W9-AZF-173

171

Economic Theory

and

Operations Analysis

PRENTICE-HALL INTERNATIONAL SERIES IN MANAGEMENT

BAUMOL *Economic Theory and Operations Analysis*

CHURCHMAN *Prediction and Optimal Decision: Philosophical Issues of a Science of Values*

GREENLAW, HERRON, AND RAWDON *Business Simulation*

HOLT, MUTH, MODIGLIANI, AND SIMON *Planning, Production, Inventories, and Work Force*

MILLER AND STARR *Executive Decisions and Operations Research*

PFIFFNER AND SHERWOOD *Administrative Organization*

PRENTICE-HALL INTERNATIONAL, INC., UNITED KINGDOM AND EIRE

PRENTICE-HALL OF CANADA, LTD., CANADA

C. BERTELSMANN VERLAG, GERMANY AND AUSTRIA

DE BUSSY, HOLLAND AND FLEMISH-SPEAKING PART OF BELGIUM

DUNOD, FRANCE AND FRENCH-SPEAKING PART OF BELGIUM

HERRERO HERMANOS, SUCS., SPAIN AND SPANISH-SPEAKING COUNTRIES OF LATIN AMERICA

MARUZEN, FAR EAST

Economic Theory
and
Operations Analysis

William J. Baumol

Professor of Economics, Princeton University

PRENTICE-HALL, INC. ENGLEWOOD CLIFFS, N. J.

To Ellen who likes marmalade and
Daniel who likes jam.

Library of Congress Catalog Card No.: 61–7763

Second printing . . . . . June, 1962

PRINTED IN THE UNITED STATES OF AMERICA
22713–C

Preface

The last few years have brought with them a happy increase in rapport between the economic theorist and the managerial economist. This development has involved their simultaneous realization that business practice can be a fertile source of more abstract analytical ideas and that the theorist's rigorous tools can make an important contribution to the analysis of applied problems. That, in essence, is the spirit in which this book was written.

The subject of this book is economic theory, *not* operations research. The volume is intended to offer the reader both a systematic exposition of received microeconomic analysis, and an intuitive grasp of the many recent developments in mathematical economics which have too long remained a mystery in the private possession of the specialists (who, it must be admitted, have always been willing and anxious to share their secrets). The discussions of applications of economic theory to the tools of operations research and to business analysis are primarily illustrative, and though a considerable portion of the body of operations research equipment is described, the result can by no means be considered to constitute a survey of the field. As one reader has suggested, this book is intended to be more helpful to an operations researcher who wishes to learn economics than to an economist who desires a systematic education in operations research.

For their helpful comments and suggestions on all or part of the manuscript I must thank Forman Acton, Wroe Alderson, S. T. Bega, W. W. Cooper, Robert Dorfman, Ralph Gomory, Herman Karreman, Robert Kuenne, Harold Kuhn, Don Patinkin, Gardner Patterson, Maurice Peston and, above all, Alvaro Lopez and Richard Quandt. The devoted labors of my research assistant, Charles Frisbie, and the extraordinary workmanship of my secretary, Mrs. C. B. Brown, were of immeasurable help. The role of my several years of experience with the management consulting firm of Alderson Associates, Inc., will be apparent in many parts of the book. I must also acknowledge my sincere gratitude to the Ford Foundation whose grant to the Department of Economics at Princeton helped to finance the research involved in the more original portions of this volume as well as the typing of the manuscript.

Finally, I must thank the editors of the several journals involved, as well as my co-authors, Ralph Gomory and Philip Wolfe, who graciously permitted me to reprint portions of the following articles: "On the Role of Marketing Theory," *Journal of Marketing*, Vol. XXI (April, 1957); "Selecting an Appropriate Model for an Operations Research Problem" Vol. VIII (November, 1955), "Solution of Management Problems Through Mathematical Programming," Vol. IX (May, 1956), "Operations Research Applied to Marketing Problems," Vol. X (March, 1957) and "A Guide to Operations Research Methods," Vol. X (April, 1957), all in *Cost and Profit Outlook;* "Community Indifference," *Review of Economic Studies*, Vol. XIV (1946–47); "On the Theory of Oligopoly," *Economica*, Vol. XXV (August, 1958); "Marginalism and the Demand for Cash in Light of Operations Research Experience," *Review of Economics and Statistics*, Vol. XL (August, 1958); (P. Wolfe co-author), "A Warehouse-Location Problem," *Operations Research*, Vol. 6, No. 2 (March–April, 1958); "Economic Theory and the Political Scientist," *World Politics*, Vol. VI (January, 1954); "Activity Analysis in One Lesson," *American Economic Review*, Vol. XLVIII (December, 1958); (R. Gomory co-author), "Integer Programming and Pricing," *Econometrica*, Vol. 28 (1960); and "The Cardinal Utility Which Is Ordinal," *Economic Journal*, Vol. LXVIII (December, 1958).

W. J. B.

Princeton University

Contents

PART I

Analytic Tools of Optimization

CHAPTER ONE

Optimization and an example from inventory analysis

1. Optimization—a Basic Viewpoint

One of the hallmarks of the economic theorist's (and the operations researcher's) approach to the analysis of business behavior and business problems is the concept of optimization. In business practice it is common to see management's decisions made on the basis of some set of fixed numbers which are meant to represent the extent of the opportunities open to the firm. For example, businessmen frequently arrange for market surveys to estimate how much of their products they will be able to sell in the next year or some other period in the future. On the basis of such figures, which management seems to treat as fixed constants (under some such name as "market potential"), it decides how much raw material to put into inventory, how many salesmen to hire, etc.

This sort of reasoning is the antithesis of the approach of the economic theorist and the operations researcher. In their analyses, one starts from the position that there is no one fixed amount of any commodity which buyers are prepared to purchase. Rather, sales will depend on price, advertising expenditure, and a host of other variables whose values may be under the businessman's control. For this reason, the number of salesmen to be hired should not be based on any fixed estimate of future sales, for *the size of the sales force helps, in turn, to determine the sales volume.*

Instead of a fixed sales figure, optimality analysis therefore deals with an array of possibilities, often infinite in number. Which of these possibilities will in fact occur depends on the decisions made by the executives in question. The analyst, then, does not confine his analysis to a single possible decision, treating it as though it were the businessman's only option, because ordinarily he will have a wide set of choices open to him, any one of which may permit him to stay in business or even to prosper. He may, with relative impunity, surely spend somewhat more or somewhat less on advertising, make an upward or downward change in the size of his sales force, in his inventory levels, and often in his prices, though the effects of these alternatives are rarely investigated in the standard market survey. The approach of optimality analysis is to take these alternatives into account and to ask which of these possible sets of decisions will come *closest* to meeting the businessman's objectives, i.e., which decisions will be best or *optimal*.

2. *Optimality Analysis in Operations Research*

The foregoing does not mean that in applied operations research work the analyst even pretends to be able to find the best of all possible decisions. The data are too inaccurate, the tools of analysis are often too blunt, and the operations researcher's acquaintance with the details of the firm's operations and his general business "know-how" are usually too limited for him to be able to come up with anything more than approximations to the ideal of the true optimum. Nevertheless, an analysis which is specifically designed to look for optimal decisions, crude and approximative though it may be, is very likely to do much better than the workable but relatively arbitrary rules of thumb of obscure origin which play so prominent a part in business practice.

It is easy to provide illustrative examples of these standard business decision rules:

1. *Inventory levels.* The quantity of any product which company X carries in inventory is kept (approximately) equal to the amount which its customers normally buy in 60 days or some other such fixed period.

2. *Pricing.* The price of any of company X's products is set at its cost per unit plus a standard fixed percentage "mark-up."

3. *Advertising budgeting.* A fixed per cent of the firm's revenues (sales) is more or less automatically set aside for advertising.

These crude rules often exhibit serious shortcomings. For example, we will see later in this chapter that the inventory rule of thumb (1) is likely to result in excess inventories of some items and insufficient stocks of others, and in later chapters it will be shown that the pricing rule (2) is unlikely to maximize profits or sales or anything else which the businessman may be expected to consider important.

Most businessmen recognize these rules of thumb for what they are—rough but serviceable management tools. The operations researcher, by systematically seeking to determine the very best of the available possibilities, may at least hope to do better than the old standard rules of thumb.

3. The Role of Optimality in Economic Analysis

The economist's interest in optimization is of another sort entirely. At least in part his position, relative to that of the operations researcher, is somewhat analogous to the physicist's relation to the engineer. A primary aim of the economist is to understand business behavior rather than to make recommendations to businessmen. His understanding of economic processes provides part of the foundation for the analysis of the operations researcher.

The concept of optimality is important to the economist for his analysis, theoretical and applied, of public policy problems; but it also helps him to understand the behavior of businessmen, consumers, and other members of the economy. It is at least possible that sheer business acumen and experience permit management and other economic units to arrive at decisions which come close to being optimal. Moreover, in business, competition may soon eliminate firms whose decision-making is consistently poor. To the extent that these assertions are valid, optimality analysis should serve as a relatively good predictor of economic behavior; that is, it should provide a reasonably good explanation of actual economic decisions and activities. In economic theory it is therefore customary to employ an optimality premise in discussing the behavior of firms, consumers, and other economic units. It is simply assumed that these units' decisions are approximately optimal, and the consequences of this assumption are then usually presented as a rough description of economic behavior in the real world. Thus, in effect, the economist tells us only what a rational individual, who is also a well-trained and efficient calculator of optimal decisions, would do in his economic activities.

Because of this orientation of so much of economic analysis, the theory of optimal decision-making will constitute a central theme of this book.

4. Illustration: A Simple Inventory Problem

The reader may well feel, with some justification, that he has always believed in optimal decisions and that the concept involves relatively little that is new. Two aspects of the approach, however, are likely to be novel. The first is the explicit consideration of the entire relevant range of possibilities. Rather than considering whether the firm can maintain its position with a $2 million advertising budget, we try to examine the effect of each and every possible budget, say between a half-million and \$4 million. A second feature of the optimality calculation which is apt to be novel is the drawing together of these materials into a more systematic and rigorous analysis. These two aspects of optimization are, perhaps, best brought out by illustration. For this purpose let us examine the simplest (and, therefore, the crudest) of the models of inventory analysis. It is to be emphasized that this model is selected only for expository purposes; the reader must keep in mind that for this reason it is necessary to ignore many crucial features of real inventory problems. He should notice, however, how far the analysis carries us on the basis of very little initial information. It pulls implications from the model much as a magician pulls rabbits out of a hat—we know that the rabbits must have been there to begin with, but their presence was by no means obvious, and the skill with which they are produced is often impressive.

Our analysis deals with a retailer who (perhaps on the basis of contracts) confidently expects to sell some fixed amount, call it Q^* units, of one of his commodities over the next year at a predetermined price, with demand spread evenly throughout the year.[1] How much inventory should he keep on hand? He has considerable choice in the matter. For example, if $Q^* = 100$ thousand units he can meet his demand by having the entire amount delivered to his warehouse at the beginning of January, keeping it in stock until it is gradually depleted by shipments to his customers; alternatively, he can have 50 thousand units delivered to him right after the first of the year and another equal amount on July 1. Still another alternative is to have four quarterly deliveries of 25 thousand units, and so on.

Now the first alternative (receipt of the whole amount at the beginning of the year) involves an inventory which begins with 100 thousand units and ends with zero,[2] so that his average inventory is 50 thousand units. Similarly, the second (two-delivery) procedure involves inventories which begin with 50 thousand units and end with zero, so that in this case the average stock on hand is 25 thousand units, etc. Thus, by ordering more and more frequently, the required average inventory level can be made smaller and smaller.

---

[1] An asterisk is written after the Q to indicate that this letter represents a definite number which is known to the firm. This convention will be used throughout this section to distinguish such numbers from the variables whose values are the unknowns of the analysis.

[2] Of course, in practice it is normally never planned to have inventory run out altogether. For unexpected demands or delays in deliveries could then embarrass the businessman who had no stocks on hand to service waiting customers. In the analysis which follows the reader can, therefore, if he wishes substitute some minimum inventory quantity M^* for this zero whenever it appears. He will find that no change in the analysis results.

Here, then, is the range of possibilities which our optimality analysis must consider: The basic quesion is, how far should this process of cutting down on inventory be carried? A smaller inventory, of course, saves money on his inventory *carrying costs:* that is, on storage costs, interest cost on the cash used to buy the inventory, etc. But, on the other hand, there is a *reorder cost* involved in placing and delivering an order, and since a smaller inventory involves more frequent orders and deliveries, if management decides on too small an average inventory level these costs may become prohibitive. Determination of the optimal inventory level involves a systematic balancing of the savings in inventory carrying costs against the increased reorder costs which reduced inventory will require.

5. Determination of the Cost Relationship

To find the optimal inventory level (the level which does the job at minimum cost) we must now go through the rather painful process of finding mathematical expressions for these two types of costs:

1. *Carrying cost.* We saw in our example that the average inventory level is one-half the amount received in a shipment. Thus, in general notation, let the quantity delivered to our retailer be D units per shipment (if it is all delivered in January, $D = 100$ thousand units in our example). Then, as has been assumed, if demand is spread evenly throughout the year, inventory would fall at a steady rate from the day it is delivered until it is used up. Thus the inventory must fall gradually from D to zero so the average inventory level must be

$$\frac{D + 0}{2} = \frac{D}{2}.$$

Now let k^* (dollars) represent the interest and other carrying cost involved in holding one unit of inventory for one year. Then the total carrying cost will be the annual carrying cost per unit times the (average) number of units in inventory $= k^*D/2$.

2. *Reorder cost.* If 100 thousand units are to be sold and 25 thousand units are delivered per shipment, then clearly $4 = 100/25$ deliveries will be required over the course of the year. More generally, if Q^* is to be sold over the course of the year and D is delivered each time, the required number of deliveries is Q^*/D.

Suppose, moreover, that the cost per delivery is related to the amount delivered, by the expression $a^* + b^*D$ where a^* and b^* are some numbers. Here b^* may be interpreted as the shipping cost per item so that the cost of sending D items is b^*D dollars. Similarly, a^* represents costs such as bookkeeping and long-distance telephoning for orders—in other words, costs whose magnitude is not seriously affected by the amount involved in the shipment.

We can now calculate the total annual reordering cost; it will equal the number of deliveries multiplied by the cost per delivery, i.e.,

$$\frac{(a^* + b^*D)Q^*}{D} = \frac{a^*Q^*}{D} + \frac{b^*Q^*D}{D} = \frac{a^*Q^*}{D} + b^*Q^*.$$

The total cost which our retailer lays out on his inventory is the sum of these two costs: the carrying and the reorder cost. It is therefore equal to

$$C = \frac{k^*D}{2} + \frac{a^*Q^*}{D} + b^*Q^*.$$

This is the relationship which we have been seeking.

6. The Optimality Calculation

Let us pause now to examine what has so far been accomplished. In effect, the only unknown in the preceding equation is the (optimal) value of D, the amount to be delivered per shipment. Once this number is determined the entire problem is solved, because we can automatically know the corresponding average inventory level ($= D/2$) and the number of times per year shipments should be ordered ($= Q^*/D$).

But once we have found our equation, the solution of the problem is reduced to a simple problem of computation. For the equation gives us a direct relationship between costs and the alternative values of our variable, D. For example, suppose the numbers in the equation were $Q^* = 100$ (thousand), $k^* = 8$, $a^* = 60$, and $b^* = 3$. Then the equation becomes

$$C = \frac{8D}{2} + \frac{60 \times 100}{D} + 3 \times 100$$

or

$$C = 4D + \frac{6000}{D} + 300.$$

With such an equation the optimal value of D can be approximated by a number of trial calculations. One can simply take a number of alternative values of D, substitute them in turn into the equation, and compute the corresponding values of C, thus finding, roughly, the value of D which gives the lowest cost. For example, setting $D = 10$ (thousand units) we obtain $C = 40 + 600 + 300 = 940$, and similarly, when $D = 20$, $C = 680$, and so on, as shown in the following table:

D	10	20	30	40	50	60	70	80	...
C	940	680	620	610	620	640	666	695	...

Examination of this table readily suggests the (correct) conclusion that the optimal value of D is approximately 40 (thousand) units per delivery.

Thus, by finding the inventory cost equation we have obtained all the information required for the solution of our problem. An equation of this variety is called an *objective function* because it shows how the firm's objective (cost minimization) is affected by the different values of the variable in question. We shall encounter such objective functions throughout this book.

In effect, then, the inventory problem has now been solved. However, an additional bit of mathematical analysis will enable us to extract a great deal of additional information from this solution. The standard methods of the differential calculus (Chapter 4) can be used to obtain from our cost equation another equation which gives us the optimal value of our variable D. This equation is[3]

$$D = \sqrt{\frac{2a^*Q^*}{k^*}}.$$

This result gives us the optimum average inventory level, $D/2$, and the optimum reorder quantity, D, corresponding to any levels of sales volume, Q^*, unit carrying cost, k^*, and unit reorder cost, a^*. The result is, therefore, not tied to any particular numbers such as $Q^* = 100$, $k^* = 8$, etc., as was our numerical computation. As a result, this equation can be used to see what happens to the optimal value of D when some of these numbers change. It can readily be seen to indicate, as might be expected, that the optimum inventory level, $D/2$, should be increased when sales, Q^*, go up. It also calls for an increase in the size of each delivery, D, (a reduction in the number of deliveries) when the reorder (delivery) cost, a^*, increases. Similarly, inventory should be reduced if the carrying cost, k^*, goes up (because k^* appears in the denominator of the fraction).[4]

More surprising, and perhaps more important, is that this formula

---

[3] *Proof:* The optimal value of D is that which minimizes total inventory cost, C. We therefore differentiate C with respect to D, set the derivative dC/dD equal to zero, and solve for D. We obtain

$$\frac{dC}{dD} = \frac{k^*}{2} - \frac{a^*Q^*}{D^2} = 0 \quad \text{or} \quad \frac{k^*}{2} = \frac{a^*Q^*}{D^2}.$$

Multiplying both sides by $2D^2/k^*$ we obtain

$$D^2 = \frac{2a^*Q^*}{k^*} \quad \text{or} \quad D = \sqrt{\frac{2a^*Q^*}{k^*}}.$$

[4] Note that b^* does not appear in the equation for optimal D. This means that no change in the value of b^* should lead to any change in inventory level in this situation. Intuitively, this perhaps slightly surprising result can be explained by noting that if the total amount, Q^*, to be shipped over the year is fixed, then there is nothing that can be done to save on shipping charges which are proportionate to the amount shipped. These charges will add up to b^*Q^* dollars over the year and no change in inventory levels can reduce this number.

indicates *inventory should increase only in proportion to the square root of sales*. In other words, if sales of some item double, inventory should not be doubled—it should be increased to much less than 200 per cent of its original amount. As was mentioned earlier in this chapter, many firms fix their inventory at some constant percentage of sales volume (a fixed number of weeks' worth of sales are kept in inventory) so that, if one item sells five times as much as another, they will tend to keep five times as large an inventory of the former which, as our result shows, means that they are keeping too much of the former, too little of the latter, or both. In fact, substantial savings have often been achieved because the last equation and related results have led analysts to recognize that the standard rule of thumb tends to yield excessive inventories of the popular, large-sales-volume items and insufficient inventories of the goods whose sales are relatively modest.[5] Thus we see that even with our highly oversimplified inventory model an optimality analysis can, if used with sufficient caution, produce significant practical results.

REFERENCES

Introductory Books

Magee, J. F., *Production, Planning and Inventory Control*, McGraw-Hill, New York, 1958.

Whitin, Thompson M., *The Theory of Inventory Management*, 2nd edition, Princeton University Press, Princeton, 1957.

More Advanced Volumes

Arrow, Kenneth J., Karlin, Samuel, and Scarf, Herbert, *Studies in the Mathematical Theory of Inventory and Production*, Stanford University Press, Stanford, 1958.

Morse, Philip M., *Queues, Inventories and Maintenance*, Wiley, New York, 1958.

[5] This conclusion can be made intuitively plausible in a closely related problem—that of maintaining inventory against unforeseen customer demands. Items whose sale is small are frequently bought by just a few customers so that demand for such a good is likely to be erratic, because it is subject to the sudden caprice of its few buyers. Hence, if the firm is to be reasonably sure it has enough on hand to meet these demands, it must carry relatively large stocks of these low- but erratic-sales-volume goods. On the other hand, the demand for a commodity which has many customers is unlikely to be much affected in an unforeseen manner by the whims of any particular buyer because when some demands are low those of other customers are apt to be high. Hence for such larger-volume goods an inventory which is not nearly as high in proportion to its sales may be expected to provide an adequate reserve against most unforeseen demands. Thus, here again, the optimal size of inventory will normally increase less than proportionately with sales volume.

CHAPTER TWO

*Some elementary mathematics**

This chapter provides an explanation of a number of elementary but fundamental mathematical ideas. It discusses the meaning of and notation for a function of one and of many variables, the equation of a straight line and a few other simple relationships, the definition of "slope," the definitions and elementary rules of manipulation of exponents and matters of notation—the Σ (sigma) representation of a sum. All of these concepts appear frequently in the literature of economics and occur later in the book. The reader who is not sure of himself on these topics would therefore do well to master this material before proceeding; he should not find it difficult. Readers who are familiar with these concepts clearly need not waste their time on this chapter.

1. Functions

The expression $y = f(x)$, which is read "y is a function of x" (and does *not* represent some number x multiplied by another number, f), means that there is some, perhaps unspecified relationship between the values of the variables y and x. That is, for some values of x, such a relationship specifies corresponding values for y. Such a functional relationship is summarized in the following table:

* The material in this chapter is far more rudimentary than the contents of the chapters which follow. However, many readers may have forgotten the logic behind such fundamental concepts as linear equations, negative exponents, etc. This material is therefore presented for review to facilitate the reading of some subsequent portions of this book.

x	1	5	6	9	10
y	15	-22	0	9	12

This states that when $x = 1$ then $y = f(1) = 15$. Similarly, the value of y which corresponds to $x = 5$, i.e., $f(5)$, is equal to -22, etc. Basically then, $y = f(x)$ is a symbol which represents such a table of values. Sometimes it may represent a specific algebraic relationship such as $y = 15x^2 \log x + 3$ from which we can compute the corresponding table of values, but this will not always be the case.

There are many economic examples of such functional relationships. Thus, some simple models contain a demand function of the form $Q_d = f(P)$ which states that Q_d, the quantity demanded of some commodity, depends on P, the price of the item. If it is desired to introduce a second functional relationship (e.g., a supply function) which is to be distinguished from a functional relationship that was previously introduced, then other symbols such as F, g, ϕ (the Greek letter phi), or f_1 may be used instead of f. Thus, the supply function might be written $Q_s = g(P)$, where Q_s represents the quantity of the commodity which is supplied.

The quantity of the commodity which is demanded may, and in fact does, also depend on the values of variables other than price. For example, it may depend on the level of consumer income, Y, and on the volume of advertising expenditure, A. This is a multivariable demand function which is written symbolically as $Q = f(P, Y, A)$. A somewhat more general notation is $Q = f(x_1, x_2, \ldots, x_{15})$ which states that the value of Q is dependent on the values of 15 different variables. Here x_1 may represent price, x_2 consumer income, etc. Still greater generality can be achieved by representing the number of variables by the symbol n, in which case we write $Q = f(x_1, x_2, \ldots, x_n)$, meaning that the value of Q depends in some way on the values of each of some unspecified number of variables.

2. Slope

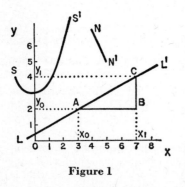

Figure 1

The slope of a line is a measure of steepness. For this purpose the following convention is employed: one simply calculates how much the line rises per unit move *to the right*. That is, if moving four units to the right involves a two-unit rise in the graph, we say that its slope is $\frac{2}{4} = 0.5$, i.e., that it rises at an (average) rate of $\frac{1}{2}$ unit as one moves one unit to the right.

This is illustrated in Figure 1. As we move four units to the right below straight line LL' from point A to point B, the curve climbs two units to point C. Specifically, the slope of the curve is given by the increase in the vertical coordinates of points A and C divided by the increase in their horizontal coordinates. That is, it is equal to

$$\frac{y_1 - y_0}{x_1 - x_0} = \frac{4 - 2}{7 - 3} = \frac{2}{4} = 0.5.$$

A line such as segment NN' which goes downhill as we move to the right is said to have a *negative slope*. In this case, since its level diminishes two units as we move one unit to the right, it is of slope -2.

The difference between a line which is straight and one which is not is that the slope of a straight line never changes. The line LL' is equally steep in the vicinity of point A and in that of point B. By contrast, at the bottom of curve SS' the line is fairly flat, but it grows steeper as we move up along it either to the right or the left, so that its slope increases.

3. Linear and Other Simple Equations

The equation $y = \frac{1}{2}x + 3$ and the more general equation $y = ax + b$ (where a and b are any numbers) are called *linear*. If the reader were to use such an equation to compute a table of values for x and y, and then plotted these figures on a graph, he would find that he had drawn a set of points all of which lie along a straight line; $y = ax + b$ is therefore called a *linear equation*.

We can prove that this must be so without much difficulty. In the preceding section it was indicated that a straight line may be defined as one whose slope never changes. To prove that $y = ax + b$ is represented by a straight line, we must therefore show that the slope of the graph is a constant (a fixed number such as a or b). Now consider any two points such as W and V (Figure 2) which lie on the graph of this equation, where the remainder of the graph of the equation is not shown in order to avoid prejudging its shape. As we have seen, the slope of this graph is

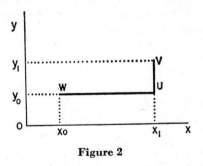

Figure 2

$(y_1 - y_0)/(x_1 - x_0)$. But, since both points lie on the graph of $y = ax + b$, this equation tells us that there is a relationship between y_0 and x_0 and a similar relationship between y_1 and x_1: $y_0 = ax_0 + b$ and $y_1 = ax_1 + b$. Substituting these expressions for y_0 and y_1 into the expression for the slope we obtain

$$\text{slope of } (y = ax + b) = \frac{y_1 - y_0}{x_1 - x_0} = \frac{(ax_1 + b) - (ax_0 + b)}{x_1 - x_0}$$

$$= \frac{ax_1 + \not b - ax_0 - \not b}{x_1 - x_0} = \frac{ax_1 - ax_0}{x_1 - x_0}$$

$$= \frac{a(x_1 - x_0)}{(x_1 - x_0)} = a.$$

Thus we have proved that *the slope of the graph of $y = ax + b$ is always equal to the number a, the coefficient of the term ax.* For example, the graph of $y = 6x + 3$ is of slope 6 which remains unchanged throughout the length of the graph. Hence that graph must be a straight line, as was to be proved.[1]

The constant, b, in our linear equation can also be given a simple interpretation. Consider the point on the graph where $x = 0$, i.e., the point where the graph crosses the y axis. There we have

$$y = f(0) = a \cdot 0 + b = b.$$

In other words, b is the y *intercept*—the value of y (the height of the graph) at the point where it crosses the vertical axis.

It can be shown by similar arguments that the graph of a three-variable relationship such as $y = 3x + 4z - 6$ is the three-dimensional analogue of a straight line—a plane in a three-dimensional diagram whose three axes represent the values of x, y, and z. More generally, by analogy, we use the term *linear equation* for any relationship such as

$$y = a_1x_1 + a_2x_2 + \ldots + a_nx_n + b$$

where $y, x_1, x_2, \ldots, x_n$ are all variables, $a_1, a_2, \ldots, a_n$ and b are all constants.

The second-degree nonlinear equation $y = x^2 + 3$ has the graph SS' in Figure 1, as may be verified by plotting some points. Similarly, other types of equation have characteristic graphic forms, some of which are indicated in Figure 3. Note that the number of "bumps," B, in an nth-degree polynomial equation

$$y = a_1x^n + a_2x^{n-1} + \ldots + a_nx + b$$

is (usually) one less than the degree, n, of the equation (though there are exceptional equations for which this is not true). Thus, the third-degree equation

$$y = ax^3 + bx^2 + cx + d$$

has one hill and one valley, the quartic has one peak and two valleys, etc. The next graph, the exponential $y = ka^x$, exhibits an explosive, roughly geometric (cumulatively increasing) growth rate. The inverse

---

[1] It is easily shown that the converse is also true, i.e., that any straight line will have an equation of the form $y = ax + b$. For let a be the slope of any such line and let b be its y intercept (see below). Then this line must be the graph of $y = ax + b$.

type of relationship $y = k/a^x + b$ can level off, with the fractional term

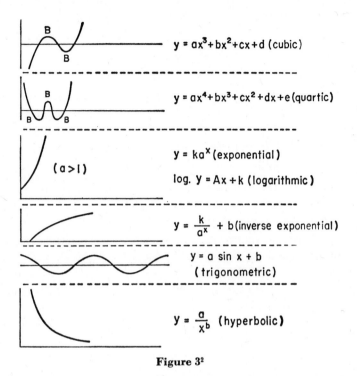

Figure 3[2]

gradually approaching zero. The trigonometric functions, $y = a \sin x + b$ and $y = \cos x + b$, form a perfectly symmetrical and repetitious cyclical pattern. Finally, the relationship $y = a/x^b$, of which the frequently encountered rectangular hyperbola, $y = a/x$ or $xy = a$, is a special case, approaches the axes asymptotically; that is, it comes closer and closer to the axes but never quite reaches them. Of course, many other types of relationship exist and each has its characteristic graph.

PROBLEMS

Show that $3y + 6x + 9 = 0$ is a linear equation. Prove that its slope is -2. Generalize this result to explain why any equation of the form

$$a_1x_1 + a_2x_2 + \ldots + a_nx_n = b_1y_1 + b_2y_2 + \ldots + b_ny_n + k$$

is linear. Here the a's, b's, and k are any (unspecified) constants (numbers).

[2] For reasons which will become clearer in Sections 4 and 5 below, exponential and logarithmic equations are very closely related and, indeed, one can usually be translated into the other. That is, of course, why they have similar graphs.

4. Exponents: Definitions and Elementary Rules of Manipulation

Negative, fractional, and zero exponents may seem puzzling at first, but these are all extensions of the standard definition

$$x^n = x \cdot x \cdot \ldots \cdot x \quad (n \text{ times})$$

i.e., x multiplied by itself n times. *As a special case of this definition we have* $x^1 = x$.

Now suppose we multiply, say, x^2 by x^3. By this definition,

$$x^2 \cdot x^3 = (x \cdot x) \cdot (x \cdot x \cdot x) = x \cdot x \cdot x \cdot x \cdot x = x^5.$$

Generalizing, we obtain the fundamental

RULE 1. *Multiplication:* $x^a \cdot x^b = x^{a+b}$, that is, the product of two identical terms, each raised to a different power, is equal to that same term, this time raised to the *sum* of the two powers.

In other words, to multiply power terms we add their exponents. An analogous rule applies to division. For example, to divide x^6 by x^2 write

$$\frac{x^6}{x^2} = \frac{x \cdot x \cdot x \cdot x \cdot x \cdot x}{x \cdot x} = x \cdot x \cdot x \cdot x = x^4.$$

Hence we conclude

RULE 2. *Division:* $x^a/x^b = x^{a-b}$.

Thus, to divide exponent terms, subtract the exponent of the denominator from that of the numerator.

This rule seems obvious so long as a is greater than b ($a > b$). But it is also extended verbatim to cases where this does not hold, e.g., to division of x^4 by x^6 which is then written $x^{4-6} = x^{-2}$. Several significant consequences follow. If we divide x^a by x^a the result is clearly equal to unity. But by Rule 2, $x^a/x^a (= 1) = x^{a-a} = x^0$. Hence,

RULE 3. *Zero exponents:* $x^0 = 1$, for *any* (nonzero) number x.

A consequence of Rule 2 and Rule 3 can be obtained by taking the reciprocal of x^a. This is equal to $1/x^a$, which by Rule 3 is equal to x^0/x^a, or by Rule 2, it is equal to $x^{0-a} = x^{-a}$. This, then, yields the definition of a negative exponent, i.e.,

RULE 4. For any x and a, the expression x^{-a} represents the reciprocal of x^a.

To raise a term, x^a, to a higher power, e.g., to square x^3 we multiply this term by itself to obtain

$$x^3 \cdot x^3 = (x \cdot x \cdot x)(x \cdot x \cdot x) = x^{3 \cdot 2} = x^6.$$

More generally,

RULE 5. *Powers:* x^a raised to the bth power is equal to x^{ab}, so that, to raise such a term to the power b, one multiplies the old exponent by b. Similarly, to undo this operation, e.g., to take the square root of x^6 we get $\sqrt{x^6} = x^3 = x^{6/2}$. More generally,

RULE 6. *Roots:* The bth root of x^a is $x^{a/b}$. In particular, $x^{1/b}$ is the bth root of x ($= x^1$).

5. *Logarithms*

The ways of manipulating exponents just described are widely used to simplify computational problems. The facts that multiplication can be reduced to *addition* of exponents and that a number can be raised to a higher power by multiplication provide the basis for logarithmic computation. This section is not intended to teach the reader how to use logarithms in computation; a much longer and more detailed exposition is required for this purpose. Rather, it seeks to illustrate how the results of the previous section can be employed and to review the simple basis of the elementary theory of logarithms which is often forgotten by many who use the device.

Given any number k, we define the logarithm of k (to the base 10) to be a number which satisfies the following relationship: $k = 10^{\log k}$. That is, $\log k$ is a number such that, if one raises 10 to the power $\log k$, then the result is equal to k.

Since these so-called "common logarithms" are all powers of 10, they can be combined according to the rules for the manipulation of exponents. For example, to multiply two numbers, a and b, observe that (by Rule 1 of the previous section)

$$a \cdot b = 10^{\log a} \cdot 10^{\log b} = 10^{\log a + \log b}.$$

Hence we conclude

RULE 7. *Logarithmic multiplication:* To multiply two numbers, a and b, use a table of logarithms to find the number whose logarithm is equal to $\log a + \log b$.

Similarly, to raise any number k to the power a we note that (by Rule 5)

$$k^a = (10^{\log k})^a = 10^{a \log k}.$$

Therefore

RULE 8. *Logarithmic calculation of powers:* To raise any number k to any power a, find the number whose logarithm is equal to $a \log k$.

To illustrate the economy which these rules permit, the reader may wish to consider what sort of labor would be involved, without the use of logarithms, in calculating, e.g., $100 \, (1.05)^{25}$, the value after 25 years of a

$100 security which carries an interest of 5 per cent, compounded annually, and where the interest is allowed to accumulate.

6. Σ *Notation*

A final item in this collection of miscellaneous mathematical background material is a standard notation for addition, employed at a number of points in this volume. Let x_1, x_2, x_3, and x_4 be symbols used to represent four numbers, say $x_1 = 5$, $x_2 = 0$, $x_3 = -2$, and $x_4 = 12$. The Greek letter Σ (upper-case sigma) is used to indicate summation. The addition of these four numbers is then written as

$$\sum_{i=1}^{4} x_i$$

This means: add the numbers x_i which are obtained, successively, by letting i be equal to 1, then letting i be equal to 2, all the way up to $i = 4$. This is the significance of the notation above and below the Σ. The number (called a *summation index*) which is below the Σ indicates the first term to be included in the sum, and the number above the Σ represents the last term in the sum. Several examples should make this clear:

$$\sum_{i=1}^{4} x_i = x_1 + x_2 + x_3 + x_4 = 5 + 0 - 2 + 12 = 15.$$

Similarly,

$$\sum_{i=1}^{3} x_i = x_1 + x_2 + x_3 = 5 + 0 - 2 = 3$$

and

$$\sum_{i=2}^{4} x_i = x_2 + x_3 + x_4 = 0 - 2 + 12 = 10.$$

A slightly more subtle example is the Σ representation of the power series

$$1 + y + y^2 + y^3 + y^4 + y^5 + y^6 \quad \text{which is just} \quad \sum_{i=0}^{6} y^i.$$

Where a large number of terms is involved, this notation saves both space and time.[3]

PROBLEMS

1. Write out in Σ notation
   (a) the linear equation

$$y = a_1 x_1 + a_2 x_2 + a_3 x_3 + a_4 x_4$$

[3] The reader will recall from Rule 3 of Section 4, above, that any number raised to the zeroth power is equal to 1. Specifically, $y^i = 1$ when $i = 0$.

(b) the polynomial equation

$$y = a_0 + a_1 x + a_2 x^2.$$

2. Write out term by term

(a) $\sum\limits_{i=0}^{3} a_i x^{3-i}$

(b) $\sum\limits_{i=1}^{3} i^2.$

CHAPTER THREE

Marginal analysis

1. Marginal Reasoning and the Logic of Decision-Making

There is a common element to all decision problems which is expressible in the apparently trivial question, "Is it worth while?" A firm considering an improvement in product quality, a consumer considering the purchase of a bottle of wine, or a government agency considering the organization of another research project must all ask the same question—whether the action in question will *add* sufficiently to the benefits enjoyed by the performer to make it worth the cost. This is the heart of marginal decision-making—the statement that an action merits performance if and only if, as a result, the actor can expect to be *better off than he was before*.

Although this proposition seems obvious enough, the fact that it is frequently vio'ated in practice suggests that it requires some examination. First let us see how a decision which runs counter to this rule is likely to arise. Consider the following example: A manager is empowered to hire an additional salesman. He decides to send this man to St. Louis rather than to Cleveland because last year's orders per salesman were $60,000 in St. Louis and $43,000 in Cleveland. But it is possible that the difference in returns per salesman in the two cities occurred just because the size of the sales force in the former was well adapted to the number of retailers whereas the sales force in the latter was spread too thinly. If so, the new salesman may *add* little, if anything, to the company's orders in the salesman-saturated St. Louis market, but in Cleveland he might produce a substantial increase in sales. Clearly, if the firm's objective is to maximize its orders, it would in this case be better to send the man to Ohio.

The figure giving the size of orders per salesman is referred to as the *average* return per salesman, whereas the *increase* in sales which results from the presence of an additional salesman is called the *marginal* return. The manager in the illustration was (inadvertently) acting contrary to the firm's interests by sending a salesman to the city where the *average* return per salesman was higher rather than to the area where his *marginal* return (the amount he could add to company sales) was higher. A basic theorem of this section, then, is that *the best interests of a firm, a consumer, or any other economic unit require that any decision take into account the magnitude of the marginal yield which it promises.*

As will be shown in the next chapter, the marginal analysis is very closely related to the classical mathematical tool of optimality analysis— the differential calculus. A marginal datum may be interpreted, roughly, as a first derivative, and most of the findings of this chapter can readily be translated into calculus terms as is shown occasionally in footnotes.

Marginal analysis, because it can be explained with the aid of arithmetic examples, has a distinct expository advantage. But, on the other hand, in this form it is a relatively blunt calculating instrument to which many of the powerful analytic theorems of the differential calculus described in the next chapter do not apply.

2. *Theorems on Resource Allocation*

To emphasize further its importance for decision-making, let us now examine two fundamental propositions of the marginal analysis. The first of these is designed to determine the *magnitudes* of the variables which constitute an optimal decision: How much should be spent on newspaper advertising? How far should price be cut? How many pounds of plums should a consumer buy? The paradoxical answer to a question of this sort is

RULE 1. *Optimal activity level:* The scale of an activity should if possible be expanded so long as its *marginal* net yield (taking into account both benefits and costs) is a positive value; and the activity should, therefore, be carried to a point where this *marginal* net yield is zero.[1]

---

[1] This is no more than the standard calculus proposition that to maximize any $y = f(x)$ it is necessary that the first derivative, dy/dx (the marginal effect of x on y), be zero. It is, however, very important to realize that this is a necessary but not a sufficient optimality condition, i.e., all optima to which it is relevant must satisfy Rule 1, but not all situations which meet the requirements of the rule will be optima. To separate the sheep from the goats we must satisfy in addition the very important *second-order conditions* described in Section 5 of the next chapter. See also Section 2 of Chapter ten for an illustrative application of this point.

This result is paradoxical because it suggests the question, "Why shouldn't we quit while we're still ahead?" Why not stop advertising when the marginal return on a dollar of advertising is, say, $1.75? The answer, here, is that a firm which takes such a decision is voluntarily missing the opportunity to make even more money. An additional dollar spent on advertising will leave the firm 75 cents (= $1.75 − $1.00) ahead, and failure to take advantage of the opportunity therefore leaves the firm 75 cents poorer.

Of course, the firm may not have any more funds to lay out on advertising. In that case the rule cannot be followed. That is the significance of the proviso in Rule 1 that the marginal yield of any activity should be reduced to zero *whenever possible*. As we shall see in later chapters, this remark lies behind the role of mathematical programming.

Another possible objection to Rule 1 is that the firm may have a better use for its money than expansion of the scale of the activity that happens to be under discussion. A dollar spent on improved quality control may perhaps yield $1.97, as against the $1.75 return to an additional advertising dollar; therefore advertising should not be increased until something is done to take advantage of the quality-control profit opportunity. By itself this argument leads only to the conclusion that more should ultimately be spent on both activities. If there is enough money available, and both of these types of expenditure yield diminishing marginal returns, an optimal budget will provide enough funds to expand *both* activities until each of them has a zero marginal yield. But where funds are limited so that this ideal cannot be attained, we have a second fundamental rule of marginal analysis:

RULE 2. *Relative activity levels:* For optimal results activities should, wherever possible, be carried to levels where they all yield the same marginal returns per unit of effort (cost).

For, where this condition does not hold, the decision-maker is missing an opportunity to benefit by reallocating some of his resources from an activity with the smaller marginal return to one with a larger marginal yield. In the previous example, he can benefit by budgeting more money for quaity contro rather than for advertising. The transfer of one dollar from advertising (marginal yield $1.75) to quality control (marginal yield $1.97) must yield a clear gain of $1.97 − 1.75 = 22 cents, in effect giving him something for nothing! Hence, general y, unless Rule 2 is satisfied, he cannot possibly be getting the maximum yield from his resources; his resource allocation among alternative activities can only be optimal if all his expenditures y eld the same marginal return.

3. Totals, Averages, and Marginals: Their Arithmetic Relationships

It is customary to explain the arithmetic of marginal analysis with the aid of a table such as Table 1.

TABLE 1

No. of Units	Total x	Average x	Marginal x
0	0	—	0
1	80	80	80
2	180	90	100
3	270	90	90
4	280	70	10
5	250	50	−30

The last three columns have been labeled "Total," "Average," and "Marginal x" to indicate that these are purely arithmetic relationships which are valid whether we are interested in total, average, or marginal revenue, cost, profit, or utility. That is, the reader can substitute any of these words for the letter x and end up with a valid table.

One may, perhaps, get a better grasp of the relationship if the numbers are, for the moment, interpreted as the examination grades of a group of five men. The first row indicates that before any of the papers has been marked the total grade is zero. The marginal grade is then, by convention, also considered zero (nothing has yet been added to the total), but there is no meaning to the concept of "average grade" when there are no papers. The first paper, however, gets an 80 (marginal grade = addition to total grade = 80) so that the total of all grades so far is 80, and the average grade is also 80. The second paper gets 100 (marginal grade 100) which brings the total up to 180 and pulls the average up to $(80 + 100)/2 = 90$, and so on.[2] We see, then, that *the marginal figure is defined as the amount which is added to the total by each additional paper.* The average (arithmetic mean), of course, has the usual connotation: the total divided by the number of units.

Three relationships emerge from this illustration, each of which will play some role in the subsequent discussion:

RULE 3. *First units.* The total, average, and marginal figures for the first unit are identical, (so long as total x for the zeroth unit is zero).

---

[2] The fifth man must have done something unusual, since his paper receives a grade of minus 30!

For example, the total, average, and marginal grades of the first paper in Table 1 are all 80. Similarly, if a farmer sells one cow for $50, his marginal revenue (the addition to his income produced by selling one cow) is $50, his revenue per cow sold (average revenue) is $50, and his total revenue is also $50. An exception to this apparently inviolable rule will emerge in Section 6 of this chapter.

RULE 4. *Relation between total and marginal figures:* The total figure is always the sum of the preceding marginal figures.

For example, the total grade of the first three papers, 270, is the sum of the grades of these papers, 80 + 100 + 90. This rule follows from the definition of the marginal figure as the addition to the preceding total figure (the current total is the sum of the preceding increments to it). Finally, we have the somewhat more complicated

RULE 5. *Relation between average and marginal figures:* For the average to rise, the marginal figure must be above the average figure; for the average to remain unchanged, the average and marginal figures must be equal; for the average to fall, the marginal figure must be below average.[3]

For example, in Table 1, when the average figure rises from 80 to 90, the marginal figure, 100, *lies above* the corresponding average figure, 90. The reason is easily seen—the average of a group of grades can only be raised by adding a paper whose grade is above average.

For similar reasons, the table shows that when the average remains unchanged at 90, the latest grade (the marginal figure) must itself be just average, i.e., 90. And when the average grade then falls to 70 it must have been pulled down by a below-average grade, i.e., 10.

This last rule is often misunderstood to state that, when the average figure falls, the marginal must also *fall;* when the average remains unchanged, the marginal must remain unchanged, etc. Such a conclusion is false. For example, while the average figure remains unchanged at 90 when the third paper is graded, the marginal figure *falls* from 100 to 90.

---

[3] A general proof of this result can also be obtained with the aid of a little differential calculus:

Let Q represent quantity, or number of units (the item in the first column of Table 1) and let A be an average figure. Then the corresponding total figure is AQ (e.g., total revenue equals average revenue multiplied by the number of units sold). The marginal figure, M, is the derivative of tht total figure with respect to the independent variable Q, i.e.,

$$(1) \qquad M = \frac{dAQ}{dQ} = A + Q\frac{dA}{dQ}.$$

From this equation Rule 5 follows readily. For example, when the average figure is rising, we have $dA/dQ > 0$, and it follows that $M > A$, etc.

4. Geometry of Marginal Analysis: Total x Curves

The preceding rules help us to find geometric relationships among the average, marginal, and total concepts. First, let us draw a graph describing the *total* profitability of advertising expenditure (Figure 1) and show how the corresponding marginal and average figures can be read off from it. This total profit curve, as its name implies, indicates how total profits will vary with the firm's advertising expenditure. It plots data like those in Column 2 of Table 1 against the information in Column 1. For example, point A in Figure 1 indicates that $3 million spent on advertising will yield

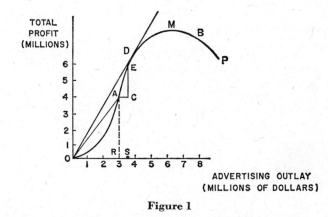

Figure 1

a total of $4 million in profit to the firm. The average profit (profit per advertising dollar) is then $4 million/$3 million = $1.33, approximately. But, in this ratio the $4 million is represented by line segment RA, while the $3 million is depicted by OR. Hence, the average profitability of expenditure OR is RA/OR *which is the slope of OA, the straight line from the origin to point A.* In other words, we have

RULE 6. *Average x and total curves:* Given any point A on a curve representing total *x*, the corresponding average *x* figure at that point is the slope of the straight line, OA, which connects point A with the origin.

This rule permits us to conclude by inspection that between points A and D the average profitability of advertising has risen, for the slope of line OD is clearly greater than that of OA. In fact, the point of maximum *average* profitability is D, the point of tangency between the total profit curve, OP, and the straight line, OD, to the origin. The reader may readily check that at points to the right of D, such as M, the average profit will be lower than it is at D because the corresponding line segment through the origin, OM, is less steep than OD.

The *marginal* productivity of advertising at point A is also measured by a slope, but this time by the slope of the total profit curve itself. For marginal profitability is defined as the increment in profit per unit addition to advertising expenditure. But if advertising expenditure goes up from OR to OS, i.e., by amount AC, equals say \$500,000, the curve shows that total profit will rise by amount CE, equals say \$1,800,000. Hence, marginal profitability will equal

$$\frac{1,800,000}{500,000} = \frac{CE}{AC} = \text{the slope of the total profit curve at } A.$$

Thus, the general

RULE 7. *Marginal x and total curves:* Given any point, A, on a curve representing total x, then marginal x is equal to the slope of the curve at point A.

As an exercise in the use of Rules 6 and 7, we may note that at point A the total profit curve slopes more steeply than does straight line OA. This means that marginal profits at A must exceed average profits so that, by Rule 5, above, average profits must be rising. We have already seen that this is in fact the case since the slope of OD exceeds that of OA. Observe also that at point D, just at the point where average profit stops rising, OD has the same slope as the total profit curve, so that average and marginal profits are equal, again as Rule 5 would lead us to expect.

The graphic interpretation of marginal x as the slope of the total x curve (Rule 7) also casts some light on the fundamental Rule 1 of this chapter, that the optimal level of any activity requires its marginal yield to be zero. Thus, in Figure 1 we note that at advertising expenditure \$3 million, the profit curve has a positive slope (a positive marginal profit yield of advertising). At point B the curve is going downhill (negative marginal profit). Neither of these can be a (profit) optimum advertising expenditure, for at A profits can be increased by advertising more, whereas from B the firm can raise its profits by advertising less. Only at M, where the profit curve is neither rising nor falling, so that the slope of the profit curve is zero, can the advertising expenditure level have reached its optimum value. But that is precisely what Rule 1 asserts for this case—an optimal advertising outlay for a profit maximizing firm requires that the marginal profit yield of advertising (the slope of the total profit curve) be zero.

5. *Marginal and Average x Curves*

So much for the "total x curves." We can also draw both "average x" and "marginal x" curves in a similar way (Figure 2). Their general relationship is largely determined by Rule 5 and Rule 3. Rule 3 tells us that the two curves must start out together (point C).[4]

To the right of point C the relative height of the two curves is governed by Rule 5. Thus, it will be observed that output OQ_2 is the point of minimum average costs, Q_2M, so that there the average cost curve is horizontal

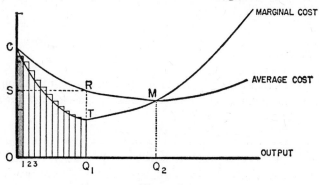

Figure 2

(average neither rising nor falling). At that output marginal and average costs are equal (intersection point M). To the right of this point, where average costs are rising, marginal costs lie above them. To the left of Q_2, where the average cost curve has a negative slope, the marginal cost curve lies below the average cost curve.[5]

Just as marginal and average x can be shown on a total x diagram, it is possible to represent total cost in terms of Figure 2. This can be done in two different ways—one in terms of the average cost curve and one in terms of the marginal cost curve.

(a) *Average curve representation of total x.* Since total cost equals average cost (cost per unit) multiplied by the number of units produced, then the total cost of output OQ_1 is $OQ_1 \times Q_1R$, which is the area of the rectangle OQ_1RS. In other words

---

[4] There is a minor difficulty here. Average cost is not defined for zero units and is only equal to marginal cost when output = 1 unit (compare Table 1). Hence they should meet somewhere to the right of the vertical axis. However, it is usually implicitly assumed, as is done here, that the unit of measurement is very small, so that our first unit lies at a microscopic distance from the origin. The two curves can then be taken to start out from a point practically on the vertical axis.

[5] But it will be noted that in the interval Q_1Q_2 marginal cost is *rising* even though average cost is falling.

RULE 8. *Total x and average curves:* The total cost of any output, OQ, is the area of the *rectangle* inscribed under the average cost curve which has OQ as its base.

(b) *Marginal curve representation of total x.* Alternatively, we can find another area which represents total profit, this time with the aid of the marginal revenue curve. By Rule 4, total cost is the sum of the preceding marginal costs. But the marginal cost of the first unit is the area of the thin, shaded rectangle next to the vertical axis, since its height is the height of the marginal cost curve at that point. Similarly, the marginal cost of the second unit produced is represented by the next rectangle, etc. Therefore the total cost of producing OQ_1 units = the sum of the preceding marginal costs = the sum of the areas of all the thin rectangles = area OQ_1TC. More generally,

RULE 9. *Total x and the marginal curve:* The total cost of producing OQ units of any commodity is that portion of the area under the marginal cost curve which lies above line OQ.

We can use these two representations of total x to derive a construction for the marginal curve from any average curve which is given to us. First, we assume that both curves are straight lines (Figure 3). It will now be

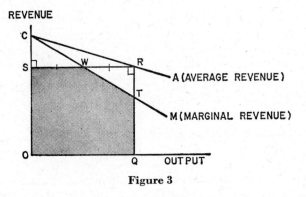

Figure 3

proved that, given the average revenue curve CA, we obtain the marginal revenue curve by drawing in *any* horizontal line SR which ends on this average cost curve, finding the midpoint W of SR, and drawing in the straight line CM which (in accord with Rule 1) begins at the same point as the average revenue curve and goes through this midpoint, W. To prove the theorem the reader will have to go through the painful process of re-calling a bit of high school geometry.

Step 1. The total revenue from any output, OQ, is given either by the area of rectangle $OQRS$ inscribed under the average revenue curve or by area $OQTC$ under the marginal revenue curve. Hence, if the two curves are drawn correctly, the two areas must be equal.

Step 2. Since these two areas have shaded area $OQTWS$ in common, it follows that right triangles CSW and WTR must be equal in area.

Step 3. Moreover, angle SWC must be the same as RWT (opposite angles of a vertex are necessarily equal). Therefore triangles SWC and WTR must be similar (two angles in common) as well as being equal in area.

Step 4. These triangles must, as a result, be congruent so that we must have $SW = WR$, as was to be proved. In sum,

Rule 10. *Straight line marginal and average curves:* Given any straight line average curve, to find the corresponding marginal curve, draw a straight line which begins where the average curve cuts the vertical axis, and goes through the midpoint of any horizontal line to the average curve.

Where the average curve is not a straight line the construction is a bit more complex. We operate, in effect, by approximating the curve by a number of straight line segments and using the preceding construction on these segments one at a time. For example, given the curved average revenue curve VA^* (Figure 4), to find the marginal revenue at output OQ, draw the straight line tangent CA to the average revenue curve at that output, and construct the corresponding straight line marginal curve (call it the marginal line), CM, by the method just indicated (Rule 10). The point, T, on CM at output OQ, is then also on the marginal revenue curve to our original average curve, VA^*, at that output. Similarly, we find the marginal revenue at output OQ' by drawing the tangent line $C'A'$ to average curve VA^* through point R' (output OQ'). Now treat that straight line as an average revenue curve and find the corresponding marginal line $C'M'$, and the point T' on that line which corresponds to output OQ' is the marginal revenue for this output. In this way we can obtain as many marginal points $T, T', \ldots$ as we wish, and the locus of these points, WM^*, is the marginal revenue curve which we seek. In sum,

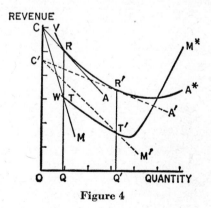

Figure 4

Rule 11. *General marginal and average curves:* To find the marginal curve to an average curve which is not straight, draw a straight line tangent to the average curve at some output, Q, find the corresponding marginal line to this tangent by Rule 10, and thereby find the marginal point on that line at output Q. The marginal curve which we seek is the locus of all such marginal points.[6]

6. Marginal Analysis and Fixed Costs

Fixed costs are defined as costs whose magnitude does not vary with the level of output, at least within some range. For example, the rent of a factory may be the same whether that factory is going full blast or running at half capacity (but once demand exceeds the factory's capacity, rental becomes a variable cost if a second factory is put into operation). Similarly, the cost of an automobile license is the same whether the car is used to travel 5000 or 30,000 miles in a year. The special features of a fixed cost are (a) that it all comes in one big lump once it is decided to enter on the operation, but (b) after it is incurred a further expansion in output makes no difference in its magnitude.[7]

These features are illustrated by the fixed cost figures in Table 2. This table is completely analogous to Table 1 (which should now be interpreted,

TABLE 2

No. of Units	Total Fixed Cost	Average Fixed Cost	Marginal Fixed Cost
0	2000	—	2000
1	2000	2000	0
2	2000	1000	0
3	2000	666 ⅔	0
4	2000	500	0
5	2000	400	0

for purposes of comparison, as a table of total, average, and marginal *variable* cost).

It will be observed that the total fixed cost figure ($2000) remains the

[6] A short proof can be given with the help of Equation (1) of footnote 3, above. This equation states that

$$(1) \qquad M = A + Q\frac{dA}{dQ}$$

where M is marginal x, A is average x, and Q is quantity (number of units). Consider, now, the straight line average curve CA and curved average curve CA^* which are tangent at point A. At that point the outputs OQ are equal on both curves, their average revenues QR also coincide, and because they are tangent, their slopes dA/dQ must also be the same. Hence, by Equation (1), at that output the marginal values QT corresponding to the two curves must be the same—find one and you have the other.

[7] It is also shown in the chapter on integer programming that fixed costs can cause computational difficulties because of these characteristics.

same throughout, no matter what the number of units, even if no units are produced or sold. Thus, once a train runs, it costs the same even if it goes empty, and (in the absence of bankruptcy) a contract to buy a fixed amount of raw material must be honored even if none of it is used.

Skipping to the marginal fixed cost column, we see that it, too, follows a very simple pattern. The very decision to go into an operation saddles management with its fixed costs—even before anything is produced. So the zeroth unit is taken to incur the entire $2000 obligation (the marginal cost of the zeroth unit is $2000). Thereafter, production of any further units adds nothing to fixed costs (the marginal fixed cost of the first unit, and any unit thereafter, is zero).[8] A curve of marginal fixed costs, therefore, must always have the same shape—it coincides with the axes of the diagram. For, to the right of the origin, marginal fixed cost is always zero so that there the marginal cost curve lies along the horizontal axis, while at the origin the marginal cost is not zero (it rises above the horizontal axis along the vertical axis).

The pattern of the average fixed cost curve is hardly more complicated. As our table shows, and for obvious reasons, the larger the number of units produced, the smaller will be the average fixed cost. The fixed costs are thereby spread over more units. However, the decline in average fixed costs is gradual, and though the average figure becomes smaller and smaller as the number of units increases, it never reaches zero. No matter by how large a number we divide $2000 (no matter how thin the overhead costs are spread), there will still remain *some* unit cost which is greater than zero.[9]

As a final observation on fixed costs, as illustrated by Table 2, notice that, for the first unit, *average* fixed cost is 2000, whereas *marginal* fixed cost is, as usual, zero. We see, then, that fixed costs violate Rule 3 of Section 3 of this chapter, which states that for first units marginal x and average x are always equal. That rule holds only so long as the total cost (or total x) of zero units is zero.[10]

So much for the purely fixed costs. In practice, of course, costs are

---

[8] In calculus terms, if T is total cost and Q is the number of units, then marginal cost is dT/dQ which equals zero whenever T is a constant (as it is for a fixed cost).

[9] The average fixed cost curve satisfies a simple mathematical relationship. Let K be total fixed cost and x be the number of units produced. Then average fixed cost, y, is the total fixed cost divided by the number of units, i.e., we have the equation $y = K/x$. This is an equation which is rather familiar in the literature. Its graph, which is called a rectangular hyperbola, is doubtless one of the economists' most popular curves—second only to the straight line. A rectangular hyperbola is depicted in Figure 3a of Chapter 8 and some of its properties are described in Section 4 of that chapter where it enters into the discussion of the theory of consumer demand.

[10] For if the zeroth unit has a positive marginal (total) cost, M_0, then the total cost of the first unit produced will be $M_0 + M_1$ where M_1 is the marginal cost of that unit. As a result, the average cost of that one unit will be $(M_0 + M_1)/1 = M_0 + M_1$ which is not equal to M_1, the marginal cost of the first unit.

usually neither entirely fixed nor entirely variable. If we refer to such expenses as combined costs, we have, by definition,

total combined cost = total variable cost + total fixed cost.

It is then easy to show from this definition that we have completely analogous relationships for average and marginal costs:

average combined cost = average variable cost + average fixed cost[11]

and finally

marginal combined cost = marginal variable cost + marginal fixed cost.[12]

Moreover, since (except for the zeroth unit) marginal fixed cost is always zero, we have

marginal combined cost = marginal variable cost

that is, (except at a zero output level) fixed costs never affect marginal costs in any way—a result which will be applied at a number of points later in this volume.

7. *Average vs. Marginal Figures in Business Practice*

In business operations one often encounters rule-of-thumb calculations which serve as substitutes for the operations researcher's optimality computations. When these business calculations are explicit, they are frequently made in terms of *average* rather than marginal quantities, that is,

---

[11] *Proof:* Writing TCC for total combined cost, etc., we have from our definition $TCC = TVC + TFC$. Dividing both sides of this equation by Q, the number of units, we obtain, $TCC/Q = TVC/Q + TFC/Q$. But, again, by definition, $TCC/Q = ACC$, etc., so that we have our result, $ACC = AVC + AFC$.

[12] *Proof:* Let TCC (20) represent the total combined cost of the 20th unit produced, etc. Then, from our definition, we have

TCC (20) $= TVC$ (20) $+ TFC$ (20)　and　TCC (19) $= TVC$ (19) $+ TFC$ (19).

Subtracting the latter equation from the former, we obtain

TCC (20) $- TCC$ (19) $= TVC$ (20) $- TVC$ (19) $+ TFC$ (20) $- TFC$ (19).

But since, by definition,

MCC (20) $= TCC$ (20) $- TCC$ (19),　etc.,

we have our result, MCC (20) $= MVC$ (20) $+ MFC$ (20). More generally, the same argument also obviously holds for any Qth unit, as well as for the 20th. Alternatively, this follows directly from the rules of the differential calculus, for if $TCC = TVC + TFC$, we have

$$dTCC/dQ = dTVC/dQ + dTFC/dQ.$$

in terms of the elements of the third rather than those of the fourth column of Table 1. We have already seen in Section 1 that decisions based on such average data are not likely to be anywhere near optimal, yet it is tempting to reason on the basis of unit (average) costs or revenues or profits, largely because of the difficulty of marginal data collection. It is almost always harder to obtain marginal figures than to acquire average data, for several reasons:

1. Almost all accounting information is in the form of average or total rather than marginal figures. Tax computations and a number of other uses of accounting data require that this be so and this usage is well ingrained by tradition.

2. By its very nature, marginal information often represents the answers to hypothetical questions—information beyond the range of the firm's actual experience. One must ask, for example, what will be the effect on the firm's profits of an increase in expenditure of type A (the marginal profitability of A), whether or not the firm has ever tried it. But note that this hypothetical question is precisely what *must* be answered in rational decision-making to determine whether or not to increase expenditure A. That is exactly why these difficult-to-obtain marginal figures are essential for good decision-making.

3. Even where some relevant data are available from the past history of a company, it is much easier to collect the statistics required for average than for marginal figures. A single observation, that the total cost of producing 500 units of some output is $15,000, yields the information that its average cost is $15,000/500 = $30. But it takes at least one more observation—say, that the total cost of 510 units is $15,050, to yield the guess that the marginal cost is $5 (since it costs an additional $50 to increase output by 10 units). And, in practice, many more than two observations will usually be required for any sort of reliable guess on marginal magnitudes. As we have seen, marginal x (e.g., cost) is the slope of a total x (cost) curve, and it is surely rash to guess at the slope of any such curve on the basis of only two statistical observations.

Another reason for the popularity of the concept of the average cost or unit profit is that it is so simple and straightforward. Anyone knows that if profits per unit are high, the firm must be making money. But, as we have already seen, this sort of "practical" reasoning can be seriously fallacious. To illustrate the point once more, the decision to produce more of a commodity which brings in a healthy profit per unit (average profit) may be very costly to the firm, as Table 1 readily shows. There the unit profit on the product varies between $50 and $90 and this may appear to be a very healthy rate of return if the average cost of the item is, say, in the vicinity of $30. Nevertheless, the decision to increase the output of this good from 4 to 5 (million) units is tantamount to incurring a loss of $30 (marginal profit = −30)! As is shown there, the increased output can actually reduce the firm's total take by this amount, despite the high level of average profit.

The use of average data in *any* optimization problem can lead to such unsatisfactory results. The logic of the difficulty is not hard to explain. For example, in any allocation problem—say the reassignment of advertising funds—the question is not whether money *already* spent in publicizing product *A* has brought high returns. What must be determined is whether the spending of *additional* money can be justified. It may well be that the public is already saturated with singing commercials, contests, and free samples of product *A*, and although the money already spent on the item brought in very satisfactory returns, more such company expenditures on this product might even repel the public. Rather, the money may be better spent on the promotion of some product, *B*, on which previous outlays were so niggardly as to be almost completely ineffective, but where the payoff to *additional* expenditures may be large because they permit some sort of public perception threshold to be reached.

8. *Averages as Approximations to Marginal Figures*

It is clear, then, that wherever there is a difference between average and marginal data, it is the latter which must be given prior consideration in an optimization problem.[13] Unfortunately, as has been shown, marginal data may be difficult and in some cases, for practical purposes, impossible to come by. It is therefore sometimes necessary to make do with average figures. For this purpose one must understand the relationship between average and marginal figures to recognize the circumstances under which the one can be expected to provide a reasonably good approximation to the other, and to determine, when this is not the case, what sort of rough adjustments in the average data can be made to bring them closer to the unknown marginal figures.

For this purpose we can again employ Rule 5 of Section 3 [and Equation (1) of footnote 3]. This yields the following correction procedures:

1. Suppose the average figure rises as the number of units increases (e.g., as production, advertising expenditure, warehouse size, or the number

---

[13] However, average figures must also always be consulted—marginal data may show the *best* that can be done, but if even this "best" arrangement involves an average loss of $2.00 per unit, it may be optimal to drop that segment of the business altogether.

of trucks used by the company goes up). Then, since marginal x must be above average x, any average figure must be revised upward to obtain an estimate of the corresponding marginal figure. Moreover, the more rapid the rise in average x, the greater will be the correction required.

2. Similarly, when average x is falling, the marginal figure will lie below the average figure, so that any average should be reduced to obtain the corresponding marginal datum.

3. Only when average x is neither increasing nor decreasing will the two figures coincide so that the average figure will need no readjustment.

In more concrete economic terms, this means that the following types of adjustment must be made to estimate marginal from average data:

(a) In cost figures, if there is reason to believe there are economies of large-scale production (falling average costs), marginal cost will be less than average cost, so that the average cost figure must be adjusted downward to yield a better approximation to the marginal cost figure. On the other hand, if observation suggests the presence of important diminishing returns, the average cost figure must be adjusted upward.

(b) In the case of productivity figures, the reverse holds. Economies of large scale (increasing average product per dollar of outlay) require an upward revision of average product figures to yield a "guestimate" of marginal product, and diminishing returns require that the average figure be reduced.

(c) In the case of revenue data, evidence that a market is saturated suggests that the average figure overestimates the marginal revenue, whereas an underexploited market may involve a marginal revenue which is higher than average revenue.

A little experience in looking about and asking the proper questions should soon permit the analyst to recognize the presence of such phenomena as economies of large scale and diminishing returns, and on this basis to use the preceding rules to obtain rough marginal data.

These results show that there is something intermediate between the counsel of perfection which regards anything but marginal data as absolutely useless for decision-making and the uncritical calculations which employ average or total figures largely as they are received from the accountants' records. Because economic information is, in any event, notoriously inaccurate, it may be that the crude and approximative marginal figures which are obtained with the aid of the preceding rules will often be as satisfactory as anything that can reasonably be hoped for. Even if this is not quite true, experience seems to suggest that such rough adjustments will in many cases eliminate the bulk of the error which arises from the use of average data as a basis for decision-making. It is even plausible that efforts to obtain better marginal data will sometimes cost more to obtain than they can add to the profits of the firm.

REFERENCE

Robinson, Joan, *The Economics of Imperfect Competition*, Macmillan, London, 1933, Chapter 2.

CHAPTER FOUR

Maximization, minimization, and elementary differential calculus

1. Differential Calculus and Marginal Analysis

Before we get down to the differential calculus and its relationship to marginal analysis, it is necessary to translate the marginal concept into algebraic notation. Suppose, for example, that an additional $5 in advertising expenditure were to increase a firm's sales by $100. We then evaluate the marginal sales contribution of advertising as $100/5 = 20$. In algebraic notation, if S represents sales volume and A symbolizes the amount of advertising, it is customary to represent an addition to (change in) S and A by ΔS and ΔA respectively,[1] so that the marginal sales contribution of advertising may be written as $\Delta S/\Delta A$.

It will be noted that this expression does not specify whether the change in advertising expenditure is large or small—in the numerical example we took $\Delta A = \$5$. But this ambiguity leads to a further difficulty because it means that the value of the marginal yield figure itself may not be determined. For example, suppose we encounter a rather extreme diminishing-returns case in which the first thousand dollars adds $40,000 to the sales of a small retailer, but a second thousand in advertising adds very little more, and a third thousand poured into a saturated market repels customers and actually reduces sales by $10,000. If we take $\Delta A = \$1000$, then the marginal yield,

---

[1] Δ is the (upper-case) Greek letter, delta.

$$\frac{\Delta S}{\Delta A} = \frac{40,000}{1000} = 40.$$

But if $\Delta A = \$2000$, we have

$$\frac{\Delta S}{\Delta A} = \frac{40,000 + 0}{2000} = 20$$

and finally, if $\Delta A = \$3000$, we obtain

$$\frac{\Delta S}{\Delta A} = \frac{40,000 + 0 - 10,000}{3000} = 10.$$

In other words, the value of the marginal yield of advertising varies with the magnitude of ΔA, the magnitude of the increment in advertising expenditure whose effect we decide to consider, and it is easy to see that a similar problem arises even in less extreme examples.

The heart of the difficulty is that if ΔA is a large number, the marginal measure becomes a rather crude over-all representation of the effects of a change in expenditure, and it therefore becomes a relatively blunt decision-making tool. For example, if a marginal computation is made using $\Delta A = \$3000$ in the preceding illustration, we have already noted that we obtain

$$\frac{\Delta S}{\Delta A} = \frac{40,000 + 0 - 10,000}{3000} = 10.$$

In other words, this calculation indicates that a dollar in advertising adds $10 to this retailer's sales and may suggest to him that it pays hand over fist to spend even more on promotion. But a more detailed calculation shows that he should actually have stopped after his first $1000 promotional outlay.

We see, then, that the larger the magnitude of the investigated change in a decision variable whose effect we calculate, i.e., the larger the value of the denominator in the marginal value fraction, the cruder becomes the marginal measure. It becomes a rough average measure of the effects of advertising or whatever we happen to be examining, and, as in the preceding example, it may conceal more than it reveals.

This naturally suggests that we ought to stick to very small changes. But, at least in principle, so long as we pick any fixed value for the increment in the decision variable, i.e., if we take $\Delta A = \$2$, we are faced with the problem that a calculation employing an even finer unit of change might give us even more detailed and perhaps different information.

The basic approach of the differential calculus is designed to cope with precisely this problem. It proceeds by operating, conceptually, with smaller and smaller units and *taking as the value of the marginal fraction the limit of the value of these fractions as the magnitude of the denominator decreases indefinitely.* For example, suppose we obtain the data in the following table:

ΔA	8	4	2	1	0.5	0.25	etc.
ΔS	30.4	13.6	6.4	3.1	1.525	0.75625	...
$\Delta S/\Delta A$	3.8	3.4	3.2	3.1	3.05	3.025	...

As we consider smaller and smaller changes in advertising expenditure, their contribution to sales also grow correspondingly insignificant,[2] e.g., as advertising expenditure drops from 8 to 2, its contribution to sales falls from 30.4 to 6.4. But the ratio of these magnitudes, $\Delta S/\Delta A$, may nevertheless vary relatively little because both numerator and denominator are going in the same direction. In our rather obviously cooked-up example the ratio $\Delta S/\Delta A$ shows a remarkably simple pattern, and it is easy to see where it is heading. Keep up the process of cutting down on ΔA long enough and the difference between the corresponding value of $\Delta S/\Delta A$ and the number 3 will not be worth mentioning—it can be made to approximate 3 to whatever degree of accuracy we desire. In standard mathematical terminology we say that *as ΔA approaches zero the fraction $\Delta S/\Delta A$ approaches the limit* 3. This limit number, 3, is represented by the symbol dS/dA or, sometimes, by S' and is called the *first derivative of sales with respect to advertising expenditure.*

More generally, then, *the first derivative, dy/dx, of any variable, y, with respect to another variable, x,* may be described as the limit value of the marginal change in y per unit change in x when the change in x is made to be smaller and smaller, i.e., when the change approaches zero. This combination of concepts—the notion of a limit number which is approached by an infinite sequence of numbers and the definition of the derivative are the fundamental concepts of the differential calculus.

2. Rules of Differentiation

Let us see now how these definitions can be employed. Suppose that we have, by statistical or other means, obtained an algebraic relationship between sales and advertising expenditure. To illustrate the logic of the procedure, we consider three (rather implausible) cases:

---

[2] Of course it must be recognized that this illustration is economic nonsense. Increases in most types of advertising cannot be bought in units as small as $8—one cannot even talk to an advertising man for that price. It should also be noted that a minimum level of expenditure is likely to be required before the advertising has any impact on sales, but the table does not assume that we start off with zero advertising. We may be asking whether the firm should *increase or decrease* its current million-dollar budget so that even if ΔA is only $6 the total A is increased to $1,000,006.

(a) $S = 50{,}000$ (S a constant unaffected by A).

(b) $S = 3A$ (relationship of proportionality).

(c) $S = 3A^2$ (second-degree relationship).

The first two cases are trivial and we can easily guess at the derivatives that will be involved. In the first case sales are fixed and independent of the level of advertising so that we may conclude, correctly, that $dS/dA = 0$, i.e., that the marginal sales yield of advertising is zero. This is a special case of the general

RULE 1. *Constants:* The derivative of any constant with respect to any variable is always zero.

The second (linear) case is only slightly more complex. It is obvious that the expression in question tells us that every unit increase in A increases sales by \$3, for sales then increase from $3A$ to $3(A + 1) = 3A + 3$. Therefore, $dS/dA = 3$. We thus have

RULE 2. *First-degree terms:* In any first-degree relationship, $y = bx$, where b is any number, we have

$$\frac{dy}{dx} = b.$$

It is only in the third-case relationship, $S = 3A^2$, that the calculation becomes slightly more complicated and that it seems worth going through a systematic derivation of the value of dy/dx. The following rather simple algebraic argument is typical of the procedures used in arriving at the various differentiation formulae which are listed below. If the reader understands it thoroughly he will have some comprehension of the elements of the logical structure of the differential calculus.

Our object is to evaluate dS/dA in the case $S = 3A^2$. For this purpose we begin by determining the marginal fraction $\Delta S/\Delta A$, then finding what happens to it as ΔA approaches zero, just as described in the previous section. We start off by adding any increment, ΔA, to the A in our equation $S = 3A^2$ to see what effect this has on S. This changes the value of S, so that, by the definition of ΔS, the procedure replaces S by $S + \Delta S$. We therefore obtain

$S + \Delta S = 3(A + \Delta A)^2 = 3[A^2 + 2A\Delta A + (\Delta A)^2]$ (by squaring and multiplying out)

$$= 3A^2 + 6A\Delta A + 3(\Delta A)^2.$$

But we are looking for ΔS, not for $S + \Delta S$. To obtain an expression for ΔS, we simply subtract the expression $S = 3A^2$ from the preceding $S + \Delta S$ equation. This gives us

$$\Delta S = S + \Delta S - S = 3A^2 + 6A\Delta A + 3(\Delta A)^2 - 3A^2 = 6A\Delta A + 3(\Delta A)^2.$$

That is, $$\Delta S = 6A\Delta A + 3(\Delta A)^2.$$

From the preceding expression for ΔS we now find the marginal sales contribution of advertising, $\Delta S/\Delta A$, by dividing both sides of the equation through by ΔA to obtain

$$\frac{\Delta S}{\Delta A} = \frac{6A\Delta A}{\Delta A} + \frac{3(\Delta A)^2}{\Delta A} = 6A + 3\Delta A.$$

But the derivative, dS/dA is the limit of $\Delta S/\Delta A$ as ΔA approaches zero (written $\Delta A \to 0$), i.e., in conventional notation

$$\frac{dS}{dA} = \lim_{\Delta A \to 0} \frac{\Delta S}{\Delta A} = \lim_{\Delta A \to 0} (6A + 3\Delta A) = 6A$$

that is, the term $3\Delta A$, which clearly approaches zero when ΔA approaches zero, simply drops out in the limit. Hence we have our result for $S = 3A^2$, that in this case $dS/dA = 6A$.

More generally (the derivation follows the preceding one step by step)[3] we have

RULE 3. *Power terms:* For any constants a and b, if $y = ax^b$, then

$$\frac{dy}{dx} = bax^{b-1}.$$

Example: The derivative of $4x^{10}$ is $4 \cdot 10x^9 = 40x^9$.

Several other frequently used rules of the differential calculus are now given and their use illustrated:

RULE 4. *Sums:* The derivative of a sum of several terms is the sum of the derivatives of these terms, i.e., if $y = y_1 + y_2$, then

$$\frac{dy}{dx} = \frac{dy_1}{dx} + \frac{dy_2}{dx}.$$

Example: Given $y = 500 - 2x + 5x^4$. We know by Rules 1–3 that the derivative of 500 is zero, that of $-2x$ is -2, and that of $5x^4$ is $4 \times 5x^3 = 20x^3$. Hence, in this case,

$$\frac{dy}{dx} = 0 - 2 + 20x^3 = -2 + 20x^3.$$

[3] There is one complication. Raising $(x + \Delta x)$ to the bth power is ordinarily more complicated than squaring it. If b is an integer (a whole number) we employ the binomial theorem of high school algebra to multiply out $(x + \Delta x)^b$. The proof then proceeds exactly as above.

Note that Rules 1 and 2 are both special cases of Rule 3 in which $b = 0$ and $b = 1$ respectively.

RULE 5. *Miscellaneous formulas:*

(a) if $y = a \sin bx$, $dy/dx = ab \cos bx$

(b) if $y = a \cos bx$, $dy/dx = -ab \sin bx$

(c)[4] if $y = ae^{bx}$, $dy/dx = bae^{bx}$.

Thus, in particular, ae^x is an expression (indeed the only expression) which is equal to its own derivative, i.e.,

(d) if $y = ae^x$, $dy/dx = ae^x \ (= y)$

(e)[5] if $y = a \log_e bx$, $dy/dx = a/x$.

RULE 6. *Products:* The derivative of the product of two expressions is the product of the (undifferentiated) second expression multiplied by the derivative of the first plus the first multiplied by the derivative of the second; that is, if $y = y_1 y_2$, then

$$\frac{dy}{dx} = y_2 \frac{dy_1}{dx} + y_1 \frac{dy_2}{dx}.$$

Example: Given $y = 6x^4 \sin \left(\frac{1}{3}x\right)$ find dy/dx. We know by Rule 3 that the derivative of $6x^4$ is $24x^3$, and by Rule 5a that the derivative of $\sin \left(\frac{1}{3}x\right)$ is $\frac{1}{3}\cos \frac{1}{3}x$. Hence by Rule 6,

$$\frac{dy}{dx} = 24x^3 \sin \left(\frac{1}{3}x\right) + 6x^4 \left[\frac{1}{3}\cos \left(\frac{1}{3}x\right)\right]$$

$$= 24x^3 \sin \left(\frac{1}{3}x\right) + 2x^4 \cos \left(\frac{1}{3}x\right).$$

RULE 7. *Division:* If y is the ratio of two expressions, its derivative is the denominator multiplied by the derivative of the numerator *minus* the numerator multiplied by the derivative of the denominator all divided by

---

[4] Here e ($= 2.718$ approximately) is the number that represents the principal which would accrue after one year if one dollar were compounded at *every* instant over the year at a 1 per cent (annual) rate of interest. This number occupies an extremely important position in the differential calculus, particularly in the theory of growth.

[5] $\log_e x$ (the logarithm of x to the base e) is defined by the relationship $x = e^{\log_e x}$. In other words, $\log_e x$ is a number L, such that, when e is raised to the power L the result is equal to x. This number has most of the convenient properties of the common logarithm (i.e., the logarithm to the base 10; $x = 10^{\log_{10} x}$). For example, by the definition that $e^a \cdot e^b = e^{(a+b)}$, for the product of any two numbers x and z,

$$x \cdot z = e^{\log_e x} \cdot e^{\log_e z} = e^{\log_e x + \log_e z}.$$

Thus two numbers can be multiplied by adding up their logarithms (to the base e) and then finding the number whose logarithm is equal to this sum.

One reason logarithms to the base e are employed in much scientific work is that they have such a simple differentiation rule.

the square of the denominator;[6] i.e., if $y = y_1/y_2$ then

$$\frac{dy}{dx} = \frac{y_2(dy_1/dx) - y_1(dy_2/dx)}{y_2^2}.$$

Example: If $y = \log_e x/e^{3x}$ then, since the derivative of $\log_e x$ is $1/x$ and that of e^{3x} is $3e^{3x}$, we have

$$\frac{dy}{dx} = \frac{e^{3x}(1/x) - 3(\log_e x)e^{3x}}{(e^{3x})^2}$$

where, by definition, $(e^{3x})^2 = e^{6x}$.

RULE 8. *Function of a function:* If y is a function of some variable z whose value is, in turn, a function of another variable, x, then the derivative of y with respect to x equals the derivative of y with respect to z multiplied by the derivative of z with respect to x, i.e.,

$$dy/dx = dy/dz \cdot dz/dx.$$

Example: If $y = \log_e (3x^2)$, write $z = 3x^2$ so that $y = \log_e (z)$ and by rule 8 we can now differentiate these two simpler expressions one at a time and just multiply the results to obtain

$$\frac{dy}{dx} = \frac{d(\log_e z)}{dz} \cdot \frac{dz}{dx} = \frac{1}{z} 6x = \left(\frac{1}{3x^2}\right) 6x = \frac{2}{x}.$$

PROBLEMS

Differentiate the following:

1. $y = 11x^7 - 16x^2 + 3$

2. $y = -4x^{12} + 17^2 + 2 \cos 4x$

3. $y = 7x^{-6}(= 7/x^6)$

4. $y = e^{3x} \sin x$

5. $y = e^{3x}/\sin x$

6. $y = e^{3x}/\log x$

7. $y = 3 \sin 5x^4$

8. $y = 8e^{2x^{-2}}$

[6] Rule 7 is a direct consequence of Rules 6 (multiplication), 3 (powers), and 8 (function of a function). For $y = y_1/y_2$ can be written as $y_1 y_2^{-1}$ (by definition of the power -1). Hence $dy/dx = y_2^{-1} dy_1/dx + y_1 dy_2^{-1}/dx$. But, by Rules 3 and 8,

$$\frac{dy_2^{-1}}{dx} = \frac{-1y_2^{-2} dy_2}{dx} = \frac{-(dy_2/dx)}{y_2^2}.$$

Hence, substituting this into our last expression for dy/dx, we have

$$\frac{dy}{dx} = \frac{y_2^{-1} dy_1}{dx} - \frac{y_1(dy_2/dx)}{y_2^2}$$

and (since $y_2^{-1} = 1/y_2 = y_2/y_2^2$) this is equal to

$$\frac{y_2(dy_1/dx)}{y_2^2} - \frac{y_1(dy_2/dx)}{y_2^2} = \frac{(y_2 dy_1/dx) - (y_1 dy_2/dx)}{y_2^2}.$$

3. *Geometric Interpretation*

It is useful at this point to translate the derivative into graphic terms. Consider the relationship between the quantity, Q, of a commodity marketed by some firm and the total profit, R, which accrues to it. Such a graph is depicted as curve PP' in Figure 1.

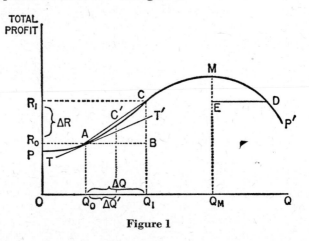

Figure 1

First, it will be recalled that the slope of a line is defined as the increase in its height per unit move *to the right*. For example, as we move to the right from point Q_0 to Q_1, the curve rises from R_0 to R_1. Hence its (average) slope over this stretch is $(R_1 - R_0)/(Q_1 - Q_0)$ or CB/AB. Similarly, we note that as we move to the right from point E to point D, the graph goes downhill, so that the slope, EM/ED, is negative (there is a *negative* increase in the height of the curve).

Now the marginal profitability of an increase in output, ΔQ, is defined as ΔR over ΔQ. But it will be observed that ΔQ, the increment in Q, is $Q_1 - Q_0$ and, similarly, that ΔR is $R_1 - R_0$. Hence the slope of the curve and the marginal profitability are the same number. More generally, let y be some variable whose value depends on x. Then the slope of the curve of this relationship represents the marginal effect on y of a change in x.

It will be noted that the slope of the curve changes as we move along the diagram. That is why the value of $\Delta R/\Delta Q$ is ambiguous and why we turn to the concept of the derivative. By letting the interval which represents ΔQ grow smaller and smaller, it more and more closely approximates a single point. That is, if from ΔQ we shift our attention to smaller interval $\Delta Q'$, and so on, we ultimately approach a state where nothing is left but point Q_0. We then interpret the derivative of the function at point Q_0 as the slope of the graph at that point.

However, this slope itself cannot be defined in the same way as the slope of a finite interval, because at a point there is neither a change in Q nor any change in R. That is, at A there is neither a ΔQ nor a ΔR, or if we wish, they are both equal to zero.

This is where the limit process is invoked. The slope at A is *defined* as the limit of the slope of AC as ΔQ approaches zero. Geometrically, this limit turns out to be the slope of the tangent TT' at point A. We see this by noting that our original marginal figure, $\Delta R/\Delta Q$, is the slope of straight line chord AC. Our second approximation is the slope of AC' and so on. It is clear intuitively that this sequence of slopes approaches the slope of the tangent TT'.

In sum, the derivative of any relationship between y and x with respect to x at some value x^* of x is represented by the slope of the tangent (at point $x = x^*$) to the curve which represents the relationship.

We can use this interpretation to discuss the problem of optimization. Suppose management desires to maximize the firm's total profits. The total profit graph in Figure 1 is shaped like a hill, and the output, OQ_m, which maximizes profits is the point directly below the peak of the hill, M.

This gives us a derivative criterion for locating point M. At points to the left of Q_m the slope of the curve (the derivative) is positive. Such points cannot be optimal because a movement to the right from any one of them will increase profits. Similarly, any point to the right of Q_m cannot be optimal because there we are going downhill (negative derivative) so that a retreat (a reduction in the size of output, Q) will increase profits. Only when the derivative is zero so that we are neither at the upgrade nor downgrade side of a profit hill is it possible for us to be at an optimal point. Note that this condition is satisfied at point M, the top of the profit curve, which is level because it is the borderline between the uphill and the downhill segments of the curve.

This result, it should be noted, corresponds to our earlier Marginal Analysis Rule (Section 2 of Chapter 3) that any activity should, if possible, be carried to a point where its marginal net benefit is zero.

Example: Find the output, Q, which maximizes profit, R, when given the relationship $R = 300 + 1200Q - Q^2$.

Differentiating, we have

$$\frac{dR}{dQ} = 1200 - 2Q.$$

Hence the only point at which this derivative is zero is where

$$1200 - 2Q = 0$$

i.e., where $2Q = 1200$ or $Q = 600$.

4. *Nondifferentiability and Limited Variable Range Problems*

The results of the preceding section at first sight seem to suggest the following rule: To find the value of x which maximizes the value of y, given some relationship $y = f(x)$ between these variables, find the derivative, dy/dx, set it equal to zero and solve for x. There is, indeed, some validity to this procedure but it has important limitations which must be understood clearly. We shall now examine several cases in which the rule is meaningless, inapplicable, or completely incorrect. Each of these cases is of fundamental importance and not just a minor exception to be acknowledged summarily and then forgotten.

Case 1. *Discontinuities and Kinks*

In Figures 2a and 2b we represent relationships between y and x which exhibit two important types of irregularity. At point B there is a sharp corner or *kink* in the graph. Above point x_a there is an even more serious type of irregularity—the graph has a complete break or *discontinuity*, AA'.

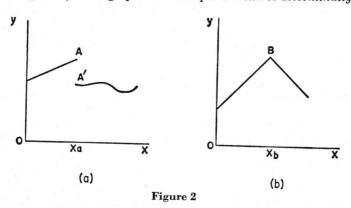

(a)   (b)

Figure 2

The difficulty is that at such points the slope, that is the derivative, is not even defined. There is no tangent to the curves at the points directly above x_a or x_b. It is to be noted that points A and B both represent maxima of the functions, i.e., at x_a or at x_b y becomes as large as possible. But at neither point is dy/dx equal to zero because we cannot even impute the usual meaning to the concept at such a point. Hence we conclude:

In the presence of kinks or discontinuities the derivative is not defined, so it may not be possible to employ the maximization criterion $dy/dx = 0$.

Case 2. *Limitations on the Values of the Variables*

In Figures 3a and 3b are represented two cases in which the levels of output Q are restricted. The unlikely situation in Figure 3a might be referred to as the crop restriction subsidy case. Here the firm is in the peculiar position that the less it produces and sells, the higher the profit it makes. Clearly, however, the smallest output, Q, which the firm can produce is zero, so that this is the point of maximum profits. Actually, analogous situations are frequently encountered in the multi-product firms which are

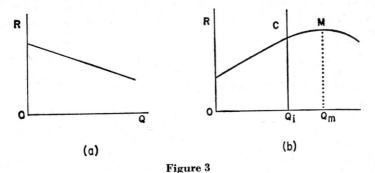

(a)   (b)

Figure 3

typical of our economy. If the production of one of the outputs of the firm incurs a loss, the most profitable (least costly) output of that product will be zero though the total profit of the firm as a whole (R) may be a positive number because its other products bring in enough money to keep the company in the black.

In this situation we note that at the point of maximum profits the slope of the graph is negative ($dR/dQ < 0$) so that a further decrease in output, if it were possible, would appear to be called for. But, since such a reduction is not possible, we must be satisfied with a level of production at which the calculus maximization criterion fails: dR/dQ, i.e., the marginal profit yield of Q is not equal to zero.

A similar difficulty occurs in somewhat more striking form in the situation shown in Figure 3b. Here we assume that the firm has a limited output capacity and that it can therefore produce no more than quantity OQ_i. In this diagram there is a level maximum point, M, at which the derivative maximum condition $dR/dQ = 0$ is satisfied. However, this maximum is economically irrelevant because the firm cannot attain it even though it might well like to do so. The maximum profit feasible point is, in fact, C where $dR/dQ > 0$ so that the derivative maximization rule is violated.

The two cases so far considered in which this rule breaks down can be handled effectively only by means of a totally new approach for the determination of optimal values of the variables. In the simple examples shown in Figures 2 and 3 the optimal values of x and Q are, of course, obvious on inspection. Particularly in Figure 3b the answer seems easy—to maximize its profits the firm should produce as much as it can. But when the number of variables involved is considerable, as it usually is in practice—for example, when the firm is dividing up its limited productive capacity among many hundreds of products—the answer is far from obvious.

To deal with such optimization problems (frequently encountered in economics) where the marginal maximization condition fails, a new body of analysis, called *mathematical programming*, has been developed. This analysis, which has turned out to be of very great significance for economics and business decision-making, is discussed in considerable detail in the next three chapters.

5. Curvature Conditions of Maximization and Minimization

A totally different but less serious sort of difficulty for the calculus maximum rule is illustrated in Figure 4. It will be observed that the condition $dR/dQ = 0$ is satisfied not only at the maximum point A. It also holds at point B where profit is at its minimum (!) and at any point in the

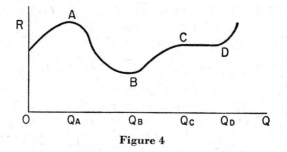

Figure 4

level stretch CD. Except in the mathematical programming cases discussed in the previous section, we may conclude that wherever profits are maximized, $dR/dQ = 0$ but the converse is *not* true: we may be at an output such as OQ_B where $dR/dQ = 0$ and yet profit will not be maximized at that point.

The source of the difficulty is easily seen. The marginal maximization condition dR/dQ assures us only that we are at a level stretch on the profit hill—we are neither going uphill nor downhill. But being on a piece of level ground is obviously no guarantee that we are on top of a hill.

To take care of this difficulty we need some more information. We require another condition (called a *second-order condition*) which assures us that we have just stopped going uphill, and that if we go any further we will begin to descend. If this is true, and if we are at a level point, we must clearly be at the top of a hill. This elementary and apparently trivial argument lies behind a considerable body of relatively deep analysis.

Unlike the problems of the preceding section, our present difficulties can normally be taken care of with the help of the differential calculus. The second-order condition which has just been described is essentially a requirement about the behavior of the slope of the curve. The (first-order) condition $dR/dQ = 0$ states that the slope must be zero at a profit-maximizing point. The second-order condition states that the slope must previously have been positive, i.e., that there $dR/dQ > 0$ (we must have been going uphill as we moved toward point A from the left) and that thereafter the slope must become negative (further movement to the right, i.e., further increases in production after output level OQ_A must reduce total profit). In sum, the second-order condition requires that dR/dQ fall as output increases. These two requirements are summarized graphically in Figure 5. Here, rather than representing *total* profit on the vertical axis, as we did before, we have instead measured the *marginal* profitability of output, dR/dQ, along that axis. The first-order condition, then, requires that the graph cut the horizontal axis ($dR/dQ = 0$) at the profit-maximizing output OQ_A. *The second-order condition requires that the slope of the curve at that point be negative*, so that dR/dQ will be positive to the left of Q_A and negative to its right.

This second order is then a condition which refers to the behavior of the curve in Figure 5. It states that the slope of the dR/dQ curve must be negative. But dR/dQ is, in turn, itself a slope—the slope of the profit graph. Hence our second-order condition is a statement about the slope of a slope. It involves what is called *a second derivative*.

The process used to find a second derivative (written d^2y/dx^2 or y'') is a simple repetition of that used to find the first derivative. We just differentiate (to find a slope) and then differentiate again (to find the slope of the slope curve). For example, given $y = 4x^3$, we know that $dy/dx = 12x^2$ and (by repeated differentiation) $d^2y/dx^2 = 24x$.

We then have the following summary rule: To find the maximum value of any relationship between two variables, y and x, compute dy/dx and determine the values of x for which this has the value zero. If for any of these values of x we also find d^2y/dx^2 is negative (dy/dx falling, as in Figure 5) then this is a true maximum point.

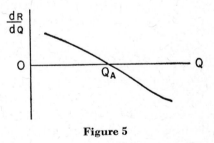

Figure 5

Minimization, too, can occur in an optimality calculation. For example, instead of maximizing profit we may wish to find the output level which minimizes total cost. The preceding rule is easily modified to deal with this sort of problem. The reader should convince himself that the only required change is that in minimization the second derivative must be positive.[7]

Example: Find the maximizing value of x for

$$y = 100 + 12x - x^3.$$

Here $dy/dx = 12 - 3x^2$, so that if $dy/dx = 0$ we must have

$$12 - 3x^2 = 0, \quad \text{i.e., } 3x^2 = 12, \quad x^2 = 4, \quad x = \pm 2.$$

To find which of these two numbers (if either) yields a maximum value of y, we find that $d^2y/dx^2 = -6x$ which is negative for $x = +2$ and positive for $x = -2$. Hence $x = +2$ yields a maximum value of y:

$$100 + (12)(2) - (2)^3 = 116$$

and $x = -2$ yields a minimum value of y:

$$100 + (12)(-2) - (-2)^3 = 84.$$

PROBLEMS

1. Find the second derivatives of
     (a) $y = 3x^5 + 15x$
     (b) $2 \log 4x$.

2. (a) Does $y = 50 + 90x - 5x^2$ have a maximum or a minimum? What is the value of x at that point?
     (b) How about $y = 15x^2$?

6. *Local and Global Optima*

One more important warning is still required. There is a pitfall in the definition of the words "maximum" and "minimum" as used in ordinary discussions involving the differential calculus. A maximum is used to denote the top of a hill in the graph of the function. But the graph may contain several hills (each is then called a *local maximum*) and the calculus procedure as described offers us no guarantee that we have found the highest hill (called a *global maximum*). Moreover, the graph may contain higher points which are not hilltops. This was in fact the case in the last example whose graph is shown in Figure 6. It is to be noted that our (local) maximum point A is below points such as B and our (local) minimum point C is above points such as D. In this case no global maximum or minimum points exist because y keeps going downhill indefinitely as we move to the

---

[7] Actually, slightly weaker conditions will do in both cases. If the second derivative is zero but the fourth derivative, d^4y/dx^4, is negative, the point in question is still a maximum; if this derivative is positive it is a minimum. A similar result holds for the case where the fourth derivative is also zero but the sixth is not, and so on.

right beyond A and it rises indefinitely to the left of C. Hence it is pointless to look for a global maximum or minimum here. But even in a problem in which there are a number of local maxima, one of which is a global optimum, the differential calculus methods just described will not do the trick.

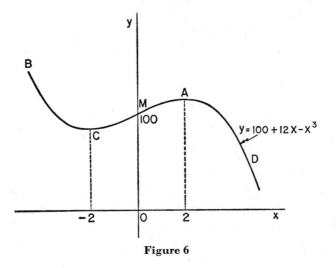

Figure 6

However, mathematical programming has made some progress in dealing with this problem as will be indicated in the chapter on integer programming.

7. *Maximization in Many Variable Relationships:* *Partial Differentiation*

Usually more than two variables will be involved in an economic relationship. For example, total profit, R, will depend not only on the level of output, Q. It will also depend on the firm's advertising expenditure, A, on the price, P, charged for some competing product, and so on. If these four variables, R, Q, A, and P, were the only ones involved we would write

$$R = f(Q, A, P)$$

which is read, "R is a function of Q, A, and P." This means only that the level of total profit depends in some specified manner on the levels of the firm's output, its advertising expenditure, and the price of the competing product.

Given such a multi-variable relationship, we may again ask about the effect of a change in Q, A, and P on total profits. In doing so we investigate the marginal profit effects of a change of one or more of these variables. In particular, we may wish to see what happens when we vary the value of one of the variables and the values of the others do not change from given amounts. As is to be expected, there is a form of the derivative which corresponds to such an "other things being equal" marginal concept. It is called the *partial derivative*. For example, if we wish to examine the effect (at a point) of a change in advertising expenditure on total profit for any specified and unchanging levels of Q and P, we compute the partial derivative of total profit with respect to advertising expenditure, which is written $\partial R/\partial A$.

The procedures for partial differentiation are a simple and intuitively comprehensible extension of the ordinary differentiation process. We just treat as constants all variables other than the two which are directly involved. This is the natural interpretation of the idea that the values of all other variables are held constant. An example will make this clear. Given

$$y = 5x^4 + 55x^3 \log z + 3xz - 12z^2 + 4$$

to find $\partial y/\partial x$ we treat z as a constant so that the relationship may be rewritten as

$$y = 5x^4 + (55 \log z)x^3 + (3z)x - (12z^2 - 4).$$

None of the terms in parentheses contains either a y or an x, so that each such term is treated as a constant number, i.e., for purposes of partial differentiation it is treated like the equation

$$y = ax^4 + bx^3 + cx + d$$

where a, b, c, and d are constants. Thus we have

$$\frac{\partial y}{\partial x} = 4ax^3 + 3bx^2 + c = 20x^3 + 3(55 \log z)x^2 + 3z.$$

The term $d = -(12z^2 + 4)$ drops out in partial differentiation with respect to x because the derivative of a constant is always zero.

Employing the partial differentiation concept, we can now extend our discussion of the calculus minimization and maximization criteria. We shall discuss only the first-order conditions because the second-order conditions are rather complex in this case and because they will not be used in the subsequent discussion.[8]

Figure 7 is a geometric representation of a three-variable case. Here the graph of the profit relationship is a three-dimensional hill. Any point on the "floor" of the diagram represents a pair of values of Q and A. For

---

[8] These conditions have in fact played an important role in comparative statics analysis. The conditions are discussed and used in the Mathematical Appendix to J. R. Hicks' *Value and Capital*, 2nd Edition, Oxford University Press, New York, 1946, and in Chapter IV and Appendix A of Paul A. Samuelson's *Foundations of Economic Analysis*, Harvard University Press, Cambridge, Mass., 1948. For a good introductory exposition see James M. Henderson and Richard E. Quandt, *Microeconomic Theory*, McGraw-Hill Book Company, Inc., New York, 1958, especially Chapters 2 and 3.

example, point K represents a situation in which the firm decides on output level OQ_k and on advertising expenditure OA_k. Moreover, the profits

to be earned by this output-advertising expenditure combination are represented by the length of the vertical line KK' from point K to the point K' on the profit surface directly above it.

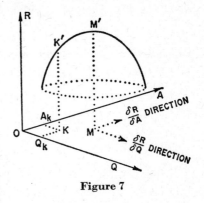

Figure 7

Here the profit-maximizing output-advertising expenditure combination is obviously M, and it will be noted that at its highest point, M', the profit surface is again level. This means that the slope of any cross section is zero at that point (for otherwise we would be going uphill or downhill and hence we would not be at a maximum). In particular, this means that as we move directly toward the right (increase Q and hold A constant) we must find the profit surface level, i.e., we must have $\partial R/\partial Q = 0$. Similarly, a small move directly toward the rear of the diagram (increasing A and holding Q constant) must also encounter a level profit surface so that $\partial R/\partial A = 0$.

More generally, in the $n + 1$ variable case, $y = f(x_1, \ldots, x_n)$, if we are to be at a maximum point we must have the n relationships

$$\partial y/\partial x_1 = 0, \quad \partial y/\partial x_2 = 0, \quad \ldots, \quad \partial y/\partial x_n = 0$$

so that no small change in value in any of the variables $x_1, x_2, \ldots, x_n$ will increase y. These are the first-order maximum or minimum conditions in the many-variable case.

The way this helps us to find the maximizing or minimizing values of the variables $x_1, x_2, \ldots, x_n$ is now straightforward, at least in principle. The conditions $\partial y/\partial x_1 = 0$, etc., are n equations in the n unknowns; and if they can be solved simultaneously for the values of the x's, they will yield the maximum or minimum values (if the appropriate second-order conditions are satisfied).

Example: Assuming that the second-order conditions are satisfied, find the profit-maximizing values of Q and A. Given the relationship

$$R = 400 - 3Q^2 - 4Q + 2QA - 5A^2 + 48A$$

we take $\partial R/\partial Q$ and $\partial R/\partial A$ and set them equal to zero to obtain

$$\frac{\partial R}{\partial Q} = -6Q - 4 + 2A = 0, \quad \text{i.e.,} \quad -6Q + 2A = 4$$

$$\frac{\partial R}{\partial A} = 2Q - 10A + 48 = 0, \quad \text{i.e.,} \quad 2Q - 10A = -48.$$

To eliminate the terms containing the A's, multiply the first equation by 5 to obtain

$$-30Q + 10A = 20$$

and add this to the second equation to yield

$$-28Q = -28 \quad \text{or} \quad Q = 1.$$

Substitution of this value into the very first equation gives

$$-6 \times 1 + 2A = 4 \quad \text{or} \quad 2A = 10, \quad \text{so that } A = 5.$$

Hence $Q = 1$ and $A = 5$ are the output and advertising expenditure levels which maximize total profit.

PROBLEMS

Which values of the variables satisfy the first-order maximum or minimum conditions in the following relationships?

1. $R = 737 - 5Q^2 + 22A + QA - 4A^2 + 17Q$

2. $y = 83.4 + x^2 + 26x - 6xz - 36z + 2z^2.$

8. Constrained Maxima: Lagrange Multipliers

We have already come across a number of cases in which the range of variation of the variables was restricted. Maximization or minimization in such cases becomes a problem of finding the largest or smallest values which can be achieved within the permitted ranges of the variables. A problem of this sort is said to be one of *constrained* maximization, and the relationships which restrict the range of variation of the variables are called *constraints* or *side conditions*. Problems involving constraints occur frequently in economics, as we shall see in the next chapter.

The relationship between a constrained and an unconstrained maximization problem can be illustrated with the aid of a geographic analogy. If we seek the location of the highest point on earth, we will end up with the latitude and longitude of the peak of Mount Everest. But if this altitude maximization problem is constrained by the condition that we must remain within the continental limits of the United States, two changes will occur: (1) we will end up with different latitude and longitude numbers, and (2) the height of the maximum point will be decreased. Of course, if the constraint had instead only required us to stay within the Asiatic continent, rather than the United States, our original (unconstrained) answer would have remained valid. Hence we conclude that a constraint usually will, but need not always, change the values of the "independent variables"; it usually will (but need not) decrease the value of the item being maximized, and, at best it will leave that value unaffected.

Let us now consider a specific maximization problem. A firm has 100 (thousand) dollars to spend on labor and raw materials in the next year. Let L be the quantity of labor it hires and let its (annual) price per unit be 2 (thousand dollars). Moreover, let the quantity of raw material bought be M, and let it have a price of 1 (thousand dollars) per unit. Then the firm is operating under the budget constraint that its total expenditure on these two items be 100, i.e., that

$$2L + M = 100.$$

For subsequent reference it is important to note that this constraint is an *equation*. Suppose, moreover, for purposes of illustrative simplicity that the firm's output, Q, is related to L and M via the following improbable production function:

$$Q = 5LM.$$

To get as much output as possible out of its budget the firm must find the values of L and M which maximize Q but which satisfy the budget constraint. Again, in this section we deal only with first-order conditions.

One fairly straightforward way of solving this constrained maximum problem is to use the constraint to eliminate one of the variables. Thus $2L + M = 100$ gives $M = 100 - 2L$, and substituting this expression for M in the production function $Q = 5LM$ gives

$$Q = 5L(100 - 2L) = 500L - 10L^2.$$

We are then left with an ordinary unconstrained maximization problem involving only the two variables Q and L. This is solved, as before, by setting the first derivative equal to zero to determine the value of L, i.e., by solving

$$500 - 20L = 0$$

which gives $L = 25$. Now, substituting this into the budget constraint equation, we find that $M = 100 - 2L = 50$. This, then, is the solution. It will pay the firm to obtain 25 units of labor and 50 units of raw material.

Before discussing a second and far more powerful method of solving such constrained maximum or minimum problems, let us examine the problem geometrically. In Figure 8a the straight line BB' is the graph of the budget constraint $100 = 2L + M$. This graph shows how the budget constraint restricts the range of values of the variables L and M. It does not just set fixed upper or lower limits on their values. Rather, it states that only certain combinations of these values are admissible, i.e., those which satisfy the budget equation so that (like combination L_A and M_a) they are represented by points on this line. In economic terms, only combinations of labor and raw material quantities whose total value is equal to 100 are to be considered. All other points such as C or D represent input combinations which do not meet the firm's budget requirements.

Now, suppose we place Figure 8a flat on the floor and erect over it a

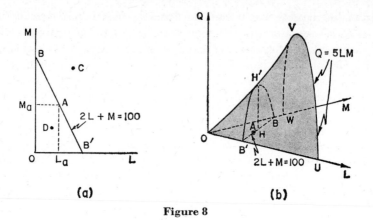

(a)   **(b)**

Figure 8

graphic representation of the production function $Q = 5LM$. This is done
in Figure 8b in which surface $OUVW$ represents the production function,
i.e., for each combination of inputs L and M it shows how much will be
produced.

In the constrained maximization problem we are not interested in the
entire production surface. We consider only that part of the surface which
corresponds to admissible input combinations whose locus is line BB' on
the floor of the diagram. The locus of the corresponding outputs is the arc
$BH'B'$ above line BB'. The optimum point which we seek is clearly point
H, which lies below the highest point on this arc, i.e., it yields the highest
attainable production level, HH'.

The method of solution which already has been described involves our
using the budget constraint to eliminate one of the variables. This is tantamount to our taking a cross section of the diagram which contains both
line BB' and arc $BH'B'$. In this way one of the dimensions is eliminated
from the diagram and we are left with an ordinary maximization problem
in two dimensions (variables).

Unfortunately, the method does not always work. The constraint does
not always take the simple form of our budget equation, so that it is not
always possible to eliminate one of the variables directly. For example, if
(in some nightmare) we encountered the constraint

$$\frac{L^M \log LM}{\sqrt{1 - L^2/M^5}} = 4$$

we would find it difficult to solve for M in terms of L as we did before. Such
cases must be dealt with by the method of *Lagrange multipliers* which is,
in any event, of far greater theoretical interest. Rigorous justification of
this procedure is beyond the scope of this book but it will be described and
explained intuitively.

It will be recalled that in the unconstrained maximization problems we proceeded by differentiating partially with respect to each variable in turn and setting each of these partial derivatives equal to zero. This gave us as many equations as variables and normally these could be solved for the optimum values of the variables. This method usually breaks down when there are constraint equations in the problem; for, in addition to the "partial derivative equal to zero" conditions, the constraint equations must also be satisfied. This means that the problem contains more equations than unknowns and is therefore, in normal circumstances, overdetermined.[9] To get out of this difficulty we introduce some artificial unknowns, as many as there are constraints, to increase the number of unknowns to equality with the number of partial derivative equations and constraint equations. These artificial unknowns are called *Lagrange multipliers.*

Let us rework our example to show how the method works, meanwhile offering some justification for the procedure. First we take our constraint $2L + M = 100$ and bring all the terms over to one side of the equation to obtain

$$2L + M - 100 = 0.$$

Next, we multiply the resulting expression on the left by an unknown constant, λ[10], and add the result to the production function $Q = 5LM$ to obtain the so-called Lagrangian expression

$$Q_\lambda = 5LM + \lambda(2L + M - 100).$$

The basic point is, roughly, that if the constraint is always satisfied the expression in parentheses will be equal to zero so that the Lagrangian expression Q_λ will behave exactly in the same way as does the production function. Whatever values of L and M maximize the one will automatically maximize the other. But the Lagrangian expression contains *three* symbols whose values are unknown, namely λ, L, and M. We may then solve the problem by differentiating partially with respect to each of the three unknowns, set the three results equal to zero, and solve these three equations for the three unknown values. This yields

$$\frac{\partial Q_\lambda}{\partial L} = 5M + 2\lambda = 0$$

$$\frac{\partial Q_\lambda}{\partial M} = 5L + \lambda = 0$$

$$\frac{\partial Q_\lambda}{\partial \lambda} = 2L + M - 100 = 0 \quad \text{(which is the budget constraint equation)}$$

[9] It is not true that equality of the number of equations and unknowns either guarantees or is necessary for solvability of a system of simultaneous equations. However, there is some presumption that this will be so. See below, Chapter 16, Section 1.

[10] λ is the Greek letter lambda, which is usually used for this purpose.

The three equations can be solved by multiplying the second equation through by 2 and subtracting from it the first equation to obtain $10L = 5M$ or $M = 2L$. Substituting this into the last equation we obtain $4L = 100$ or $L = 25$, and another simple substitution yields $M = 50$, $\lambda = -125$— the same result as before, except that, in addition, we have now obtained a value for λ.

It can be shown that this value of λ itself has a significant economic interpretation. In this case, $-\lambda$ is the marginal productivity of money—it indicates how much would be added to output if the input budget were increased from 100 to 101. We can check this roughly by noting that this dollar could be used to buy another unit of M, which would increase output from

$$Q = 5LM = 5 \cdot 25M = 125M \quad \text{to} \quad Q + \Delta Q = 125(M + 1)$$
$$= 125M + 125$$

so that $\quad\quad\quad \Delta Q \,(= \Delta Q/1 = \Delta Q/\Delta M) = 125 = -\lambda.$

More will be said about the interpretation of Lagrange multipliers in a later chapter.

Finally, we note that, if the problem has more than one constraint equation, to obtain the Lagrangian expression we multiply each of the constraints by a *different* unknown Lagrange multiplier and add them all to the original expression whose value is to be maximized.

Example: Maximize
$$y = 10xzw - 3w^2$$
subject to $x + z + w = 12$ and $x - w = 2$.

We rewrite the constraints as $x + z + w - 12 = 0$ and $x - w - 2 = 0$, and multiplying these respectively by λ_1 and λ_2 we can write the Lagrangian expression
$$y_\lambda = 10xzw - 3w^2 + \lambda_1(x + z + w - 12) + \lambda_2(x - w - 2).$$
The maximum (or minimum) value is then found from the equations

$$\frac{\partial y_\lambda}{\partial x} = 10zw + \lambda_1 + \lambda_2 = 0$$

$$\frac{\partial y_\lambda}{\partial z} = 10xw + \lambda_1 = 0$$

$$\frac{\partial y_\lambda}{\partial w} = 10xz - 6w + \lambda_1 - \lambda_2 = 0$$

$$\frac{\partial y_\lambda}{\partial \lambda_1} = x + z + w - 12 = 0$$

and $\quad\quad\quad \dfrac{\partial y_\lambda}{\partial \lambda_2} = x - w - 2 = 0$

where the last two lines are the constraint equations.

PROBLEMS

1. By both methods find the values which satisfy the first-order conditions for maximization of:

(a) $y = 10xw - 2w^2$ subject to $x + w = 12$

(b) $R = 737 - 5Q^2 + 22A + QA - 4A^2 + 17Q$ subject to

$$28Q + 13A = 40.$$

2. Compare your results in 1(b) with those for Problem 1 of the previous section.

3. Write out the Lagrangian expression for the problem: maximize

$$y = \log x^3 w$$

subject to

$$\cos x \cos w = 0.3 \quad \text{and} \quad \frac{x}{w^5} + e^w = 10.$$

9. Some Economic Applications of the Differential Calculus

In economics the differential calculus has had many fruitful applications. In fact, as we have already noted, economists have invented a special terminology for this technique, referring to it as *marginal analysis*. This application arises naturally in an investigation of the decision-making of business firms, consumers, and other economic units. For, in pursuing their goals, these units may be taken to *maximize* some measure of achievement, whether it be profits, national income, or some other such variable. It is convenient at this point to list some of the functional relationships which recur most frequently in the work of the economist:

(a) a production function, $Q = f(z)$, which records how the required quantity of labor or some raw material, z, varies with the production level, Q, of some commodity, e.g., Q may represent the number of shoes produced per week by a shoe factory;

(b) a cost function, $C = g(Q)$, which records the total expense, C, associated with production level Q;

(c) a demand function, $P = F(Q)$, which shows how high a price, P, can be charged per unit if it is desired to sell Q units of a commodity. In other words, it shows how much of the commodity consumers will demand at different levels of the price;

(d) a revenue function, $P \cdot Q = QF(Q)$, which shows the total income of the firm when it sells Q units of a commodity at the price P per unit;

(e) a utility function, $U(Q)$, which measures the pleasure that the individual derives from the possession of some quantity, Q, of some commodity.

Economists have then adopted the following terminology:

$$\text{marginal utility is the name given to } \frac{dU}{dQ}$$

$$\text{marginal product refers to } \frac{dQ}{dz}$$

$$\text{marginal cost refers to } \frac{dC}{dQ}$$

$$\text{marginal revenue refers to } \frac{d(PQ)}{dQ}.$$

Suppose now that a businessman desires to earn as much total profit, R, as he can. This means that he desires to make as large as possible the difference between his total receipts (revenue), PQ, and his total costs, C. In other words, he seeks to maximize

$$R = PQ - C.$$

We can now see what level of production, Q, is most profitable. In ordinary circumstances, R will be maximized when its derivative vanishes, i.e., when

$$\frac{dR}{dQ} = \frac{d(PQ)}{dQ} - \frac{dC}{dQ} = 0$$

or

$$\frac{d(PQ)}{dQ} = \frac{dC}{dQ}.$$

In other words, maximum profits require that *marginal cost be equal to marginal revenue*. This is a fundamental result in the economic theory of the firm which will be discussed again later.

Example 1: *Optimum production level.* Suppose the relevant portion of the demand function is

$$P = 100 - 0.01Q$$

where Q is the weekly production. This equation states that as more of the commodity is put on the market its price must fall. If price is measured in cents, it means that price must fall by 1 cent for every 100 additional units of the commodity which appear on the market each week. Suppose also that the cost function is given by

$$C = 50Q + 30,000.$$

It is easy to verify that

$$\text{total revenue} = PQ \quad = 100Q - 0.01Q^2$$

$$\text{marginal revenue} = \frac{d(PQ)}{dQ} = 100 - 0.02Q$$

$$\text{marginal cost} = \frac{dC}{dQ} \quad = 50$$

so that maximum profit involves

$$\text{marginal cost} = \text{marginal revenue}, \quad \text{i.e., } 50 = 100 - 0.02Q.$$

This means that the most profitable level of production will be

$$Q = \frac{50}{.02} = 2500 \text{ units per week.}$$

At that level of production, price will be

$$P = 100 - 0.01Q = 100 - 25 = 75 \text{ cents}$$

and total profit per week will be

$$R = PQ - C = 75 \times 2500 - (30{,}000 + 50 \times 2500)\cent = \$325.00.$$

Example 2: *The incidence of a sales tax.* Suppose, in the preceding example, the government decides to levy a tax of 10 cents per unit of product sold. What will happen to price, quantity sold, and total profit?

Total cost now becomes

$$C = 50Q + 10Q + 30{,}000 = 60Q + 30{,}000.$$

Maximum profit again requires marginal cost = marginal revenue, which now involves

$$60 = 100 - 0.02Q.$$

This yields

$$Q = 2{,}000 \text{ units per week}$$

$$P = \$.80$$

$$R = \$100.00$$

We thus have the results

	Before Tax	After Tax
Tax/unit...............	0	10
Weekly output..........	2,500	2,000
Price (cents)...........	75	80
Weekly profit ($)........	325	100

Particularly noteworthy is the result that it does not pay the businessman to pass on the full 10¢ tax rise to the consumer—rather it is most profitable in this case to raise his price by only 5¢!

Example 3: *Fixed costs.* Let the firm's total cost be given by $C = k + c(Q)$. That portion of the firm's costs, k, which do not change when its output, Q, changes, is called its *fixed cost*. The firm's marginal cost is obtained, by differentiation, to be

$$\frac{dC}{dQ} = \frac{dc(Q)}{dQ}$$

It will be observed that the constant term, k, has dropped out in the course of this differentiation. As a result, marginal costs are the same no matter what the value of k, i.e., no matter what changes occur in the firm's fixed costs (cf. Section 6 of the previous chapter).

This leads us to a rather surprising result. Since a change in fixed costs does not affect the firm's marginal cost (nor clearly, its marginal revenue), the price-output combination at which marginal cost equals marginal revenue will be unaffected by any such change. In other words, *if the firm maximizes its profits a change in fixed cost will affect neither its output level nor the price of its product!*[11]

PROBLEMS

1. Give verbal definitions of marginal utility, marginal cost, marginal revenue, and marginal product.

2. A commodity is sold at a fixed price P per unit. A consumer, in buying Q units of the commodity, tries to maximize the difference between the utility, U, he derives from his consumption of the commodity and the total amount, PQ, which he has to pay. Show that he should buy so much of the commodity that its marginal utility is equal to its price.

3. Elasticity of demand is a measure of the responsiveness of quantity demanded to price changes, which is given by

$$\frac{\% \text{ change in quantity demanded}}{\% \text{ change in price}} = \frac{100 \, dQ/Q}{100 \, dP/P} = \frac{P}{Q}\frac{dQ}{dP}.$$

If the demand function is such that when price is cut, consumer purchases increase by an amount just sufficient to keep total revenue unchanged, the demand equation is $PQ = K$ (a constant). Show that in this case elasticity of demand $= -1$.

4. Let c represent the cost per unit of producing a commodity, C the total cost of producing that commodity, and Q be the number of units produced. Then, by definition, $C = cQ$. Prove that if Q is at such a level that costs per unit are at a minimum (is this an efficient level of production?), we will also have marginal cost equal to c.

5. Suppose $C = 120Q - Q^2 + 0.02Q^3$ and $P = 114 - 0.25Q$.
  (a) What level of Q yields minimum costs per unit, c?
  (b) Does this level of output yield maximum profit?
  (c) At how many levels of output is marginal cost equal to marginal revenue?
  (d) Are these all profit-maximizing outputs? (Evaluate the second derivative of the total profit.)
  (e) Explain by sketching the graphs of P and c (unit cost) plotted against Q.

6. Consider the demand and cost functions

$$P = a - bQ$$
$$C = w + vQ$$

where a, b, w, and v are positive constants. Suppose the government imposes on the producer a tax of t dollars per unit of output and that as a result it pays to raise price from P dollars to P^* dollars. Show that $P^* - P = \frac{1}{2}t$,

[11] The rationale of the rule that the profit maximizer's prices should not be changed when fixed costs change is discussed in Chapter 10, below.

i.e., that it pays the manufacturer to shift only one-half of the tax onto the consumer.

7. Find the sign of the second derivative of the profit functions in the preceding problem. Why is it relevant?

REFERENCES

Allen, R. G. D., *Mathematical Analysis for Economists*, Macmillan, London, 1938, Chapters VI–XIV.

Crum, W. L., and Schumpeter, J. A., *Rudimentary Mathematics for Economists and Statisticians*, McGraw-Hill Book Company, Inc., New York, 1946.

Johnson, R. E., and Kiokemeister, F. L., *Calculus with Analytic Geometry*, Allyn and Bacon Inc., Boston, 1957.

Taylor, A. E., *Calculus with Analytic Geometry*, Prentice-Hall, Inc., Englewood Cliffs, N. J., 1959.

Thomas, G. B. Jr., *Calculus and Analytic Geometry*, Addison-Wesley Publishing Co., Inc., Cambridge, Mass., 1955.

CHAPTER FIVE

Linear programming

Programming, both linear and nonlinear, is entirely a mathematical technique. Its economic content is therefore nil. This is no mere classificatory quibble. It means that programming per se can never tell us anything about the operation of any part of the economy. Like the calculus or any other branch of mathematics, it can only help us to find the implications of the economic information which we already have or are willing to assume. To the extent, then, that econom'sts were responsible for the development of programming,[1] they may be said to have been productive in areas outside their own fields, as they have been in the past when they formulated the largely technological law of diminishing returns, or when, by inventing the marginal analysis, they stumbled, a few centuries too late, on what is essentially a crude version of the differential calculus.

1. Some Standard Programming Problems

Programming is concerned with the determination of the optimal solutions to problems. As a result, it is well suited to the analysis of rational behavior. It has, therefore, like the marginal analysis, been somewhat less

---

[1] Several economists have made important contributions. Notable among these are T. C. Koopmans, R. Dorfman, and W. W. Cooper. But if any one person is to be named as the father of programming, we must undoubtedly award the honor to mathematician George Dantzig, inventor of the first successful (and still one of the most efficient) general computational techniques, the simplex method. Important contributions have been made by mathematicians such as the Russian L. V. Kantorovich, who first formulated the problem, H. W. Kuhn, A. W. Tucker, A. Charnes, and others.

successful in describing what is than in indicating what (given some pre-assigned goals) ought to be. Some of the most fertile applications of programming have involved welfare economics and advice to businessmen, both of which aim to tell the relevant persons how they can most efficiently go about working toward their objectives. Let us indicate briefly a few of the business problems to which programming is most frequently applied.

(a) *Optimum product lines and production processes.* When operating at a high output level a firm is likely to run into a variety of capacity limitations. Its factory size, the amount of time available on different machines, its warehouse space, and its skilled personnel—any or all may constitute bottlenecks, some of which are prohibitively expensive or even impossible to eliminate in the short run.

A crucial characteristic of such a situation is that the production of a relatively unprofitable item or the use of a production process which makes liberal use of the scarce facilities may take up valuable capacity that can better be used in more economical processes and in the manufacture of more lucrative commodities.

There is no simple solution, such as complete specialization in the one "most efficient process" for producing the one item which makes "most profitable" use of scarce facilities since, except by pure accident, there may be no process or no product which is economical in its use of all of the firm's limited facilities at once. One item may make good use of machine capacity and may therefore yield the highest profit per scarce machine-hour, whereas another may make more effective use of limited warehouse space. Production of only the former would find warehouses completely loaded before machine time was fully employed, while the latter product, since it is not bulky, might leave warehouses half empty even if the firm's machines were to turn out nothing else.

(b) *Transportation routing.* In the selection of transportation routes, especially where a firm has many plants and its processes involve trans-shipment of items in various stages of production, substantial savings can be expected from careful planning of commodity movements. If the firm employs its own trucks or other transport facilities, the problem is to route them in a way that incurs as little cost as possible. Where the firm employs others to do its transporting, the computations may be further complicated by peculiarities in the transportation rate structure, for then the firm's objective is not to minimize ton-miles but to minimize payments to the carrier, and the two do not always correspond.

(c) *Meeting product specifications.* Many contracts include a number of minimum specifications which must be met by the product, and sometimes the manufacturer will set up such standards for himself. Usually there is a variety of ways in which these specifications can be met. For example, an animal feed may require X units of protein per bag, Y of carbohydrates, Z of vitamin B, etc. Each of the grains combined in the animal feed contains some of the nutrients, and it is therefore possible to make a bag of feed meet these specifications in many different ways. A very inexpensive ingredient may contain much starch and very little else, so to meet the standards it may be necessary to add some more expensive ingredients. But which ingredients should be added and in what proportion? Or will it prove cheaper to begin with somewhat more costly ingredients which supply a better balance of all the nutrients?

The least-cost combination of meeting specifications is basically a programming problem. This technique has, for example, been employed in just this fashion, i.e., in mixing animal feeds, as well as other areas such as in the blending of gasolines. Programming techniques have been employed in many other business problems. They can help determine optimum inventory levels and have been used to solve production problems such as cutting of paper and cloth in a way which minimizes raw material waste, and in the job assignment of specialized personnel.

2. Characteristics of Programming

What is the common element in all of these situations which makes them amenable to programming analysis? It is clear that all of them require a search for "best" values of the variables. But there is something more involved which makes the usual tools of the calculus or marginal analysis inapplicable. In many problems of optimization there is a complication in that the outcome, to be acceptable, must meet certain conditions. For example, the problem of fencing in 20 square feet at minimum cost involves the determination of that shape of plot which will save on fencing most effectively. But any saving which is achieved by fencing only 19 or 21 square feet w ll be unacceptable. This, then, is essentially a problem of finding the best way of meeting a very precise specification which the mathematician calls "a side-condition." So long as the specifications are so precise (the area must be 20 square feet, no more or less; or the starch content of a 100-pound bag of feed must be exactly so many calories, etc.), the optimization problem can usually still be dealt with by calculus (marginal) techniques as was shown in section 8 of the previous chapter.[2]

However, it is characteristic of many business problems that specifica-

---

[2] Even here there is an important exception. The mathematical form of the precise specification (side-condition) is an equation. If the graph of the equation is discontinuous or kinked, calculus methods cannot be depended on to work. The reason is that these techniques find an optimum by computing the slope of the relevant graphs to investigate whether it is possible to go "uphill" (toward higher profits). Where the graph of a function is discontinuous or kinked, its slope is, for obvious reasons, not even defined.

tions are not precise but provide only minimum requirements that must be met. Or the specification, rather than stating the precise extent to which a facility will be used, may indicate only the maximum capacity which is available. Any output which overshoots the quality standards or does not fully utilize some part of capacity is not necessarily ruled out. Here the side-conditions are inequalities rather than equations. That is, they do not state that X must equal 500 but only that X must be no less than 500.[3]

This sort of side-condition characterizes each of the business problems which has been described. In the optimum product line and production process problem there are maximum capacities to be dealt with. In meeting specifications at minimum cost, each specification is such an inequality. In the transportation routing and plant location problems, the presence of such restrictions on the businessman's decisions is less obvious, but they are nevertheless there and play a fundamental role in the computation. There can be limitations on the size and cargo-carrying capacity of the trucks, trains, or ships to be routed. But the more relevant capacity limitation is a peculiar one which states that in no case is it possible to ship negative amounts from one place to another! This rather silly-sounding restriction is important partly because things like this are never obvious to an electronic computer and, unless it is specifically forbidden to do so, the computer will assign negative shipments from some supply sources to some destinations. For the machine will reason that if it is profitable to reduce some shipments to zero, it may be still more profitable to reduce these shipments even further!

For the economic theorist, such non-negativity requirements are important for a far more fundamental reason. Like an electronic computer, marginal analysis is, by itself, incapable of taking account of them. To return to the more familiar optimum output problem, for the competitive firm we note that the rule of the marginal analysis is that the output of any item should be at a level at which marginal cost is equal to price. But for an unprofitable item marginal cost may only be equal to price at

---

[3] The reason marginal techniques break down in the presence of inequality side-conditions is easily illustrated with the aid of a simple graph (Figure 3b of Chapter 4). Marginal analysis finds, e.g., the point of maximum profits by locating the point at which marginal profit (the slope of the total profit curve) equals zero (output OQ_m in the figure). That is the meaning of the standard marginal-cost-equals-marginal-revenue condition. But suppose output is limited by the inequality that production cannot exceed OQ_i. Then our problem is to find out whether the point of maximum attainable profit is OQ_i or some point to its left (which is no easy problem in the N-dimensional N-variable case). But for this the first-order conditions of the marginal analysis cannot be employed, for at the optimum point in the diagram, OQ_i, the marginal criterion, marginal profit = the slope of the total profit curve = zero, is obviously invalid. See Chapter 4, Section 4, for a more complete discussion of the cases in which the calculus maximization criteria are not directly applicable.

an impossible negative output level. That is, in a case of increasing costs, even at zero output cost need not have fallen back to the level of price. Of course, no moderately sane economist making a graphic analysis will ever recommend a negative output. But where a large number of inter-dependent decisions have to be made, the calculations may all have to be done with the help of mathematical reasoning. And a mathematical analysis, based on marginal equalities such as marginal cost equals price, must in such a case yield nonsense results unless we impose on the calculation the explicit requirement that the variables be given no negative values. We will come to this point again later.

Programming, then, is the mathematical method for the analysis and computation of optimum decisions which do not violate the limitations imposed by inequality side-conditions. In almost all cases the method of computation is a so-called "iterative procedure." Just as the term "ragout" disguises the fact that it is only stew, though presumably an elegant one, this fancy term is used to dignify a systematic trial-and-error procedure. The answer to a programming problem will ordinarily not be arrived at directly. Instead the solution is found by groping toward it. But the trial-and-error procedure is not pure guesswork. It is systematic in that it usually involves at least the first two of the following features:

1. There is a mechanical rule which determines, after each step, ex-actly what the next step is to be on the basis of the results of the trial just completed. One purpose of this feature of the method of solution is that it makes electronic computation possible. Most of these mechanical brains unfortunately possess no judgment of their own so they must be told what to do in every contingency. This is like teaching a human the rules of algebra before giving him an algebraic problem to solve. In any event, a mechanical rule stating what must be done at each succeeding trial in the trial-and-error procedure is useful because in a problem complicated by a great number of variables and interrelationships, human judgment can go badly wrong and can result in an inefficient, even totally ineffective, search for the answer.

2. A second characteristic feature of the systematic trial-and-error pro-cedure is a proof that the method has been constructed in a way which guarantees that each trial will yield values which are closer than the pre-ceding one to the correct answer. This very important feature assures the computer that he is always getting closer to his result and is not wasting his time by going off in a wrong direction. We shall see later, in our dis-cussion of the simplex method, how this sort of guarantee can be built into a computation procedure. Of course, such a guarantee can only be provided where there is a mechanical rule which specifies step by step what will be done. Otherwise, successive steps are unpredictable, and it is then not

possible to say in advance whether they will be closer to or farther from the correct answer.

3. For a large class of problems there are available trial-and-error procedure rules which are guaranteed to yield precisely the correct result after a finite number of steps. In other cases where this is not possible, one can hope to calculate a maximum error, and to be able to say, for example, that the result of the most recent trial is at most one-tenth of 1 per cent from the correct answer.

Where the problem is one involving *linear* programming, there are several computational methods which yield a precise answer after a finite number of steps. The simplex method, the method of fictitious play, and the complete-description method are all linear programming computational techniques. In the next section we will see what is invo ved in the linearity of a programming problem.

3. *Algebra and Geometry*

First, let us set out the equations of a typical linear programming problem.

Consider a profit-maximizing firm which can produce any of the four products w, x, y, and z whose outputs are W, X, Y, and Z and whose profits per unit of output are, respectively, 5, 3, 2, and 7. Then the total profits of the firm are given by $5W + 3X + 2Y + 7Z$. (Here, e.g., W and X may represent outputs of the same product manufactured by different "processes," i.e., with the use of different input proportions.) Suppose, moreover, the firm has available only 50,000 square feet of warehouse space and 32,000 machine hours. If the manufacture of one unit of w requires 0.5 hours of machine time, that of x requires 2 hours of machine time, etc., we have an inequality relationship (which is called a "constraint" or "side-condition") such as:

$$0.5W + 2X + 1.9Y + 3.1Z \leq 32,000$$

which states that no more of these outputs can be manufactured than the available machine time permits. Assume also that there is a similar warehouse-space constraint which is written out below. We can see now that the programming problem can be written:

(1)
$$
\begin{cases}
\quad \text{maximize profits:} \quad 5W + 3X + 2Y + 7Z \\
\text{subject to the constraints} \\
0.5W + 2X + 1.9Y + 3.1Z \leq 32,000 \text{ (available machine time)} \\
\quad 10W + 1.2X + 7Y + 4Z \leq 50,000 \text{ (warehouse capacity)} \\
\text{and the non-negativity requirements} \\
\quad W \geq 0, \quad X \geq 0, \quad Y \geq 0, \quad Z \geq 0.
\end{cases}
$$

This is the standard form for a programming problem. It consists of three parts: (1) the function (e.g., profits or costs) whose value is to be maximized or minimized, which is called *the objective function*, (2) the (capacity) constraints, and (3) the non-negativity conditions on the variables, e.g., $W \geq 0$.

This problem is called "linear" because the expression to be maximized and the inequalities involve only the variable multiplied by constants and added together (as in an equation for a straight line such as $y = 5x + 3$). There are no X^2's, 5 sin Y's, log Z's, or more complex expressions. We may note that this linear model employs an assumption of competitively or otherwise fixed input and output prices and constant returns to scale in production.[4] These premises enter in two ways. First, from the information that profit per unit of w is 5, we can only compute the profit from producing 10 units of w at $5W = 50$ because the assumption of constant returns to scale and constant input and output prices implies that costs, revenues, and profits will all rise precisely in proportion with the level of output. (We observe again that w is *defined* in such a way that it must always be produced with the same input proportions—in this analysis a change in the amount of scarce machine time used per unit of output is described as a shift from the manufacture of, say, w to that of x.) The linearity of the inequalities also rests on the assumption of constant returns to scale—the amount of warehouse space occupied by product y is assumed strictly proportionate to Y, the level of output of that item.[5]

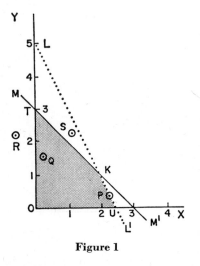

Figure 1

Let us now look at some programming geometry. First, we must see how an inequality is represented graphically. Consider the inequality $2X + Y \leq 5$. (This may be interpreted, e.g., as a warehouse capacity limitation.) In Figure 1 any point such as P on the line LL' which represents the equation $2X + Y = 5$ (and represents full use of capacity) clearly satisfies the inequality. But, in addition, any point such as Q, R, or S which lies below and to the left of LL' also satisfies the inequality because it involves values of X and Y smaller than those which completely

[4] For a definition and discussion of the "constant returns" case see Chapter 9.

[5] Where the facts of the situation do not warrant these assumptions even as an approximation, we may be forced to employ techniques of nonlinear programming. Usually these are, at best, more complicated, as indicated in the following chapter.

use up the capacity. We note, then, that while a two-variable equation is represented by a line, a two-variable inequality is represented by a region. Indeed, a linear two-variable inequality is represented by drawing a straight line which divides the plane into two regions called "half-spaces," one of which contains all points satisfying the inequality.

Let us see what happens if, in addition, the variables must satisfy a second inequality, say $Y + X \leq 3$ represented by the half-space to the left of line MM'. All of the points which satisfy both inequalities must lie below both lines MM' and LL', so that we are left with the region bounded by the broken line MKL'.[6] Further inequalities may bound the region from all sides—e.g., the addition of the inequalities $X \geq 0$, $Y \geq 0$ leaves us with the shaded region in the diagram. This area is called the *feasible region* because every point such as Q which lies within it or on its boundary represents a combination of values of the variables (the output levels of X and Y) which does not violate the constraints, i.e., any such output combination is within the firm's capacity. For this reason, every point such as Q or P, in the feasible region, represents what is called a *feasible solution* to the programming problem.

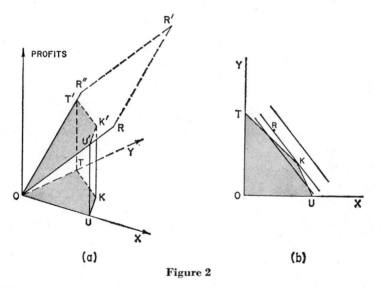

(a)   (b)

Figure 2

We can now represent the entire programming problem diagrammatically by adding to Figure 1 a third dimension which we use to represent

[6] Note that while two linear equations in two variables will normally leave us with only one possible point (the intersection of the two straight lines), two or more linear inequalities will often still leave us an unlimited number of points to choose from. Thus, there is nothing necessarily wrong with, say, a system of 5 inequalities in 3 unknowns even though we usually prefer to have no more equations than unknowns.

profits (Figure 2a). A surface, $ORR'R''$, shows the profit that can be earned by any combination of our two outputs x and y. The XOY plane which constitutes the floor of the diagram is the same as the graph of Figure 1 or Figure 2b. Thus point K, for example, is a combination of outputs X and Y. If this combination, say, is capable of yielding \$100 in profits, we erect above point K the vertical line KK' whose length is 100 units. The profit surface $ORR'R''$ is the locus of all points such as K' whose height indicates the profits which are yielded by the output combination represented by the point K directly below.

In the *linear* programming case this profit surface $ORR'R''$ is always a plane through the origin (equation: profit $= aX + bY$ where a and b are constants).

Alternatively (Figure 2b) this situation can be depicted in a two-dimensional diagram where the profits are shown by iso profit curves. Any two points on such a curve represent combinations of outputs X and Y which yield the same profits—e.g., profits at output combination R are the same as at output combination K. In a *linear* program these iso profit curves are always straight lines, and they are parallel. For, a typical profit equation in a two-variable linear program is

$$\text{profit} = 3X + 2Y.$$

The curve representing a \$50,000 profit level therefore has the equation

$$50,000 = 3X + 2Y, \quad \text{i.e.,} \quad Y = -\tfrac{3}{2}X + 25,000$$

so that the profit indifference curve is a straight line whose slope is $-\tfrac{3}{2}$. Similarly, the line representing a \$70 000 profit level will be higher than and of the same slope as the \$50,000 line. The indifference curves of a linear program will therefore be a series of parallel straight lines. Further, moving to higher and higher curves will always increase profits.[7]

The objective of a programming calculation is to pick the *optimal* (in our examples, the most profitable) among the feasible output combinations. In geometric terms, this is represented by the point in the feasible region which happens to lie beneath the highest point on the profit surface, $ORR'R''$, i.e., the feasible point which lies on the most valuable profit indifference curve.

It follows from the result that a move to a higher indifference curve always increases profits, that the optimal point of a *linear* program will always lie on the boundary of the feasible region.[8] The logic is simple. Any

---

[7] There is an exception to this result when the outputs in question bring in losses rather than profits. In such a case profits may decrease when we move to higher indifference curves. However, this exception does not affect the rest of the argument.

[8] It will be shown in the next chapter that where a programming problem is nonlinear, most of the preceding theorems need not hold. The profit surface need not be a plane, the iso profit curves need not be parallel straight lines, and an optimal point need not occur on the boundary of the feasible region.

commodity whose production is profitable will continue to be lucrative as its output expands because there will be neither diminishing returns to scale nor unfavorable effects on input and output prices. It will, therefore, always pay to expand production until some capacity limit is reached, i.e., until the boundary of the feasible region is attained. In fact, in a linear program, since the profit indifference curves are straight lines, there will always be at least one optimal solution (an optimal point) which occurs at one of the corners, O, T, K, or U of the feasible region. For the optimal point will always either be a corner "tangency" point, such as K in Figure 2b, or, if the straight line indifference curves are parallel to one of the segments of the feasible region's boundary, say to TK, then the entire segment *including corners T and K* will be optimal. Such a corner point is the geometric representation of what is called a *basic solution* of the linear programming problem. We may then sum up our result by stating that in any *linear* problem an optimal solution can always be found by searching among the basic solutions (the corner points of the feasible region). This will next be shown to lead to a result which has been called *the basic theorem of linear programming:*

> Suppose there are, say, five inequality (capacity limitation) or equation constraints in a linear program (here we do not count the non-negativity requirement inequalities such as $X \geq 0$); then an optimal solution can be found which involves no more than five nonzero values of the variables, i.e., it will pay to produce no more than five products (or use no more than five production processes).[9]
>
> Moreover, if this optimal solution, say, tells us to produce just three products, exactly three facilities will normally be used to capacity (so that the other two will have unused capacity); i.e., *in this optimal arrangement there will normally be exactly as many commodities produced as there are facilities used to capacity.*

This is really a rather surprising result. It states that a firm which has, say, 12 fixed factors and is producing 150 products, can maximize its profits by cutting its product line down to no more than 12 items! The result should properly be viewed with suspicion and it must be recognized to be a direct consequence of the linearity assumption. In practice, a businessman must be very careful to make sure the assumption is valid before accepting this sort of radical advice.

We can prove the theorem graphically in the case where there are only

---

[9] Sometimes there will be other types of optimal solution but they will offer no advantage over such a basic (five-product) solution. The phenomenon of degeneracy, discussed briefly in the next footnote, requires some modification of this theorem, but the details will not be pursued here.

two variables (call them outputs X and Y) in Figure 3. We assume there is only one capacity restriction (say, a crowded warehouse) represented by line CC' and the region below and to the left of that line. At any point on CC' (including points C and C') our single limited facility (the warehouse) is used right up to capacity. With the requirements $X \geq 0$, $Y \geq 0$ the feasible region is reduced to the triangle $OC'C$. We have just seen that an optimal point must occur at one of the corners O, C, or C'. Consider each of these in turn. At either C or C' there is just one output (Y or X respectively) and one facility used to capacity, whereas at O there is no output and nothing used to capacity. Thus, at any such corner optimum point, the theorem holds. With one constraint it will pay to produce at most one of our two commodities, and, if one commodity is produced, it will pay to fill our one facility (the warehouse) to capacity.

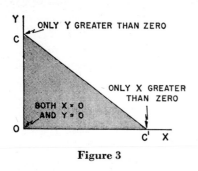

Figure 3

Only where there are two or more facilities of limited capacity can a corner optimal solution occur which involves nonzero outputs of both commodities. For example, at point K in Figure 1 there are positive outputs of both X and Y (and both facilities are used to capacity—K lies on both LL' and MM').[10]

But why should this be so—why should the optimal number of products equal the number of fully used facilities? Roughly, the answer is that if there is only one constraint, say only machine time is limited, it will pay to produce *only* the one item which yields the highest profit per machine hour. But if warehouse space, too, is really limited (if it is used to capacity), it will usually also be profitable to introduce a second item which makes good use of warehouse space, and so on.

4. Slack Variables

For later use both the programming problem and the basic theorem of linear programming need to be restated somewhat. First, let us employ

---

[10] The theorem runs into trouble only if a third constraint line happens to pass exactly through point K, the intersection of the other two constraint lines, so that at that point *two* products are manufactured but *three* facilities are used to capacity. A programming problem in which this occurs is said to be *degenerate* and the phenomenon leads to additional computational difficulties. This phenomenon is ignored throughout the discussion of this chapter. However, it may be observed that it can usually be handled quite satisfactorily by the introduction of a tiny artificial shift in one of the constraints, so that its graph no longer intersects precisely with the junction of the other constraint lines.

our numerical example to illustrate the required reformulation of the linear programming problem. For this purpose we make use of two additional symbols, T and C, to represent unused machine time and warehouse capacity, so that the statement $C = 10,000$ means that 10,000 square feet of warehouse space remains unused. T and C are called *slack variables* (in contrast, variables such as W, X, and Y will be referred to as *ordinary variables*). With the aid of these symbols our problem (1) can be written in a manner to which we shall refer as the *equality form* of the program:

(2)
$$\begin{cases}
\text{maximize}\quad 5W + 3X + 2Y + 7Z \\
\text{given the constraints} \\
\quad 0.5W + 2X + 1.9Y + 3.1Z + T = 32,000 \\
\quad 10W + 1.2X + 7Y + 4Z + C = 50,000 \\
\text{and the non-negativity requirements} \\
\quad W \geq 0, \quad X \geq 0, \quad Y \geq 0, \quad Z \geq 0, \quad T \geq 0, \quad C \geq 0.
\end{cases}$$

Thus by adding two new *non-negative* slack variables, we have been able to change all of the inequalities into equations except, of course, for the non-negativity requirements. To interpret T and C in a manner comparable with the other variables, we may consider these slack variables to represent costless processes whose function is to "use up" otherwise unemployed machine time and warehouse capacity. In solving a programming problem we are interested also in the optimal values of these slack variables, for they indicate which of the firm's facilities will constitute bottlenecks (facilities whose slack variables have value zero) and to what extent there should be idle capacity in the remaining facilities.

We can now proceed to reformulate the basic theorem of linear programming, which, in our previous version, stated that there is always an optimal solution to any linear problem in which as many processes are employed as there are facilities used to capacity. Suppose, in a problem, that there is some number of constraints, M (say, $M = 5$) and that in this optimal solution some other number, K ($= 3$), of these facilities are used to capacity. By the previous version of the basic theorem it follows that $K = 3$ ordinary variables will then take nonzero values. But, since the remaining two ($M - K$) facilities are normally not used to capacity, the corresponding two ($M - K$) slack variables must then also take nonzero values. Hence, exactly 3 (i.e., K) ordinary variables and 2 ($= M - K$) slack variables, or a grand total of 5 ($= 3 + 2 = K + M - K = M$) variables will take positive values, where 5 ($= M$) is the number of constraints in the problem. Here, then, is the revised version of the basic theorem:

There is always an optimal solution of any linear programming problem in which the total number of nonzero valued variables of both kinds (ordinary and slack) is exactly equal to the number of capacity limitations, i.e., to the number of equations in the equality form of the programming problem.

A solution which satisfies this requirement on the number of nonzero variables is called a *basic solution*. As we have just seen, any such solution is represented by a corner of the feasible region in our diagrams.

5. The Simplex Method: Outline

The observation (the basic theorem) that some corner of the feasible region will always be optimal lies behind the simplex method[11] of computation, for this at once reduces the possibilities to a finite set. In looking for an optimal solution we can ignore all of the rest of the feasible region.

The simplex method, whose conceptual simplicity is one of its great merits, can be outlined as follows:

1. Find any basic solution—i.e., any corner of the feasible region (this is not as easy as it sounds—if the origin is a corner of the feasible region as in our diagrams it can save a lot of trouble to start here). Suppose then we start at O (Figure 1).

2. Compute the profits at point O and at the adjacent corners T and U.[12]

3. If one or both of the latter yield higher profits than does O, move to the corner which offers more profit (per unit of output), say to U.

4. Now repeat steps 2 and 3 substituting point U for point O. Thus compute profits at K and see if they are higher than those at U; if so, move to K; otherwise stay at U. In this way, by successive elimination, we must eventually find the optimal point.[13] This sounds much easier than it is in practice. Most of the work arises in just locating the (adjacent) corners of the feasible region.

6. The Initial Basic Solution, Feasibility and Optimality Criteria

For reasons which will soon be given it is convenient to make one slight and final modification in the formulation of Problem (2) by bringing all of

[11] The name was not chosen to imply that the procedure is simple. Roughly, a simplex may be described as the N-dimensional analogue of a triangle. The outline of the computations, below, indicates that the method consists in successive investigation of adjacent corners of a figure which can be broken up into a series of simplexes.

[12] This is not quite accurate. In practice, we only compute the change in profits resulting from a small move in the direction of T or U. A theorem states that in a linear problem if such a small move is profitable, so is the move all the way to T or U (because in a *linear* program there are no diminishing returns).

[13] We do not have to try every point because it can be shown that if no move to an *adjacent* corner increases profits we are at an optimum. If both O and K are less profitable than U, it is unnecessary to try T.

the terms involving ordinary variables over to the right-hand side of the equations:

$$\text{maximize} \quad \text{profits} = 0 + 5W + 3X + 2Y + 7Z$$

subject to

$$T = 32{,}000 - 0.5W - 2X - 1.9Y - 3.1Z$$

$$C = 50{,}000 - 10W - 1.2X - 7Y - 4Z$$

or, in more general notation,

(3a) $$\max Z = a_{00} + a_{01}X_1 + \ldots + a_{0n}X_n$$

subject to

$$t_1 = a_{10} + a_{11}X_1 + \ldots + a_{1n}X_n$$

(3b) $$\cdots \cdots \cdots \cdots \cdots \cdots$$

$$t_m = a_{m0} + a_{m1}X_1 + \ldots + a_{mn}X_n$$

(3c) $$\text{all} \quad t_i \geq 0 \quad \text{and all} \quad X_j \geq 0$$

where the X_j are ordinary variables, the t_i are slack variables, and the a_{ij} are constants. (The notation X_j is used to represent any one of the numbers, $X_1, X_2, \ldots, X_n$ and similarly t_i and a_{ij} represent any one of the t variables and any one of the a's respectively.)

This form (3) has substantial advantages, because, as will now be shown, it permits us to accomplish three important things. Just by inspection we can (a) write out a basic solution; (b) check whether this solution is feasible; and (c) check whether it is optimal.

(a) *The basic solution.* The first step in the simplex method is to find some (any) basic feasible solution. In many cases, there is an easy way of doing this. Recall that a basic solution is defined as one which contains as many nonzero variable values as there are constraints. Then, obviously,

RULE 1. *A basic solution:* A basic solution of (3) is

(4) $$T = 32{,}000, \quad C = 50{,}000 \quad \text{and} \quad W = X = Y = Z = 0$$

or, in the more general case [Equations (3a) to (3c)],

(4a) $$t_1 = a_{10}, t_2 = a_{20}, \ldots, t_m = a_{m0} \quad \text{and} \quad X_1 = X_2 = \ldots = X_n = 0.$$

Since there are exactly as many nonzero variables as there are equations (two), (4) is clearly a basic solution.

This is the solution in which all facilities are left idle and the only nonzero activities are disposal activities. It is the basic solution represented by the origin in the previous diagrams. It will ordinarily be far from an optimal solution since, if it were optimal, the best alternative open to the businessman would be for him to close up his firm altogether. Nevertheless, this basic solution is so easily found that it is usually a good idea to employ it as a starting point for the calculation.

(b) *Feasibility check.* If and only if all of the constant terms a_{10}, $a_{20}, \ldots, a_{m0}$ in (3b) are non-negative the basic solution (4a) is feasible, i.e., it satisfies all of the requirements (3b) and (3c). Equations (3b) are clearly satisfied by (4a), as we can see by substitution, and since the variables take on the non-negative values $a_{10}, a_{20}, \ldots, a_{m0}$, and zero, the non-negativity requirements (3c) are also clearly satisfied. Hence, we can tell at once by just looking at (3b) whether (4a) is feasible since

RULE 2. *Feasibility:* The basic solution (4) is feasible if and only if all of the constant terms $a_{10}, a_{20}, \ldots, a_{m0}$, in (3b) are non-negative.

Before describing the equally simple optimality test, it is necessary to outline the rest of the computational procedure. It will be observed that all of the variables which take nonzero values in our basic solution (4a) appear on the left-hand side of (3b) whereas all of the zero-valued variables appear on the right-hand side of (3a) and (3b). It is this convenient arrangement which permits us to say that the solution (4) is feasible if the constant terms in (3b) are non-negative. Therefore, whenever we try out a new basic solution in our computational procedure we will rewrite the equations in the corresponding form—the variables which at that stage are possibly nonzero on the left, and all other variables on the right. We will thus proceed as follows:

We will keep moving from basic solution to basic solution (from corner to corner in our diagrams). This means we will want one variable X_j which was previously zero to become nonzero, and one variable t_i which was formerly nonzero in solution (4) to become zero. In this way we keep the right number of positive elements in the solution for the solution to continue basic [as many positive elements as constraints (3b)].

In making these substitutions and rewriting the system in form (3) each time (with nonzero variables on the left), naturally the coefficient (a_{ij}) figures will be replaced by new values, and these new values must be computed for each step. Each time, moreover, we must stop to see whether we have arrived at the optimum which we are seeking. We then have the following convenient test for optimality

(c) *Optimality check.* Suppose we reach a stage where all of the revalued coefficients a'_{oj} of the variables in the objective function (3a) are negative (or zero). It can be seen by inspection that the corresponding solution (4) for this stage of the operation is not only basic and feasible, but it must be optimal. For if the objective function at that stage is, say, $Z = 23 - 7X'_1 - 12X'_2$ where X'_1 and X'_2 are the variables which appear on the right in (3) at that stage of the computations, then since X_1 and X_2 must take non-negative values, the largest possible value of Z (i.e., 23) will be obtained by setting $X_1 = X_2 = 0$. In other words, any other basic solution, in which either X_1 or X_2 must be positive, cannot possibly yield a higher profit, Z. Thus

RULE 3. *Optimality:* A basic solution such as (4a) is optimal if and only if none of the coefficients of the objective function (3a) corresponding to that basic solution is positive.

This condition, that the coefficients of the X_i be nonpositive, has, incidentally, a simple economic interpretation. The coefficient of X_i in the objective function is the contribution to total profit of an additional unit of X_i (the marginal profit of X_i). If the coefficients of the X_i are all negative or zero, all of the X_i will yield negative or zero marginal profits. Hence it will not pay to introduce any of these activities into the firm's operations— the optimal solution will require all of these $X_i = 0$.

Let us now examine the details of the computation with the aid of a two-variable numerical example:

$$\text{maximize} \quad 2.5X_1 + 2X_2$$

subject to

$$X_1 + 2X_2 \leq 8000$$
$$3X_1 + 2X_2 \leq 9000$$
$$X_1 \geq 0, \quad X_2 \geq 0.$$

To put this problem into our standard form (3) we must insert two slack variables, S_a and S_b, and bring all terms involving the ordinary variables X_1 and X_2 over to the right. This gives us

$$(3') \quad \begin{cases} \text{maximize} \quad Z = 0 + 2.5X_1 + 2X_2 \\ \text{subject to} \\ \quad S_a = 8000 - X_1 - 2X_2 \\ \quad S_b = 9000 - 3X_1 - 2X_2 \\ \quad S_a \geq 0, \quad S_b \geq 0, \quad X_1 \geq 0, \quad X_2 \geq 0. \end{cases}$$

We write out the table or *matrix* of coefficients corresponding to system (3') at this stage of the computation. This is just a table which provides a convenient summary of the numerical data in our system (3').

		X_1	X_2
Z	0	(2.5)	(2)
(5) S_a	8000	-1	-2
S_b	9000	(-3^*)	(-2)

Our first basic solution is clearly

$$(4') \qquad S_a = 8000, \quad S_b = 9000, \quad X_1 = X_2 = 0$$

so that in matrix (5) the zero-valued variables X_1 and X_2 appear at the top and positive-valued variables appear along the left side.

7. *The Next Basic Solution: The Pivoting Process*

Next, we wish to arrive at a new basic solution and the corresponding matrix for this following step. To do this, we must give a positive value to one of the variables which was zero in the previous solution (4′) and a zero value to one of the formerly nonzero variables. That is, in the next matrix we will want to move one of the top variables, say X_1, over to the left side, and move one of the left-hand (formerly nonzero) variables, say S_b, over to the top. In such a case where we are interchanging the roles of X_1 and S_b we say we are pivoting on the corresponding element, -3, in the S_b (horizontal) row and X_1 (vertical) column in the matrix, and we mark that element with an asterisk.

How we choose which element to interchange will be examined presently. First we must discuss the effect of the interchange. Consider first the equation in which element S_b appears,

$$S_b = 9000 - 3^*X_1 - 2X_2$$

where the asterisk is retained on the -3 to remind us that it is the pivot.

We require that this and the other constraints (3′) continue to hold since the firm's capacity limitations continue unchanged. But we now want these constraints rewritten with a new arrangement of the variables, i.e., with S_b on their right in place of variable X_1. We want the preceding equation to be replaced by an equivalent equation with X_1 on the left and S_b on the right. This new equation is obtained by dividing through by the coefficient of X_1, i.e., by the pivot element -3^*, and transposing, to obtain

$$(6) \qquad X_1 = \frac{-9000}{-3^*} + \frac{1}{-3^*} S_b + \frac{2}{-3^*} X_2 = 3000 - \frac{1}{3} S_b - \frac{2}{3} X_2.$$

This is our new third equation and its coefficients are, therefore, the elements of the last row of the next matrix (7).

			S_b	X_2
	Z			
(7) (incomplete)	S_a			
	X_1	3000	$-\frac{1}{3}$	$-\frac{2}{3}$

Similarly, to obtain the remaining terms in the matrix, we must replace the former zero-valued variable, X_1, by the new zero variable S_b in the other two equations of (3′). For this purpose we substitute the expression

(6) for X_1 into the objective function and the other constraint in the original system (3′). We obtain

$$Z = 0 + 2.5 \left(\frac{-9000}{-3*} + \frac{1}{-3*} S_b + \frac{2}{-3*} X_2 \right) + 2X_2$$

$$S_a = 8000 - \left(\frac{-9000}{-3*} + \frac{1}{-3*} S_b + \frac{2}{-3*} X_2 \right) - 2X_2.$$

By collecting terms we obtain the new coefficients of our variables S_b and X_2 in these equations and the new constant terms. These are the remaining elements of the new matrix (7). Thus, we have

(8)
$$Z = \left(0 - \frac{(2.5)(9000)}{-3*} \right) + \frac{2.5}{-3*} S_b + \left(2 - \frac{(2.5)(-2)}{-3*} \right) X_2$$

$$S_a = \left(8000 - \frac{(-1)(9000)}{-3*} \right) + \frac{-1}{-3*} S_b + \left(-2 - \frac{(-1)(-2)}{-3*} \right) X_2$$

that is,

(9)
$$Z = 7500 - \tfrac{5}{6} S_b + \tfrac{1}{3} X_2$$

$$S_a = 5000 + \tfrac{1}{3} S_b - \tfrac{4}{3} X_2.$$

These are the coefficients of the first and second rows of matrix (7):

			S_b	X_2
(7)	Z	7500	$-\tfrac{5}{6}$	$\tfrac{1}{3}$
	S_a	5000	$\tfrac{1}{3}$	$-\tfrac{4}{3}*$
	X_1	3000	$-\tfrac{1}{3}$	$-\tfrac{2}{3}$

Equations (6) and (9) or, alternatively, matrix (7) give us our next trial basic solution. By an extension of Rule 1 we have for this solution, $S_b = X_2 = 0$, so that $S_a = 5000$ and $X_1 = 3000$. By Rule 2 this is a feasible solution. Note also that we now have profit $(Z) = 7500$, which is a considerable improvement over the previous zero profit level of matrix (5).

We are now ready to choose another pivot and repeat this procedure as many times as necessary until an optimal basic solution (as indicated by Rule 3) is found. That is all there is to the simplex method. Once we have found out how to choose the pivot element (Section 9), we shall then have gone over the entire procedure.

8. Special Pivoting Rules[14]

However, before going on it is convenient to describe a method which avoids a good deal of the work involved in the preceding equation manipulating procedures. The four rules which follow reduce the entire pivoting process to some very elementary arithmetic. Unfortunately, a statement of the rules does not make light or interesting reading. However, experience indicates that once the reader has employed them on a problem he will find them exceedingly easy to use and to remember.

The coefficients of Equation (6) of the previous section illustrate the following two rules for finding the elements in the new simplex matrix which replace the elements in which the pivot previously appeared [the last row in matrix (5)]:[15]

RULE 4. *Pivot element:* The element which replaces the old pivot (-3^*) is simply the number 1 divided by the old pivot element ($1/-3^*$), i.e., it is the reciprocal of the old pivot element.

RULE 5. *Other pivot row elements:* Any other element in this row of the matrix is obtained by changing the sign of the corresponding old element and dividing by the old pivot element. For example, the lower left-hand element, 9000 in matrix (5), is replaced by $-9000/-3^* = 3000$. Similarly, Equations (8) illustrate the following rules for the replacement of the remaining elements of the matrix:

RULE 6. *Other pivot column elements:* Any other element in the (vertical) column which contained the old pivot is replaced by the corresponding old element divided by the old pivot. Thus, the number 2.5 in the second (pivot) column of (5) is replaced by $2.5/-3^* = -5/6$ in the new matrix (7).

RULE 7. *All other elements:* The last rule for the transformation of the remaining elements of (5) is also the most complicated of the four, but a

---

[14] This section makes rather tedious reading. However, it does show a way in which the simplex computation can be considerably simplified. The reader may prefer to skip this and all except the first and last paragraphs of Section 10 (in which the method is reviewed) or he may prefer to return to this material later.

[15] A general proof is the following: Let the original equation of (3b) which contains the pivot element a_{vw}^* be

$$t_v = a_{v0} + a_{v1}X_1 + \ldots + a_{vw}^* X_w + \ldots + a_{vn}X_n.$$

Then, to solve for X_w (the new nonzero variable) in terms of t_v (the variable whose value will be zero in the next basic solution) we divide through by the pivot, a_{vw}^*, and transpose terms to obtain

(6a) $$X_w = -\frac{a_{v0}}{a_{vw}^*} - \frac{a_{v1}}{a_{vw}^*} X_1 - \ldots + \frac{1}{a_{vw}^*} t_v - \ldots - \frac{a_{vn}}{a_{vw}^*} X_n$$

so that Rules 4 and 5 hold generally.

little practice can make it fairly easy to follow: To replace, e.g., the element 2 in the upper right-hand corner of (5), consider its position relative to that of the pivot element. Now find the corner elements, one in the pivot row, and one in the pivot column [the circled elements 2.5 and -2 in matrix (5)], which together with the pivot element and the element to be replaced (the other circled elements) form the four corners of a rectangle. Then follow the formula[16]

(10)   new element = corresponding old element

$$- \frac{\text{product of the two (other) corner elements}}{\text{old pivot element}}$$

e.g.,
$$\frac{1}{3} = 2 - \frac{(2.5)(-2)}{-3*}$$

so that $\frac{1}{3}$ is the upper right-hand element in the next matrix (7).[17]

9. Choosing the Pivot

We need only one more result and our description of the simplex method is complete. We need only decide which element to choose as the pivot element. Here we have two rules:

RULE 8. *Choice of pivot column:* The pivot element is (as a matter of good computational strategy) chosen to come from that column, w, which has the largest positive top element.

[16] The reader may find the following alternative formulation easier to remember because of its symmetry. Form the cross product of circled elements in (5) which is given by

     cross product = old element times pivot element minus the product of the other two corner elements.

Then we have the following formula which the reader may readily show to be equivalent to (10):

$$\text{new element} = \frac{\text{cross product}}{\text{old pivot element}}.$$

[17] In the general case Rules 6 and 7 are obtained by substituting the last equation (6a) in footnote 15 for X_w in the general (non-pivot-row) equation of (3a) or (3b)

$$t_i = a_{i0} + a_{i1}X_1 + \ldots + a_{iw}X_w + \ldots + a_{in}X_n.$$

This substitution yields

$$t_i = a_{i0} + a_{i1}X_1 + \ldots$$
$$+ a_{iw}\left(-\frac{a_{v0}}{a_{vw}^*} - \frac{a_{v1}}{a_{vw}^*}X_1 - \ldots + \frac{1}{a_{vw}^*}t_v - \ldots - \frac{a_{vn}}{a_{vw}^*}X_n\right) + \ldots + a_{in}X_n$$

or, collecting terms,

$$t_i = \left(a_{i0} - \frac{a_{iw}a_{v0}}{a_{vw}^*}\right) + \left(a_{i1} - \frac{a_{iw}a_{v1}}{a_{vw}^*}\right)X_1 + \ldots + \frac{a_{iw}}{a_{vw}^*}t_v + \ldots + \left(a_{in} - \frac{a_{iw}a_{vn}}{a_{vw}^*}\right)X_n$$

in which the bracketed expressions give us formula (10) (Rule 7) and the unbracketed coefficient gives us Rule 6, above.

Thus in matrix (5) the pivot column, w, must be the second column because its top element, 2.5, is positive and larger than that of any other column. To see why we choose the pivot column by this rule, note that by picking this second column for our pivot column we have decided to make the corresponding variable X_1 [or X_w, in the general matrix (11) in footnote 18] nonzero in the next basic (corner) solution. But the positive number 2.5 is the coefficient of X_1 in the objective function. We are, therefore, introducing a variable (an output), X_1, whose marginal profit, 2.5, is positive and greater than the marginal profit of any other formerly zero variable (e.g., the profit derivable from the introduction of a unit of X_2 is only 2). This is precisely what we want to do in order to increase profit rapidly at the next step.[18]

But which of the numbers in this column, w (the second column), should be chosen as the pivot element? Here we have another rule:

RULE 9. *Choice of pivot element:* Take each *negative* element in the chosen column and use it to divide the corresponding element in the first column. The element for which the resulting quotient is smallest in absolute value (i.e., smallest, ignoring sign) must be chosen as pivot.

For example, in matrix (5) the pivot is to be chosen from the second column whose only negative elements are -1 and -3. Dividing the corresponding first-column elements by these numbers, we have the quotients $8000/-1 = -8000$ and $9000/-3 = -3000$. The latter of these is clearly the smaller in absolute value and hence the corresponding element -3 of the column in question *must* be chosen as pivot.

[18] We choose our pivot column in this way because at each step of the computation we desire to increase the value of the objective function (total profit) which is the element in the upper left-hand corner of the matrix (a_{00}). We therefore want to choose our pivot in a way which will, by formula (10), increase the value of this element a_{00}. In the general matrix (11) we note that if a_{vw}^* is chosen as pivot the two circled corner

$$
\begin{array}{c}
\quad\quad\quad \ldots \; X_w \; \ldots \; X_n \\[4pt]
\begin{array}{c|ccccc}
Z & \boxed{\textstyle\widehat{a_{00}}} & \ldots & \widehat{a_{0w}} & \ldots & a_{0n} \\
\cdot & \cdots & \cdots & \cdots & \cdots & \cdots \\
t_v & \widehat{a_{v0}} & \ldots & \widehat{a_{vw}^*} & \ldots & a_{vn} \\
\cdot & \cdots & \cdots & \cdots & \cdots & \cdots \\
t_m & a_{m0} & \ldots & a_{mw} & \ldots & a_{mn}
\end{array}
\end{array}
$$

(11)

elements which complete the a_{00}-pivot rectangle include one element, a_{v0}, from the first column and one, a_{0w}, from the first row. The former, a_{v0}, must be non-negative because we began with a feasible solution. Hence, if we pick a_{0w} *positive and our pivot negative* (by rule 9), the fraction $-a_{v0}a_{0w}/a_{vw}^*$ must be positive. Hence by formula (10) since this is the change in a_{00}, it follows that a_{00} will be increased.

The reason we must choose this element can be explained intuitively.[19] When we introduce the new output X_1 into the solution, some of the firm's limited productive capacity must be diverted from its current outputs and used for the production of X_1. Thus, the quantities of other outputs will be reduced. We can increase the quantity of the profitable output X_1 only so long as sufficient capacity remains to be taken away from other outputs. We therefore must stop increasing the output of X_1 when the production of some other commodity, call it W, is cut down to zero, for any further increase in X_1 would require a negative output of W, which is impossible. W will, then, be the output which is cut to zero in the next basic solution, i.e., the pivot element will be in the row of the old matrix (5) which corresponds to output W.

To find which will be commodity W we must find which output is first reduced to zero by an expansion of the production of X_1. Let us therefore see what happens to each of the previously nonzero "outputs," S_a and S_b, when we increase X_1 in matrix (5). By the first constraint equation in (3'), a unit increase in X_1 decreases the output of S_a by 1 unit [the second element in the pivot column of matrix (5)—i.e., the element in the S_a row and X_1 column of that matrix]. Since there are 8000 units of S_a to begin with in the previous solution (4') [the element in the S_a row and first column of matrix (5)], it will take $8000/1 = 8000$ units of X_1 to reduce S_a to zero.

Now, compare the effect of the increase in X_1 on S_b. By the second equation in (3') a unit increase in X_1 decreases S_b by 3 units [the element, 3, in the S_b row and X_1 column of matrix (5)], and since there are 9000 units of S_b to begin with (the element in the S_b row and first column), S_b production will be eliminated altogether with a $9000/3 = 3000$ unit output of X_1. Hence S_b will be reduced to zero before we can reach the 8000-unit output of X_1 needed to eliminate output S_a. It is therefore impossible to expand the output of X_1 beyond 3000 units, and S_b will be the output

---

[19] A rigorous proof which is relatively simple but not very intuitive is the following: We require all the elements a'_{i0} in the first column of the next matrix to be non-negative so that the next basic solution will also be feasible. But by (10) that new element will be

$$a'_{i0} = a_{i0} - \frac{a_{iw}a_{v0}}{a^*_{vw}}.$$

If this is to be non-negative for every such element i we must have (for negative a_{iw} and a^*_{vw})

$$a_{i0} - \frac{-a_{iw}a_{v0}}{-a^*_{vw}} \geq 0, \quad \text{i.e.,} \quad \frac{a_{i0}}{-a_{iw}} \geq \frac{a_{v0}}{-a^*_{vw}}$$

so that the pivot element, a^*_{vw}, must yield such a fraction which is no larger than that corresponding to any other element, a_{iw}, in the same column, w.

The reader should show that if some a_{iw} is not negative we must always have $a'_{i0} \geqslant a_{io} \geq 0$ so that such elements can never be reduced to zero (a_{iw} cannot be the pivot), nor can they produce a nonfeasible solution ($a'_{i0} < 0$). That is why this proof deals only with negative a_{iw}, and why the pivot element must always be negative.

which is reduced to zero in the next basic solution; that is, the element, -3, in the S_b row and X_1 column must be the pivot in matrix (5) because the ratio 9000/3, the output of X_1 which reduces S_b to zero, is smaller than 8000/1, the corresponding figure for output S_a. This is our Rule 9 for the choice of pivot element.

10. Illustration: Another Pivot Step

This completes the discussion of the simplex-method computation. However, the reader may have found it confusing on first reading, and a careful description of the computation of the next matrix may help to pull the preceding material together into a clear pattern. We notice that in the previous matrix (7) there is only one column (the last) whose top element is positive. The pivot must therefore be chosen from this column (Rule 8). Both remaining elements in this column are negative, and to choose the pivot we must find the quotients obtained by dividing the corresponding first-column elements by these. The quotients are

$$\frac{5000}{-\frac{4}{3}} = -3750 \quad \text{and} \quad \frac{3000}{-\frac{2}{3}} = -4500.$$

Since the former is the smaller quotient in absolute value, $-\frac{4}{3}$, the element in the S_a row and X_2 column, becomes the pivot element (Rule 9). That means the roles of variables X_2 and S_a are to be interchanged in the next matrix, where S_a will be reduced to zero and X_2 will become positive. The new matrix is then produced as follows:

1. Interchange X_2 and S_a in the column and row headings so that the third column is now labelled S_a and the second row is called X_2.[20]

2. The pivot element, $-\frac{4}{3}$ in (7) is replaced by its reciprocal, $-\frac{3}{4}$, and the rest of the elements of the pivot row are replaced by the corresponding old elements in (7), each multiplied by -1 and divided by the pivot $(-\frac{4}{3})$, as shown in matrix (12a) (Rules 4 and 5):

		S_b	S_a				S_b	S_a
(12a)	Z					Z		
	X_2	$-\dfrac{5000}{-\frac{4}{3}}$	$-\dfrac{1}{3}$ $-\frac{4}{3}$	$-\dfrac{3}{4}$	$=$	X_2	3750	$\dfrac{1}{4}$	$-\dfrac{3}{4}$
	X_1					X_1		

[20] The reader who omitted the special computational techniques of Section 8 is reminded that the remainder of this section (except for matrix (12) and the last paragraph of the section) is just a review of these methods so this material should be skipped by him.

3. The remaining elements of the pivot column in (7) are replaced by the corresponding old elements each divided by the pivot $(-\frac{4}{3})$ as shown in matrix (12b) (Rule 6):

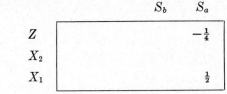

(12b)

4. Finally, the remaining elements in matrix (7) are replaced by use of formula (10) of Rule 7 as shown in matrix (12c):

		S_b	S_a
(12c) Z	$7500 - \dfrac{(5000)(\frac{1}{3})}{-\frac{4}{3}}$	$-\dfrac{5}{6}$	$-\dfrac{(\frac{1}{3})(\frac{1}{3})}{-\frac{4}{3}}$
X_1	$3000 - \dfrac{(5000)(-\frac{2}{3})}{-\frac{4}{3}}$	$-\dfrac{1}{3}$	$-\dfrac{(\frac{1}{3})(-\frac{2}{3})}{-\frac{4}{3}}$

		S_b	S_a
Z	8750		$-\dfrac{3}{4}$
$= X_2$			
X_1	500		$-\dfrac{1}{2}$

If we now combine the information in (12a), (12b), and (12c) we obtain our new matrix (12):

		S_b	S_a
Z	8750	$-\frac{3}{4}$	$-\frac{1}{4}$
(12) X_2	3750	$\frac{1}{4}$	$-\frac{3}{4}$
X_1	500	$-\frac{1}{2}$	$\frac{1}{2}$

It will be noted that all (except the first) of the elements in the top row are negative. These negative numbers are the marginal profitabilities of the items S_b and S_a, whose outputs are now zero. Hence, by Rule 3, *the corresponding basic solution is optimal* (any nonzero value of S_b and S_a must decrease profit, Z). By (4) this solution is $X_2 = 3750$, $X_1 = 500$, $S_b = S_a = 0$, and it yields $Z = 8750$ in profit.

PROBLEMS

1. Maximize $R = 3x + 7y + 6z$ subject to

$$2x + 2y + 2z \leq 8$$
$$x + y \qquad \leq 3$$

$x \geq 0, y \geq 0, z \geq 0.$

2. Maximize $R = 4x + 3y$ subject to

$$x + 3.5y \leq 9$$
$$2x + y \leq 8$$
$$x + y \leq 6$$

$x \geq 0, y \geq 0$.

3. Maximize $R = 4x + 6y$ subject to

$$\tfrac{1}{2}x + y \leq 4$$
$$2x + y \leq 8$$
$$4x - 2y \leq 2$$

$x \geq 0, y \geq 0$.

4. Maximize $R = 4x + y$ subject to

$$x + 2y \leq 5$$
$$3x + 2y \leq 4$$

$x \geq 0, y \geq 0$.

11. The Initial Basic Solution and the "Feasibility Program"

We started our discussion of the simplex computation by assuming that a feasible basic solution can be found by setting all variables except the slack variables equal to zero. In this way we obtained our first basic solution (4) from which all subsequent trial solutions were derived. Unfortunately, many programming problems are inconsistent with such a solution. Some of the constraints may lack slack variables because they were equations to begin with. Even if this difficulty does not arise, a basic solution in which all variables, except the slack elements, are given the value zero may not be feasible.

For example, consider a program with an inequality of a sort which arises typically out of a minimum-requirements specification. A simplified illustration is an advertising budgeting problem which aims to minimize the cost of reaching 30 million potential customers of whom 23 million are required to have an income of over $5000 per year. Suppose the relevant data are those shown in the following table:

	Cost Per Ad (thousands of dollars)	Audience (millions)	Audience with Income over $5000 (millions)
Magazine	28	1	0.6
Television	400	9	2
F. M. Radio	20	0.8	0.7

This states, for example, that each magazine advertisement reaches one million readers and each television program of the variety under consideration can be expected to reach 9 million viewers, etc. Now let M, T, and R respectively represent the number of magazine, television, and radio advertisements budgeted. Our program is then:

$$\text{minimize advertising cost} = 28M + 400T + 20R$$

subject to

(13)
$$M + 9T + 0.8R \geq 30 \text{ (required audience size)}$$
$$0.6M + 2T + 0.7R \geq 23 \text{ (required income)}$$
$$M \geq 0, \quad T \geq 0, \quad R \geq 0.$$

In equality form this is rewritten

$$\text{minimize} \quad 28M + 400T + 20R$$

subject to

(13a)
$$M + 9T + 0.8R - S = 30$$
$$0.6M + 2T + 0.7R - W = 23$$
$$M \geq 0, \quad T \geq 0, \quad R \geq 0, \quad S \geq 0, \quad W \geq 0.$$

Here, the non-negative slack variables S and W must be *subtracted* from the left-hand sides of the constraints because (unlike the machine time and warehouse capacity problem) the activities decided upon must produce a result (reach an audience) *greater* than or equal to 30 million, etc. (not *less* than or equal to some capacity figure). Hence, if the advertisements were to reach an audience of, e.g., 32 million, we must subtract $S = 2$ million from this number to obtain the 30 million minimum requirement figure.

Suppose, now, we try in such a case to obtain our initial basic solution in the simplex computation as we did before, by setting all but slack variables equal to zero. We would have $M = T = R = 0$ but, by (13), this has the ridiculous implication $0 \geq 30$, $0 \geq 23$, or alternatively, by (13a), this implies $-S = 30$, $-W = 23$, $S \geq 0$, $W \geq 0$, all of which obviously cannot be true simultaneously. Hence, the usual initial basic solution with all ordinary variables set equal to zero is not feasible here. In economic terms, in the previously discussed problems, where the constraints represented maximum capacities, zero outputs were always feasible (though not very profitable). But now, where the constraints are minimum acceptability requirements, zero outputs will not normally meet the stated requirements—they will not be feasible. It follows that this simple method for finding a starting basic solution does not always work.[21]

However, Dantzig has invented an ingenious procedure which substi-

[21] The remainder of this section is relatively difficult and the reader may prefer to omit it.

tutes for such an inconvenient problem another artificial programming problem for which we can start off with the usual first basic solution where all ordinary variables take the value zero. This artificial program is so constructed that its optimal solutions must be the same as the optimal solutions of the original problem. Hence we can just go ahead and solve it by the usual procedure, paying no further attention to the original linear programming problem in the course of the computation. This artificial problem is called the *feasibility program*.

The nature of the feasibility program is best explained by example. Consider again our illustrative program (13a). The corresponding feasibility program is obtained simply by adding two more artificial variables V_1 and V_2 (a sort of second set of slack variables) to give us the program:

$$\text{minimize} \quad 28M + 400T + 20R + kV_1 + kV_2$$

subject to the constraints

(14)
$$M + 9T + 0.8R - S + V_1 = 30$$
$$0.6M + 2T + 0.7R - W + V_2 = 23$$

$$M \geq 0, \quad T \geq 0, \quad R \geq 0, \quad S \geq 0, \quad W \geq 0, \quad V_1 \geq 0, \quad V_2 \geq 0.$$

Here k is some positive number which, for reasons to be given in a moment, is chosen to be very large. A basic solution for this feasibility problem is easily found by treating the V's as we treated the slack variables previously. We have the initial basic solution

$$V_1 = 30, \quad V_2 = 23, \quad M = T = R = S = W = 0.$$

Thus such a solution is always feasible even if the *original* slack variables are necessarily zero or negative as in our advertising program problem. This artificial feasibility problem can be solved by the ordinary methods of linear programming, and, as will now be shown, *the optimal solution of the feasibility problem is exactly the same as that of the original problem*, so that, by solving the former, we automatically solve the latter!

Because of the similarity in their structures, any solution of the feasibility program which involves $V_1 = V_2 = 0$ is necessarily a solution of the original programming problem since with the V's equal to zero all the terms which are peculiar to the feasibility program drop out. That is, if $V_1 = V_2 = 0$, programming problems (13a) and (14) are identical, so that any solution of (14) in which $V_1 = V_2 = 0$ must also satisfy (13a). But, if k is a sufficiently large positive number, e.g., if we set $k = 999$ billion dollars in problem (14) we can be sure that the optimal solution to the feasibility program will have the desired property, $V_1 = V_2 = 0$. For the objective function is so constructed that any nonzero V, say V_2, must add

kV_2 dollars to the "cost" figure which we are trying to minimize. In our artificial feasibility program, therefore, if we make k a very large number, $V_2 \neq 0$ can never be optimal because we thereby make V_2 so expensive that it is sure to be cheaper to set $V_2 = 0$ and adopt a nonzero level of some other less "expensive" variable instead. As a result, the ordinary programming computation will yield $V_1 = V_2 = 0$ in its optimal solution. But, as has just been noted, for the V's $= 0$ the feasibility problem and the original problem coincide so that their optimal solutions must also coincide.

To sum up, we can find an optimal solution for any linear program by finding the optimum solution of the artificial feasibility program for which we can use the usual initial basic solution (4), where all ordinary variables take the value zero.

12. The Dual Program

To every linear programming maximization problem there is an associated, sometimes somewhat artificial, minimization problem and vice versa. The mathematical significance of these associated pairs of problems is very great. Before examining its formal structure, let us see what economic interpretation has been given the second *dual* problem.

Let our original problem be that of choosing the most profitable combination of outputs under the limitations imposed by several scarce inputs such as warehouse space, and suppose an economist enters the management of this competitive firm and decides to see how the profits can be imputed to the scarce inputs which constitute the bottlenecks to output expansion. That is to say, he wishes to decide what proportion of its profits the firm owes to each such scarce factor. To do this he will set up accounting prices for these resources which are just high enough to give to these inputs a value equal to the total profit of the firm.[22] That is, *the firm's profits after paying their imputed values to its scarce factors must be zero.* Moreover, a similar condition must hold for each commodity produced by the firm— the value of the scarce resources tied up in its manufacture must not fall short of the product's maximum profit yield. In programming terms, the economist wants to find prices for the scarce resources which minimize the total accounting cost of these resources to the firm, and yet involve a scarce-input cost of producing a unit of each commodity which is no less

[22] As economists we would expect the accounting prices of these resources to reflect the values of their marginal products—i.e., the increase in profits which would accrue to the firm if it could somehow obtain another unit of such a factor. In fact, this turns out to be the case—the prices determined by the dual program do represent these marginal values of the scarce factors.

than its unit profit yield.[23] The problem of finding such prices is the dual program to the profit-maximizing program.

It must be emphasized that the zero profit condition in this problem is not related directly to the zero profit requirement for long-run equilibrium under perfect competition. In imputation, zero profit is an accounting requirement. If accounting prices are set up which do not completely exhaust profits, these prices do not impute profits completely to the scarce inputs which were used to obtain the outputs. The accounting prices must then be increased to eliminate these unimputed profits.

The term "duality" refers to a very remarkable symmetry in the mathematical statement of the two problems. One involves maximization, the other minimization. The former involves outputs *no greater than* resources permit, the other an accounting cost *no lower than* the amounts necessary to allocate all profits. Suppose, moreover, the firm has two scarce inputs, A and B, and three possible outputs, 1, 2, and 3. The maximization problem has three variables, X_1, X_2, and X_3, the magnitudes of these outputs. The dual problem has the same number (three) of inequalities stating that the profits, P_1, P_2, and P_3 of each of these outputs must be imputed fully to the firm's scarce resources. Similarly, the minimization problem has two variables, Y_a and Y_b, the accounting prices of the scarce resources, and the maximization problem correspondingly has two inequalities stating that resource capacities C_a and C_b must not be exceeded.

But the symmetry of the two problems is even more remarkable, as the algebraic statement of the two problems will show:

PRIMAL PROBLEM	*DUAL PROBLEM*
Maximize profit	Minimize imputed cost
$$P = P_1X_1 + P_2X_2 + P_3X_3$$	$$C = C_aY_a + C_bY_b$$
subject to resource limitations	subject to the requirement that all profits are imputed
$$k_{a1}X_1 + k_{a2}X_2 + k_{a3}X_3 \leq C_a$$	
$$k_{b1}X_1 + k_{b2}X_2 + k_{b3}X_3 \leq C_b$$	$$k_{a1}Y_a + k_{b1}Y_b \geq P_1$$
and the requirement that no outputs be negative	$$k_{a2}Y_a + k_{b2}Y_b \geq P_2$$
	$$k_{a3}Y_a + k_{b3}Y_b \geq P_3$$
$$X_1 \geq 0, \quad X_2 \geq 0, \quad X_3 \geq 0.$$	and the requirement that no accounting prices be negative
	$$Y_a \geq 0, \qquad Y_b \geq 0.$$

Here, e.g., k_{b3} represents the amount of scarce resource b that is required to produce a unit of output 3. Thus, the first inequality on the left

---

[23] Some commodities which the firm can but does not wish to produce will, as we shall see, yield negative profits. That is, their gross profit must be less than their opportunity cost in terms of scarce factors tied up in their production.

states that the amount of resource a used on output 1 plus the amount used on output 2 plus the amount used on output 3 must not exceed C_a, the amount available of that resource. Similarly, the first inequality on the right states that the value of the amount of resource a (valued at its accounting price, Y_a) used in a unit of output 1 plus the value of resource b used in a unit of that output must be at least as great as P_1, the net profit of a unit of this output.

Notice the position of the k's in the two sets of inequalities; e.g., k_{a3} appears on the left in the third term of the first inequality, while on the right it is the first term of the third inequality. Here is another duality symmetry.

It is now easy to prove the following very useful theorem: If it is feasible to find *any* value, P', of the variable, P, which is to be maximized and *any* value, C', of the dual variable which is to be minimized, P' will never exceed C'. In the present illustrative case the reason is obvious. P is total profit and C is total imputed cost and we have constructed imputed cost so that it will never fail to eat up profit.[24]

Two more remarkable theorems can also be proved:

DUALITY THEOREM I. The maximum value of P will equal the minimum value of C, that is, total profit from the optimal output combination will just equal the total "optimal" imputed cost.

DUALITY THEOREM II. If in an optimal solution, say, the *second* inequality in one problem involves less than full use of capacity (i.e., strict inequality: that is, the sign is $<$, not $=$), then the optimal value of the corresponding (second) variable of the dual problem will be zero.

What does this mean economically? In our illustrative problem Theorem II has two interesting interpretations. It states that if, e.g., input B, say warehouse space, is optimally *not* used to capacity (so that $S_b > 0$),

---

[24] More generally, to prove the theorem, consider first the problem on the left. Multiply both sides of the first inequality by Y_a, and those of the second inequality by Y_b, and add the corresponding sides of both inequalities. We obtain

$$Y_a k_{a1} X_1 + Y_a k_{a2} X_2 + Y_a k_{a3} X_3 + Y_b k_{b1} X_1 + Y_b k_{b2} X_2 + Y_b k_{b3} X_3 \leq C_a Y_a + C_b Y_b \equiv C.$$

In the mess on the left, e.g., the term $Y_a k_{a2} X_2$ represents the value of resource a used in producing X_2 units of output 2, so that the entire expression (call it ΣYkX) is the accounting value of all resources used in producing all outputs.

Now multiply the first inequality in the dual program by X_1, the second by X_2, the third by X_3, and add. We get

$$\Sigma YkX \geq P_1 X_1 + P_2 X_2 + P_3 X_3 \equiv P.$$

Comparing the results of the two additions our theorem follows at once: $P \leq C$.

then Y_b, the optimal accounting price of input b, must be zero. That is, warehouse space will (as seems reasonable) be considered a free good. Actually, this result merely indicates that the programming price imputation is reasonable.

The second (dual) application of Theorem II states that if, e.g., commodity 3 yields a unit profit less than the imputed cost of the resources used to produce it, then the optimal value of the corresponding variable X_3, in the dual problem will be zero, i.e., commodity 3 will not be produced. This result states essentially, and plausibly, that scarce resources will be used only on the production of commodities whose profits are no less than their marginal yield in other uses.[25]

It must be emphasized that minimization problems also have a dual. For example, here is problem (13) of the preceding section, and its dual:

PRIMAL PROBLEM	DUAL PROBLEM
Minimize	Maximize
$28M + 400T + 20R$	$30Y_1 + 23Y_2$
subject to	subject to
$M + 9T + 0.8R \geq 30$	$Y_1 + 0.6Y_2 \leq 28$
(13c) $0.6M + 2T + 0.7R \geq 23$	$9Y_1 + 2Y_2 \leq 400$
	$0.8Y_1 + 0.7Y_2 \leq 20$
$M \geq 0, \quad T \geq 0, \quad R \geq 0$	$Y_1 \geq 0, \quad Y_2 \geq 0$

where Y_1 and Y_2 are the artificial variables of the dual program. (The reader should study this illustration to see why there are only two constraints in the first problem and three in the second, why there are three variables in the primal problem and two in the second, etc. He should make certain he understands how the coefficients of the dual are obtained. Finally he should write out the dual problem for problem (1) of Section 3, above.)

Duality can often also be put to good use in the linear programming computation process. It is not difficult to show that the solution to a primal programming problem can automatically yield the solution to the dual program as well. That is because of the symmetry of the two problems, which means they will have exactly the same simplex matrices except that their rows and columns will be interchanged. For example, the initial simplex tableaus corresponding to the first two dual programs of this section are:

---

[25] One of the most impressive applications of the duality theorems occurs in the theory of games where the profit or utility maximization calculations of the two players in a "zero-sum two-person game" can be formulated as a pair of dual programs. See Chapter 18, Section 8 below.

	X_1	X_2	X_3
P	0	P_1	P_2	P_3
s_a	C_a	$-k_{a1}$	$-k_{a2}$	$-k_{a3}$
s_b	C_b	$-k_{b1}$	$-k_{b2}$	$-k_{b3}$

(Primal Matrix — P row: $0, P_1, P_2, P_3$)

		Y_a	Y_b
C	0	C_a	C_b
D_1	P_1	$-k_{a1}$	$-k_{b1}$
D_2	P_2	$-k_{a2}$	$-k_{b2}$
D_3	P_3	$-k_{a3}$	$-k_{b3}$

Primal Matrix   Dual Matrix[26]

where the s's and D's are the slack variables of the primal and dual problems, respectively. Note, in particular, that the first *row* of the primal matrix is the same as the first *column* in the dual matrix. [The reader should write out the initial matrices for the preceding pair of numerical dual problems (13c).] Suppose now that we have obtained the final (optimal) simplex matrix for the primal problem so that the solution to this problem is, as usual, given by the first *column* of that matrix. It should be plausible (and it is true) that the first *row* of that same optimal matrix contains the solution to the dual problem! For example, it will be recalled that matrix (12) of Section 10 yields the primal problem solution $X_2 = 3750$, $X_1 = 500$ (all other variables taking value zero). But, by observing the first row of that first matrix we see that the dual problem has the solution $Y_b = \frac{3}{4}$, $Y_a = \frac{1}{4}$, where Y_b and Y_a are, respectively, the second and first nonslack variables of the dual to problem (3′).[27]

---

[26] Actually all dual matrix elements below the first row should be reversed in sign. This results from the difference in sign of the slack variables in the primal and dual programs. For example, the dual constraint $k_{a1}Y_a + k_{b1}Y_b \geq P_1$ becomes in slack variable form

$$k_{a1}Y_a + k_{b1}Y_b - D_1 = P_1$$

where $D_1 \geq 0$, i.e.,

$$D_1 = -P_1 + k_{a1}Y_a + k_{b1}Y_b$$

so that the signs in the second line in our dual matrix (which corresponds to this constraint) should be reversed.

Note that the slack variable D_1 may be interpreted as the unit loss on output of commodity 1. That is, D_1 equals $k_{a1}Y_a + k_{b1}Y_b$, the imputed cost of the inputs needed to produce a unit of this good, minus P_1, the unit price of output 1. Thus this commodity will be produced ($X_1 > 0$) only if $D_1 = 0$ (no loss involved in producing the item). This is part of Duality Theorem II, above.

[27] To find which variable corresponds to which number in the solution matrix, it is necessary to replace the primal variables by the corresponding variables of the dual problem. By comparing the primal and dual simplex tables of this section (noting again that dual columns correspond to primal rows) we obtain the following rule: If $X_1, \ldots, X_n$, $s_a, \ldots, s_m$ are the ordinary and slack variables of the primal problem and $Y_a, \ldots, Y_m$, $D_1, \ldots, D_n$ are the ordinary slack variables of the dual problem, then corresponding e.g. to primal ordinary variable X_7 we have dual slack variable D_7, and, similarly, primal slack variable s_j corresponds to dual ordinary variable Y_j. Since in matrix (12) S_a and S_b are the first and second slack variables in the primal problem (3′) they must be replaced

For the same reason it is possible to solve the primal problem by first dealing with the dual problem—that is, by solving the dual problem and then obtaining the primal answer as a free bonus. Which of these methods it pays to use is a matter of convenience or computational efficiency since the dual and the primal problem are not always equally easy to solve.

In particular, if as in the problem (13) discussed in the previous section, it turns out that $X_1 = X_2 = \ldots = X_n = 0$ is not a feasible solution to the primal problem so that we cannot use this in our first basic solution, it is usually possible to solve the dual problem and to take $Y_a = Y_b = \ldots = Y_m = 0$ as a first feasible solution. To see why this is so, suppose that in the primal problem we have only "greater than or equal to constraints" such as $0.6M + 2T + 0.7R \geq 23$ in system (13). This is clearly not satisfied by $M = T = R = 0$. But the dual problem will then have only "less than or equal to constraints" such as $9Y_1 + 2Y_2 \leq 400$ which are clearly satisfied by $Y_1 = Y_2 = 0$. Hence, in such a case it is possible to work entirely with the dual problem and to avoid altogether the use of the feasibility program of Section 11 (which is likely to get rather complicated in practice).[28]

REFERENCES

Bennion, Edward G., *Elementary Mathematics of Linear Programming and Game Theory*, Bureau of Business and Economic Research, Michigan State University, East Lansing, 1960.

Charnes, A., Cooper, W. W., and Henderson, A., *Introduction to Linear Programming*, Wiley, New York, 1953.

Dorfman, Robert, Samuelson, Paul A., and Solow, Robert M., *Linear Programming and Economic Analysis*, McGraw-Hill, New York, 1958.

Dorfman, Robert, "Mathematical or 'Linear' Programming," *American Economic Review*, Vol. XLIII, December 1953. (Non-technical introductory material.)

Gass, Saul, *Linear Programming: Methods and Applications*, McGraw-Hill, New York, 1958.

---

by Y_a and Y_b respectively. And so, because in matrix (12) the number $-\frac{3}{4}$ occurs in the S_b column, we set $Y_b = \frac{3}{4}$, and, similarly, we take $Y_a = \frac{1}{4}$ in the solution of our dual problem. The reason for dropping the minus signs is indicated in footnote 26, above.

[28] But note that this approach will not work if the primal problem contains both "less than or equal to" and "greater than or equal to" constraints. Note also that we can tell directly from the simplex matrix when it is appropriate to use the dual matrix. The primal method requires that all elements in the first column be non-negative. If, however, there are some negative elements in the first column but *no* positive elements in the first row we can use the dual program in our computations. For the dual method interchanges rows and columns and changes the signs of all the elements in the matrix (see footnote 26). Hence the dual problem will in this case contain no negative elements in its first column. An important application of this principle occurs in Chapter 7.

Henderson, A., and Schlaifer, R., "Mathematical Programming," *Harvard Business Review*, Vol. 32, May–June 1954. (Non-technical introductory material.)

Harrison, J. O., "Linear Programming," in J. F. McCloskey and F. N. Trefethen (eds.), *Operations Research for Management*, Johns Hopkins, Baltimore, 1954. (Non-technical introductory material.)

Vajda, S., *Readings in Linear Programming*, Wiley, New York, 1958. (Describes a wide variety of applications.)

CHAPTER SIX

*Nonlinear programming**

In economic terms nonlinear programming may be described as the analysis of constrainted maximization problems in which diminishing or increasing returns to scale are present. For example, by doubling *all* its inputs a firm may find that it can increase its profits by only 47 per cent. This may occur because, for some reason, its physical outputs cannot keep pace, or because it becomes increasingly difficult to sell additional outputs so that selling costs yield diminishing returns and/or the prices of its products fall.

1. Algebraic Notation and Example

In a nonlinear program the algebraic expressions which occur in either the objective function (e.g., the profit or cost relationship) or in the constraints or both will involve nonlinear terms such as X^3 or 5^x or $\cos X$. Thus, rather than representing the profit relationship by a simple linear expression such as $5X + 3Y + 7Z$, we use the more general functional notation, total profit $= f(X, Y, Z)$ which states simply that profit is dependent in some way on the quantities of the three outputs, X, Y, and Z. Similar notation is used for the constraints, so that the general nonlinear programming problem may be written in the usual three parts:

* Some of the material in this chapter may be considered conceptually difficult. However, it is recommended that any reader of the preceding chapter read at least Sections 1 through 6, for only by contrast with nonlinear programming can the limitations and peculiarities of the *linear* programming case be fully understood.

1. *Objective function*

$$\text{maximize (or minimize)} \quad f(X, Y, Z, \ldots)$$

subject to

2. *Constraints*

$$g_1(X, Y, Z, \ldots) \leq c_1$$
$$g_2(X, Y, Z, \ldots) \leq c_2$$
$$\cdots \cdots \cdots \cdots$$
$$g_m(X, Y, Z, \ldots) \leq c_m$$

and

3. *The non-negativity requirements*

$$X \geq 0, \quad Y \geq 0, \quad Z \geq 0, \quad \ldots .$$

To show how such a nonlinear programming problem can arise in an economic problem, consider the case where the unit profits, P_x and P_y, of X and Y are fixed, say $P_x = 5$ and $P_y = 3$. Suppose, however, that because of customer resistance to increased purchasing (a negatively sloping demand curve) the unit profits of Z, P_z, fall continuously as more of this commodity is offered for sale, in accord with the simple *linear* relationship

$$P_z = 200 - 0.005Z$$

which states that every time another thousand units of Z are offered for sale, its price falls 5 cents. Substituting this expression for P_z into the objective function, that function becomes

$$\text{total profit} = P_xX + P_yY + P_zZ = 5X + 3Y + (200 - 0.005Z)Z$$
$$= 5X + 3Y + 200Z - 0.005Z^2 .$$

Note that this contains a Z^2, so it is no longer a linear relationship despite the fact that the demand expression which was substituted for P_z is linear.

2. *Geometric Representation: Nonlinear Constraints*

It is convenient to consider the effects of nonlinearities on the graph of a programming problem in two separate stages: (1) the effects of non-linearities in the constraints, and (2) the effects of nonlinearities in the objective function.

Let us first examine the constraints. Suppose the problem involves, for example, the inequality

$$X^2 + Y^2 \leq 1$$

As in the linear programming case, this divides combinations of X and Y

into two classes: feasible (those which meet the conditions specified by the inequality) and infeasible (those combinations of X and Y which violate the inequality). The borderline between the region of feasible points and those which represent outputs that do not satisfy the inequality is again given by the requirement that *equality* hold in the constraint:

$$X^2 + Y^2 = 1, \quad \text{i.e.,} \quad Y = \sqrt{1 - X^2}.$$

Any point on the graph of this equation represents a combination of X and Y which just manages to squeeze in "under the wire"—it just barely

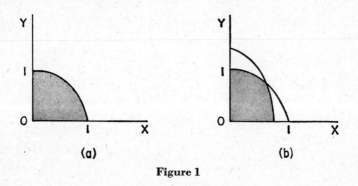

(a)   (b)

Figure 1

satisfies the inequality. By trying various values of X and computing the corresponding values of Y, or by more sophisticated means, it can be seen that the graph of this relationship is that shown in Figure 1a. Furthermore, if we require X and Y to be non-negative, the feasible output combinations are represented by the shaded region in this diagram. A second nonlinear inequality might reduce the feasible region to that depicted in Figure 1b.

We see, then, that nonlinear inequalities trace out a feasible region just as do linear inequalities. However, when they are nonlinear the borders of the feasible region will consist, at least partly, of curved lines.

3. Geometry of Nonlinear Objective Functions

For reasons analogous to those just described, the graph of a nonlinear objective function is not a plane as in the linear case. Instead profit functions may be hills or valleys or of totally irregular shape.

Several such profit relationships and the corresponding iso profit curves (profit indifference curves) are illustrated in Figures 2, 3, and 4. Figure 2a represents the "best-behaved" type of profit function. For reasons which are discussed later in this chapter, such a function makes life eas-

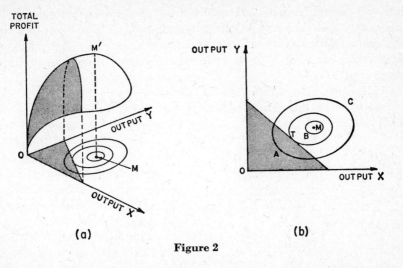

(a)   (b)

Figure 2

ier for the programmer than does the presence of other types of nonlinear profit functions.

This can be described as a diminishing-returns case—the curvature of the surface (its upside-down U-shaped cross sections) indicates that increases in output yield diminishing marginal returns (see Section 4 of Chapter 9 above). Indeed, increases in output beyond the profit-maximizing point M, must yield diminishing *total* returns, i.e., such an increase in output must obviously reduce total profits.

The iso profit curves of nonlinear profit functions are not usually parallel straight lines. In this hill-shaped profit function case they are closed curves which lie inside one another. It is also to be noted that, unlike the linear

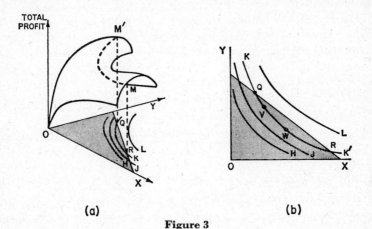

(a)   (b)

Figure 3

case, the direction of profitable movement can change. For example, in Figure 2b a movement upward and to the right (an increase in both outputs) will sometimes increase profits and sometimes reduce them. Thus the move from A to B adds to total profits, but a move from T to C reduces them.

An extreme case of this phenomenon is depicted in Figure 3. Here the iso profit curves have the traditional shape of indifference curves, but

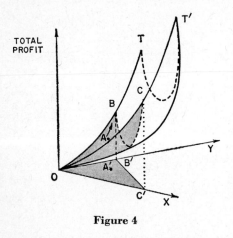

there is one difference. Profits increase as we move up from H to J to K. But curve K corresponds to the maximum profit ridge MM' in Figure 3a, so that if we move further away from the origin, say from an output combination on K to one on L, profits actually fall.

Finally, Figure 4 depicts an important extreme case, that of increasing returns, where increasing values of, say, X bring in ever-increasing marginal yields (the upward curvature of OCT').

Figure 4

After a preliminary discussion of some geometric concepts we shall return to examine some of the problems which such a situation involves.

4. Convex and Nonconvex Regions

The shaded region in Figure 5a is of a variety which is called *convex*. That is to say, it has no dents or holes as does the nonconvex region in Figure 5b. More precisely, a region is defined to be convex if the straight line connecting any two of its points lies entirely inside the region. Thus, if we draw the line connecting any two points, such as M and R in Figure 5a, that line will never leave the shaded area. But if in 5b we try to connect points A and B or B and C in this way, our lines will have to traverse some of the unshaded part of the diagram.

The distinction between convexity and nonconvexity of the feasible region is important for programming. Nonconvexity can make it more difficult for us to find the optimal point, and it can also make it more difficult for us to recognize the point to be optimal when we get there.

1. *Testing for optimality.* Suppose, for the moment, that the objective (profit) function is linear so that the iso profit curves are parallel straight lines. Then, in a feasible region which is convex, if we find a point

such as *M* from which any *small* move decreases profit, we can be sure that this point is a global optimum, i.e., no move of *any* magnitude will bring in profits higher than those at *M*. *M* is a point of "tangency" between iso profit curve *PP'* and the boundary of the feasible region.

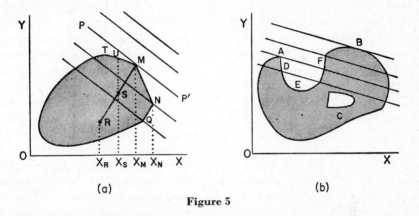

(a)   (b)

Figure 5

Because of the convexity of the region, its boundary curves further and further away from iso profit line *PP'*. Thus if a small move away from *M*, say to *N*, reduces profits, we can be sure that any further move in that direction, say to *Q*, will reduce profits still more.

However, this result does not hold for the nonconvex feasible region in Figure 5b. There, a move from point of tangency *A* over to *D* does indeed reduce profits. But if we are patient and nevertheless follow along the boundary of the feasible region, it may begin to curl back upward again (point *E*) and eventually we may even reach a point *B* which is also a point of price line-feasible region tangency and which yields profits far higher than those at tangency point *A*. A point like *A* which yields higher profit than any other feasible point in its vicinity is called a *local optimum*, whereas the point *B* which really yields maximum profits is a *global optimum*.

2. *Finding the optimum.* A related problem produced by nonconvexity is that it is more difficult under these circumstances to design an iterative procedure to find the global optimum. In the convex case (Figure 5a) any move which increases profits (e.g., the move from *Q* to *N*) is certain to get us closer to the optimal point, *M*, because there is only one profit hilltop and any uphill move must bring us nearer to it. But in the case of the nonconvex region a move which increases profits (e.g., the move from *E* to *D* in Figure 5b) can move us toward the wrong hilltop, *A*, and away from the true optimum, *B*. Hence in such a case an iterative procedure which is designed always to increase profits may very well fail to lead us to the global optimum.

What is the significance of these results? It is, in effect, that near-sighted mathematicians cannot be trusted to solve programming problems in which the feasible region is nonconvex. Any procedure that tells us to test for maximum profits by checking whether a few steps in any direction reduce profits can be considered to involve such a myopic approach. An example of such a procedure is the simple requirement of the differential calculus that the second derivative of the function whose value is to be maximized be negative at the maximum point. For this condition merely states that any move to a point *very near* the maximum point results in a reduction in the value of the objective function, so it is a satisfactory condition only where nearsightedness is no handicap. In other words there are optimality tests and resulting economies of calculation which are inapplicable to problems involving nonconvex feasible regions.

It is important to note that in a *linear* program the feasible region is *always* convex.[1] That is why, in the simplex method, to see whether some corner C of the feasible region is optimal it is only necessary to test the profitability of a move to one of the corners adjacent to C. For if a move to any such corner reduces profits (or increases costs) then any further moves must certainly be disadvantageous. In other words, the simplex method can be classified as a nearsighted calculation method.

5. Concave and Convex (Objective) Functions

A classification somewhat analogous to that just described for geometric regions also holds for the graphs of functions. A function whose graph is like that in Figure 4 is called *convex* while that in Figure 2a is called *concave*. More precisely, a function is called *strictly concave* if, when we draw a straight line connecting any two points A and B on its graph (Figure 6a), the whole of the arc AB, excluding the end points, lies above the straight line AB. The function is called *concave* (but not strictly

---

[1] To demonstrate this it is only necessary to show that if S (Figure 5a) is any point on the line connecting two feasible points such as M and R in the feasible region of a linear program, then S is also feasible (it lies in the shaded region). But S represents an output combination which can be obtained by a suitable scaling down of the activities at M and R. For example, if S is the midpoint of line MR it represents the sum of half the outputs at M and half the outputs at R (X_S is the midpoint of X_R and X_M, etc.). Now consider any scarce facility, k, whose total capacity is K. Since M is feasible, its production must require no more than K units of this facility, and the same must hold for output combination R. But because a linear program involves constant returns to scale, it follows that half of the outputs at M or at R require no more than $\frac{1}{2}K$ units of facility k in their production. Hence S will require in its manufacture no more than $\frac{1}{2}K + \frac{1}{2}K = K$ units of k, i.e., no more of this scarce resource than is available. A similar argument holds for every scarce resource needed to produce S, and it therefore follows that output S must be feasible.

concave) if its graph contains some linear stretches so that a straight line such as $A'B'$ (Figure 6b) may coincide with arc $A'B'$.

Convex and *strictly convex* functions are defined analogously, only here the connecting arc always lies *below* or coincides with the line connecting two points on the graph. It should be noted that a linear function, whose graph is a straight line, a plane, or a hyperplane (n-dimensional analogue of a plane), is always *both* concave and convex.

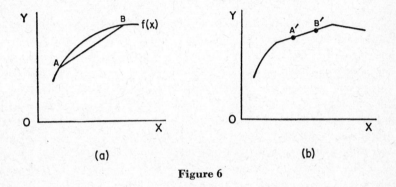

Figure 6

Objective functions of the "wrong" shape can lead to the same problem as nonconvex feasible regions—they can produce local optima which are not global optima so they can invalidate myopic computational procedures and procedures for testing for optimality. But in this case which shape is wrong depends on the nature of the problem. As we shall see now, a well-behaved objective function in a maximization problem is apt to be badly behaved in a minimization problem, and vice versa.

A moment's thought indicates why this is so. In a maximization problem, if the function is hill-shaped (concave) all uphill roads lead to the top. In Figure 2a we can confidently proceed by moving upward in *any* direction because all uphill paths end up at the peak. Hence any trial-and-error (iterative) procedure which keeps trying successive output levels which are more profitable than those in the previous attempts will (if it does not move up too slowly) eventually get us to the maximum profit output combination. Moreover, if we are at a point M from which any small move takes us downhill, we know that this point must be the true optimum. The myopic computational techniques and optimality tests both work.

But if in a maximization problem the graph of the objective function contains a valley (it is convex), going in an uphill direction is not guaranteed to get us to the top. If we start uphill from point A in Figure 4 we may land up in point B instead of point C, the global optimum in the shaded feasible region.

In a minimization problem it is easy to see that the situation is reversed—a valley is desirable and a hill is troublesome from the point of view of computation.

We may sum up by stating that nearsighted computational techniques can be used in a maximization problem if the feasible region is convex and the objective function is concave. In a minimization problem such methods can be employed if the objective function and the feasible region are both convex.

There is another way in which the economist can look at this matter. A graph of a concave function such as Figure 2, if it is a profit function, represents a situation involving diminishing returns, as already noted. But if the figure were to represent a cost function, it should be clear that it would be one involving increasing returns (decreasing marginal costs as output expands). Similarly, convex Figure 4 represents either an increasing-returns profit function or a diminishing-returns cost function. Thus a well-behaved objective function in either the maximization case (concave) or the minimization case (convex) involves diminishing returns. We can, then, restate our main theorem as:

> Myopic computational and optimality testing techniques can be used when the problem involves a convex feasible region and diminishing returns.

The role of diminishing returns in this proposition is easily visualized intuitively—if any departure from a local optimum always involves diminishing returns, then going further and further only makes things worse, so that our local optimum must be a global optimum as well. Indeed, this reasoning can be carried further to indicate that diminishing returns will tend to produce convexity in the feasible region. The stretch EF in the nonconvex feasible region in Figure 5b clearly involves increasing returns to scale (increasing marginal profits as output increases). If diminishing returns held throughout, the boundary of the feasible region would curve further and further away from the iso profit line through local optimum point A so that no other optimum point such as B would be possible.[2]

---

[2] More specifically, it is easy to show that, if the variables represent the magnitudes of several outputs, then convexity of the feasible region is tantamount to diminishing marginal rate of transformation of one output for another (see *Value and Capital*, 2nd edition, Oxford University Press, New York, 1946, pp. 80–87). For the outer (northeast) boundary of the feasible region (arc TN in Figure 5a) is the production possibility locus (the transformation curve or efficiency frontier) which represents all the maximal output combinations producible with the available quantities of scarce resources (see Chapter 16, Section 5, below). Convexity requires that as we move to the right along this arc its slope diminishes (becomes increasingly negative) or, for some stretches, remains unchanged. But the diminishing slope of TM means that we get diminishing returns in shifting resources out of the production of Y and into the production of X. Thus, an

Therefore, *only if we have diminishing returns throughout the feasible region are myopic computational techniques generally legitimate*. This is the final, most compact form of this theorem.

6. Nonlinearities and the Basic Theorem of Linear Programming

It will be recalled from the preceding chapter that there is a central theorem of linear programming which states that the number of variables (including slack variables) whose values are positive in an optimal solution will ordinarily be equal to the number of constraints in the problem. In other words there will always be a *basic* optimal solution to any solvable linear programming problem. In geometric terms, there will then always be an optimal solution which occurs at a corner of the feasible region. This is one of the great computational economies which *linear* programming makes possible. An optimal solution can always be found by examining only the corners of the feasible region, and ignoring the infinite set of points which make up the remainder of the feasible region.

In nonlinear programming this result does not hold. This is easily shown by counterexample. In Figure 2b the optimum point is the point of tangency T between the boundary of the feasible region and the highest attainable iso profit curve. It will be noted that at point T both X and Y have positive values even though there is only one constraint.

In Figure 3b an even more extreme case is depicted. Here optimal points, such as V and W, occur in the interior of the feasible region.[3] It is to be noted, then, that even though there is only one constraint both X and Y are positive. But, in addition, since the facility represented by that constraint is not used to capacity (we are not on the constraint line), the slack variable corresponding to that constraint will also have a nonzero

---

increase in the output of X from X_s to X_m results in only a small decrease in Y (from the ordinate of U to that of M), but a further equal increase in X from X_m to X_n requires a much larger fall in Y. This argument can be extended to the case where there are more variables, or variables other than outputs, to show a general connection between diminishing returns and convexity of the feasible region.

Note that, in this respect, diminishing returns is compatible with a *linear* programming problem, because the feasible region of such a problem is always convex. Cf. footnote 1, above.

[3] It is true that this figure also contains two optimal points Q and R which lie on the boundary (but *not on corners*) of the feasible region. But it is easy to see that a slight modification of the drawing could eliminate these by bending down the 3-dimensional surface in Figure 3a as it approaches the axes. A simpler example of an optimum point which occurs only in the interior of the feasible region would result if the highest point M in Figure 2 fell inside the feasible region.

value. Here, then, we have only one constraint and yet every one of the three variables' values is positive!

It is clear, then, that the so-called basic theorem of linear programming need not hold in the presence of nonlinearities. However, the connection between the number of variables whose optimal values are nonzero and the number of constraints does not just descend into chaos. A very important relationship exists between the difference in these two numbers and the structure of the problem. In general we may state that with diminishing returns (a concave maximization or a convex minimization problem) the number of positive variable values will tend to be greater than the number of constraints. In the increasing-returns case the number of positive optimal variable values will generally fall short of the number of constraints. It follows that if we try to approximate a nonlinear problem with a linear programming calculation, then if there are diminishing returns we should suspect that the answer will contain too few positive values, while if it involves increasing returns it will contain too many.

The reason for this result is not difficult to see. First we may note how this follows from the geometry. We consider only the maximization problem, but the argument for the minimization case is perfectly analogous. In Figure 2, the diminishing-returns case, the highest feasible point, that is, the optimal point, will tend to occur toward the center of the diagram where variables take nonzero values. On the other hand, in the increasing-returns case (Figure 4) where the graph curls upward toward the edges of the diagram, maximal points like B and C will occur over the axes where variables take on zero values (X is zero at point B and Y is zero at point C).

But there is an easier way to visualize the relationship between diminishing or increasing returns and the number of nonzero variable values in an optimal solution. When a linear program indicates that a firm with 2000 products and 17 constraints should cut its line down to 17 or fewer items, it is reasoned implicitly that the combination of products which yields the greatest profits with a small expansion in their outputs will also continue to be most profitable as their production increases indefinitely. It will then pay to enlarge the output of these most profitable goods as far as possible—until they take over all of the firm's scarce facilities and leave no excess capacity sufficient for the production of other items. But if there are diminishing returns to the production of these goods, then though they start off being the most profitable, after their output expands to some intermediate level the profitability of a further increment in their outputs will fall below that of some other goods and it will then pay to devote some of the company's resources to the output of these other goods, and so on.

That is precisely why our instincts are outraged by the linear programming recommendation that a 2000-product firm cut its product line down to 17 items, devoting all of its facilities to the production of these goods. We surmise that the firm has spread its production over so many different items because the market calls for them—because it will be difficult or impossible to market as much of the 17 items as the firm has the capacity to produce. There are diminishing returns because of increasing marketing costs. Often careful analysis will indicate that the 2000-item line is indeed excessive, but that the optimal set of products includes considerably more than the 17 items which will yield most profits to a small output expansion.

For similar reasons, increasing returns tend to call for considerably greater concentration in a few products than does linear programming. If an item which is most profitable becomes even more profitable as its output expands, it will pay to drop other goods from the line to achieve the full benefits of specialization.

Here again, an economic example may help to clarify the situation. In a study of the optimal number and geographic location of a company's warehouses[4] it was found that a linear programming computation might very well suggest that the firm operate a separate warehouse for every customer! For, in the linear case, if a change in warehouse location would reduce the transportation cost of shipping from factory to warehouse to some single customer, it would (if these were the only costs involved) pay to operate such a warehouse. What this computation ignores is the economies in inventory, administration, and bookkeeping, etc., which result from the operation of a small number of larger warehouses. In other words the increasing returns to size of warehouse operation are ignored in the linear programming calculation which then recommends the operation of too many warehouse installations (too many nonzero variables).

The results of this section may then be summed up in the following rule: When a linear programming calculation is employed as an approximation, and if the problem involves diminishing returns, the linear approximation will recommend too few activities, whereas if the actual problem involves economies of large scale (increasing returns) the linear approximation will call for too many activities. This rule should be helpful in making rough improvements in the results of linear approximations.

7. Methods of Nonlinear Computation

This section makes no attempt to teach the reader step-by-step procedures for nonlinear computation. The literature contains many special tricks which vary from one type of problem to another, and the field is in a state of rapid change and development. We shall discuss only two general approaches indicating the logic of the procedures which have been

---

[4] See Section 8 of Chapter 21 below, and William J. Baumol and Philip Wolfe, "A Warehouse Location Problem," *Operations Research*, Vol. 6, March–April, 1958.

employed. It will be noted that the methods which are about to be described are both of the myopic variety. They can only be relied upon to find a global optimum in a diminishing-returns problem. In a case of increasing returns these methods cannot be relied upon to produce more than local optima. There exist principles for the determination of global optima in the increasing-returns case, but they have as yet not been tested to any significant extent. Such an approach will be described in the next chapter.

Dr. Wolfe has described the simplex procedure of linear programming as a "walking" method.[5] That is, the computer steps from one corner to another adjacent corner (always in the right direction), until he finds an optimum. By contrast he has described the techniques of nonlinear programming as hopping and creeping methods. Let us deal first with the former.

The hopping approach applies only where the constraints are linear, even though the objective function is nonlinear. In fact most nonlinear programs which have so far been encountered in practice have been of this variety. In such a case the boundary of the feasible region is composed of a set of joined straight-line segments and is always convex. Indeed, it is identical with the feasible region of linear programming.

In this situation it is nevertheless possible for a unique optimal point to occur away from a corner, as witness the case of point T in Figure 2b which is an example of this sort of program. The hopping feature of the computational procedure is necessary to get us away from the corner-to-corner movement of the simplex method. In effect, starting off at any point we walk to the next more profitable corner and then hop back to any still more lucrative intermediate point.

To be more specific, let us describe one of the more frequently used hopping procedures in somewhat greater detail. Consider the situation in Figure 7. Suppose at some stage of our computation we have just passed corner K and happen to find ourselves at a point A. We then proceed in the following stages:

Step 1. Fit a plane, $pp'p''p'''$, tangent to the nonlinear profit surface above point A.[6]

Step 2. Use one "round" of the simplex method on the resulting approximative linear programming problem to find a corner, say B, which is more profitable than the previous corner K.

Step 3. Use the differential calculus or some substitute procedure to

---

[5] See Philip Wolfe, "Computational Techniques for Non-Linear Programs," Princeton University Conference, March, 1957.

[6] This is done by taking the profit function to be total profit $= aX + bY$ and setting $a = \partial f/\partial X$ and $b = \partial f/\partial Y$ where $f(X, Y)$ is the true nonlinear profit function and the partial derivatives are evaluated at point A', i.e., at $X = X_A$ and $Y = Y_A$.

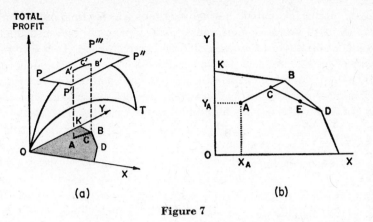

Figure 7

find the most profitable point, say C, on the straight line connecting A and B, i.e., find the point C on line AB above which the nonlinear profit function is highest. (This is always a "one-dimensional problem," i.e., the graph of alternatives is a straight line, and the computation is therefore not difficult.)

Step 4. Go back to Step 1, but start this time from point C and corner B (thus going, e.g., successively to corner D and then back to E, etc.).

These "hopping" methods are slower than the walking methods. Moreover, unlike the walking methods, they do not actually find the solution to a programming problem, but they do approximate it to any desired degree of accuracy, which is enough for all practical applications.

We come now to the "creeping" or, more correctly, the *gradient* methods for solving nonlinear programming problems. Geometrically, they involve our sliding around the feasible region, always in continuous motion (no jumps) and always in a direction which goes uphill (downhill) on the profit (cost) function. These methods can be used even when both the objective function and the constraints contain nonlinearities. Such methods were first proposed for problems relating to programming by George Brown and von Neumann. Samuelson later showed that they bear some analogy with the way in which a market mechanism can approach its equilibrium. The basic idea of the gradient methods is very simple. Suppose it is desired to find the outputs which maximize profit, $R = f(X_1, \ldots, X_n)$ where the X_i are the outputs of the firm's different products. A gradient method sets up the differential equation (in which t represents computing time elapsed):

$$\frac{dX_i}{dt} = \frac{\partial R}{\partial X_i}.$$

This states that we increase the quantity X_i of commodity i ($dX_i/dt > 0$) in the trial solution, so long and only so long as this increase in X_i results in a rise in the firm's profits. Moreover, we make this time rate of increase in output, X_i, proportionate (equal for an appropriate time unit) to its marginal profitability $(\partial R/\partial X_i)$. In other words, we increase (decrease) all quantities whose rise leads to higher (lower) profits and, in effect, give a priority ordering to the changes in the different quantities in proportion to their profit contribution. Moreover, we impose the condition that any quantity which falls to zero be stopped at that point

$$(\partial X_k/\partial t = 0 \quad \text{if} \quad X_k = 0 \quad \text{and} \quad \partial R/\partial X_k < 0$$

[i.e., if X_k has just been falling]) so that we do not get into the economic nonsense of negative outputs. This is the essence of the gradient methods. If the problem is one invo.ving diminishing returns throughout, the solution to the gradient-method differential equations will converge, over time, to the true maximum, i.e., the quantities, X_i, will all approach their profit-maximizing values. Gradient methods can also be employed in linear programming computations. There is reason to believe that they are slower than the simplex method when an accurate solution is required, but there is not yet enough computational experience for a firm statement on this matter.[7]

Still another, indeed, so far one of the most successful methods of dealing with nonlinear programming methods involves the use of "piecewise linear" approximations. Clearly, a circle can be approximated to any desired degree of accuracy by an inscribed polygon. Similarly, other well-behaved curves can be approximated by connected straight line segments. In this way the objective function and constraints of a nonlinear program can be approximated linearly, and the resulting approximation can be handled by variants of the simplex method of linear programming.

8. The Kuhn-Tucker Theorems

We come finally to a class of theorems of nonlinear programming which have been the focal point of the mathematician's interest in the subject.

---

[7] However, Wolfe, *op. cit.*, pp. 10–11 and 19, points out that the differential equations of the gradient methods of *linear* programming can be set up on ". . . conventional electronic differential analyzer equipment. This has been done by Pyne at Princeton for small-scale problems and works with relatively good accuracy and surprisingly high speed. One can view the trajectories of several X_j on oscilloscopes and see the solution of a linear programming problem traced out from an arbitrary initial point in a matter of several seconds. In addition to giving a satisfactory graphic account of a solution to the problem, the analogue method has the notable feature that the parameters occurring in the problem can be varied with a great deal of ease. One can explore large areas of parameter values quite quickly by this means, giving a good method for rough sensitivity analysis in linear problems. It is also possible to wire nonlinearities into the problem . . . but this is not so easy to do with conventional equipment." Wolfe concludes, "It is true that an analogue method will give little accuracy compared with a digital procedure; but how accurate are the data of our programming problems?"

These theorems are deeper and more abstruse than the material covered in the rest of the chapter, and it will not be possible to give a fully satisfactory account of what they involve. The reader will therefore have to be satisfied with my apology on this point. The basic theorems were contributed by H. W. Kuhn and A. W. Tucker and were later extended by Arrow, Hurwicz, and Uzawa who have also done important work extending the class of programming problems to which gradient methods can be applied.

It will be recalled from Chapter 4 that a maximum or minimum problem involving only equality constraints, and which is amenable to treatment by classical calculus techniques, can be approached by the method of Lagrange multipliers. In bare outline, this involves the following steps:

1. Take each of the constraints and bring all of the terms over to one side of the equation—e.g., rewrite $X + Y = 5$ as $X + Y - 5 = 0$.

2. Multiply each of the constraints by a constant whose value is unspecified, this constant being the Lagrange multiplier. For example, the preceding constraint becomes $\lambda(X + Y - 5) = 0$.

3. Add together all of the constraints (each multiplied by its own Lagrange multiplier) and then add this sum to the objective function. This sum is called the Lagrangian expression; e.g., if the problem is to maximize $X^2 + 3XY + Z$ subject to $X + Y = 5$ and $XZ = 10$ the Lagrangian expression is

$$X^2 + 3XY + Z + \lambda_1(X + Y - 5) + \lambda_2(XZ - 10)$$

where λ_1 and λ_2 are two different Lagrange multipliers.

We now can state the central theorem of Lagrange multiplier theory which asserts that, in a wide class of problems, any values of X, Y, and Z which maximize the value of the objective function subject to the stated constraints will also maximize the Lagrangian expression and vice versa. In other words, we are given a choice—we can either solve the original maximization problem or we can instead solve the problem of maximizing the value of the Lagrangian expression. Either procedure automatically solves both problems. Naturally, we then choose the alternative which is easier, and often the easier procedure will be the Lagrangian method. It should be recalled that in the course of the Lagrangian procedure specific numbers will be determined for the Lagrangian constants, the λ's.

Kuhn and Tucker have extended this approach to mathematical programming. Specifically they have shown:

1. That for a wide class of programming problems (including all linear problems and all diminishing-returns nonlinear problems) a Lagrangian expression can be formed in exactly the way as described above for the calculus case, and this Lagrangian expression will have the same use-

ful property—whatever values of the variables maximize (minimize) the value of the original objective function subject to its equality or inequality constraints will maximize (minimize) the value of the Lagrangian expression.

2. This Lagrangian expression has another interesting property: Suppose we are dealing with a maximization problem and it turns out that the optimal values of the variables, X_1, X_2, . . . , X_n are some numbers which we designate X_1^*, X_2^*, . . . , X_n^*. Suppose, moreover, that we substitute these numbers for the X's wherever an X occurs in the Lagrangian expression. Then we have the following rather curious theorem: Suppose we treat the Lagrange multipliers as variables and try to find the values of these λ's which *minimize* the value of Lagrangian expression (with the X^*'s substituted for the X's. The minimizing values of the λ's then turn out to be precisely the values of the constant Lagrangian multipliers required for the solution of the original maximization problem. The original problem will have been solved when and only when we have found the values of the X's which maximize the value of the Lagrangian expression *and the values of the λ's which minimize that value.* In more technical terminology we call this solution a "saddle point." [See Section 5, of Chapter 18, below, which explains the reason for this terminology—the saddle-like shape of the graph of the Lagrangian function—the optimal point is the top of a hill when looked at from one direction, and the trough of a valley when looked at from another (Figure 1 of Chapter 18)].

3. In particular, in a linear programming problem these Lagrangian multipliers turn out to be the optimal values (the "prices") of the dual problem! Moreover, given any primal problem and its dual, the Lagrangian expressions for the two problems are identical! (This theorem is a direct consequence of the duality theorems of the preceding chapter and its proof is not very difficult.)

4. In fact, this duality relationship leads directly to the maximization-minimization (saddle-point) property described in 2, above. For suppose our primal problem is a maximization problem in which the object is to maximize profit (P). Then the dual problem must be a minimization problem whose objective is to minimize accounting cost, C. Let L represent the common Lagrangian expression for the two problems. The logic of the Lagrangian approach rests on the fact that the values of the primal variables, X_1, . . . , X_n, which maximize P must also be those which maximize L. Similarly, the values of the dual variables, λ_1, . . . , λ_m, which minimize C must also minimize L. Hence we have the minimax (saddle-point) result: if we find a combination of X's and λ's which constitutes a solution to the primal and the dual problems, respectively, then for these values the Lagrangian expression will have the lowest value which any λ's can give it and the highest value which any X's can give it.

These Kuhn-Tucker theorems have a number of applications of which we outline a few:

1. They provide a helpful interpretation (as dual prices) of Lagrange multipliers in the linear and portions of the nonlinear programming theory, which sheds some light on Lagrange multiplier theory.

2. More important, they are, in many cases, helpful in computation, giving us alternative means for solving a given programming problem. In particular, they have been helpful in the gradient methods of solution.

3. Perhaps most important from the point of view of the mathematician, the Kuhn-Tucker theorems serve as so-called *existence theorems* in mathematical programming. That is, there are some programming problems which are unsolvable (they have no solution) because they involve inconsistencies or because there is no effective upper bound to the value of the objective function (so that the sky is the limit and it has no *maximum* value). Before we try to solve a problem it is desirable to know whether a solution even *exists*—because if it does not exist there is no point in wasting time looking for it. An existence theorem is a criterion which can tell us whether a solution to a given problem exists, even if it does not show us how to go about finding that solution. The Kuhn-Tucker theorems provide such an existence theorem, for they state that, for the class of programming problems for which they are valid, a problem has a solution if and only if the corresponding Lagrangian condition can be satisfied.

REFERENCES

Arrow, K. J., Hurwicz, Leonid, and Uzawa, H., *Studies in Linear and Non-Linear Programming*, Stanford University Press, Stanford, California, 1958.

Charnes, A., and Cooper, W. W., "Non-Linear Power of Adjacent Extreme Point Methods in Linear Programming," *Econometrica*, Vol. 25, January 1957. (Discussion of piecewise linear approximation methods.)

Dorfman, Robert, Samuelson, P. A., and Solow, R. M., *Linear Programming and Economic Analysis*, McGraw-Hill, New York, 1958, Chapter 8.

Kuhn, H. W., and Tucker, A. W., "Nonlinear Programming," in J. Neyman (ed.), *Proceedings of the Second Berkeley Symposium on Mathematical Statistics and Probability*, University of California Press, Berkeley and Los Angeles, 1951.

Rosen, J. B., "The Gradient Projection Method for Nonlinear Programming — Linear Constraints," *Journal of the Society for Industrial and Applied Mathmatics*, Vol. 8, March 1960. (A promising computation method.)

Wolfe, Philip, *Computational Techniques for Non-Linear Programs*, Princeton University Conference, March 1957.

CHAPTER SEVEN

Integer programming[1]

An integer programming problem is a programming problem in which the answer is required to consist entirely of integers—"whole numbers" which have no fractional or decimal parts. In other words, from among all possible integers, it is required to find values of the variables which are feasible and maximize (minimize) the value of the objective function. Let us see how the need for integer answers arises.[2]

1. Problems Where Noninteger Solutions Are Meaningless

In economics many items come in indivisible units. There is no meaningful entity such as half a locomotive or half a drill press or half a worker. It is, therefore, natural that there should arise problems in which fractional answers are inconvenient. However, for these indivisibility problems ordinary programming methods will often do as an approximation (sometimes as a very good approximation), so that the special techniques of integer programming will not contribute much. For example, if an ordinary programming analysis recommends that an automobile manufacturer produce 374,063.4 cars of some model, we may reasonably ignore the four-tenths figure in this answer. Indeed, data inaccuracy will usually require

[1] The material in this chapter may be considered relatively advanced and specialized; the reader may, therefore, prefer to omit it.

[2] For an excellent survey of the applications of integer programming, see George B. Dantzig, "On the Significance of Solving Linear Programming Problems with Some Integer Variables," *Econometrica*, Vol. 28, January 1960.

that we round off even more and report the answer as, say, a 375,000-car output recommendation.

But there are many other programming problems, more qualitative in nature, in which a fractional answer is totally meaningless and where rounding is therefore not a real alternative. For example, if we wish to decide in what order a group of cities should be visited to minimize transportation costs (including the cost of returning to the home-base starting point—this is the so-called traveling salesman problem), it is not helpful to be told that the next place to go at some stage of the tour is City No. 9.63, where City No. 9 is New Orleans and City No. 10 is San Francisco. Another example in which rounding of noninteger answers is not helpful is the following problem of choosing "the largest harmonious task force."

Suppose a personnel office is attempting to make up a working team of persons who get along together. There are n candidates, and no two candidates who can't get along with each other are to be used. Assigning a variable x_i to the ith candidate, we will interpret a value of 0 to mean that that candidate is included in the team, a value of 1 to mean that he is excluded. The variable x_i is to be restricted to these two values. The problem of constructing the largest harmonious team then is the problem of minimizing

$$\sum_{i=1}^{i=n} x_i,$$

the number left out, subject to the restrictions

$$x_i + x_j \geq 1$$

for all pairs i, j of candidates who can't get along. The effect of each such restriction is to insist that at least one candidate in the i, j pair is left out (at least $x_i > 0$ or $x_j > 0$). It is not hard to see that if the problem is solved as an integer programming problem, the variables in the minimum solution will not only be integers, but actually 0's and 1's as is required for a meaningful answer. For if any larger integer, say $3 = x_k$, is included in a trial solution it can be decreased to 1 without violating any constraints. Moreover, such a change in the value of x_k must reduce the value of the objective function, $\sum x_i$, which is to be minimized. Hence, the number 3 will never occur in an optimal integer solution—nor will any other integer larger than 1. Only zeros and ones will be included as is required. Thus the problem can be solved as an integer programming problem, but it will be noted again that an ordinary linear programming solution to this problem, if it involves any fractions, has no obvious meaning.

2. Nonconvex Feasible Region Problems

It has been known for some time that a method of solution of the general linear programming problem in which the variables are required to take integer values would also permit the solution of a considerable variety of other problems, many of which are not obviously related to it. For example, Markowitz and Manne have shown that the solution to the difficult increasing-returns programming problem which was described in Sections 3 and 5 of the preceding chapter can, at least in principle, be approximated as an integer program which permits the determination of a global, and not just a local optimum.[3] Nonconvex feasible regions can also, at least in principle, be handled by integer programming.

As we saw in the previous chapter, the difficulty with a programming problem whose feasible region is nonconvex is that it is not possible by ordinary methods to distinguish a global from a local maximum. Thus, in Figure 1, we have depicted a nonconvex feasible region (shaded area). The

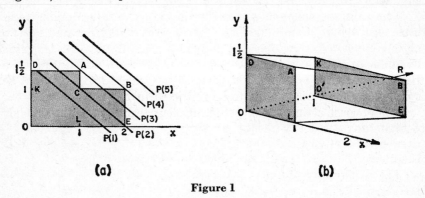

(a)   (b)

Figure 1

parallel lines marked P are the iso profit lines. B is clearly the maximum profit point, but A is a local optimum which yields lower profits than does B. Note, however, that A satisfies the simplex criterion for an optimum solution. That is, it yields higher profits than either adjacent corner C or D.

By translating this into an integer programming problem, however, it is possible to transform the feasible region into a convex region. Algebraically, we proceed by inventing an artificial variable, R, and writing

$$\text{maximize } P = ax + by$$

subject to

$$x \leq 1 + R$$
$$y \leq 1\tfrac{1}{2} - R/2$$
$$R \leq 1$$
$$x \geq 0, \quad y \geq 0, \quad R \geq 0.$$

The constraints are three variable linear inequalities which, as usual,

---

[3] Harry M. Markowitz and Alan S. Manne, "On the Solution of Discrete Programming Problems," *Econometrica*, Vol. 25, January 1957, pp. 84–87.

describe a (three-dimensional) convex region. If in addition we require R to be an integer[4] this means R must be either 0 or 1. It will be noted that if $R = 0$ the inequalities involving x and y describe rectangle $OLAD$, whereas if $R = 1$ they describe rectangle $OEBK$; hence together they describe the entire feasible region of Figure 1a.

What the variable R and the integer solution requirement have done is described geometrically in Figure 1b. Here at $R = 0$ we have re-erected rectangle $OLAD$ from Figure 1a, while at $R = 1$ we have drawn in rectangle $OEBK$ (the shaded regions). The algebraic constraints given above describe the *convex hull* of these two rectangles, that is, the smallest convex region which includes both rectangles. This convex hull is the distorted cube shown in Figure 1b.

The artificial programming problem with variable R which has just been formulated is, then, that of maximizing the value of the original objective function, $P = ax + by$, by choice of values of x, y, and R which lie in the artificial *convex* feasible region, the distorted cube of Figure 1b. Hence we have gone from a problem with a nonconvex feasible region to another in which the feasible region is convex.

Where does integer programming enter the matter? By requiring that R be an integer between 0 and 1 we force both problems to yield the same answers, so that an optimal solution of the artificial problem of Figure 1b is automatically also the optimal solution of the original problem.

The requirement that R be an integer confines us just to the shaded rectangles of Figure 1b, for at any other points of the distorted cube R is not an integer. But as we have seen, these two shaded rectangles of Figure 1b together are (when superimposed) identical with the nonconvex feasible region of Figure 1a. Hence, any values of x and y represented by a point in either shaded region of Figure 1b must also lie in the feasible region of the original problem. Thus the feasible values of x and y in the artificial problem, when R is required to be an integer, must coincide with those for the original problem. Since the two problems then have the same feasible regions as well as the same objective functions, they must clearly have the same solutions.

---

[4] Note that as described this is a "mixed" problem in which some but not all of the variables are required to be integer values. The method of integer programming which is described in this chapter does not apply directly to such problems, although there has been some exploratory work in the area. The difficulty can be evaded, at least in principle, by measuring x and y in very small units and taking their optimal *integer* values as approximations to their true optimal values. By making the units of measurement small enough this approximation can, in principle, clearly be made as close as desired, though we do not yet have enough computing experience with the method to know how rapidly it yields answers when dealing with the large numbers which are likely to result. There has also been some promising work on the mixed problem.

3. Increasing Returns: The Fixed Charges Problem

As previously mentioned, integer programming can also, at least in principle, be helpful in the problem of finding a global optimum in the increasing-returns *objective function* case—where the graph of the objective function is of the wrong shape from the point of view of myopic computational methods (cf. Sections 3 and 5 of the preceding chapter). Let us now see how integer programming enters the matter in one particularly important but intractable case—the fixed costs (charges) problem.

Several times in this volume the nature of fixed costs has been discussed. It will be recalled that they are defined as costs which do not vary with the magnitude of some operation (at least within limits), and that these costs can therefore be escaped only by closing down the operation altogether. We will now see what computational problems expenses of this type can produce.

Figure 2a represents part of the profit function of a multi-branch firm showing how company profits will vary when the scale of operation of one

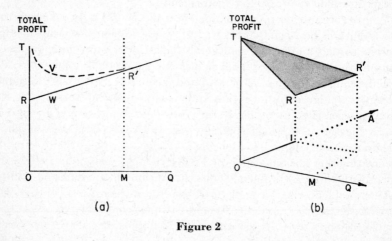

(a)   (b)

Figure 2

of its branches, B, varies, the outputs of all other branches being given. This relationship is profit curve TRR'. As the diagram shows, if this branch is kept in operation, the larger its output, Q, the larger will be the firm's profits (RR' slopes uphill toward the right). But in the case shown, if the branch goes out of operation altogether, the fixed costs (such as rent) which the firm escapes are so large that company profits (from the operation of its remaining branches) will ultimately jump from R to T. In fact (assuming that there is some upper limit, OM, to the demand for its product), even if the branch produces every bit that it can sell, the profit contribution of this branch will not suffice to cover the fixed cost, for point R', whose height represents profit at the maximum salable output, lies below T, where OT represents company profit when the plant is closed down altogether.

We see, then, that point R' is a local maximum, but T is the global maximum. Indeed, Figure 2a is clearly an increasing-returns objective function—a two-dimensional relative of the surface of Figure 4 in the preceding chapter. But, in the present fixed charges case it is to be noted that *any* computation which tells us to go uphill along the profit curve will move us in the wrong direction. Even at a point like W, which is very close to R, there is not the slightest hint in the slope of the curve that profits can be increased by reducing output. This difficulty, which results from the sharp angle in the objective function, is a particularly nasty feature of the fixed charges problem. By contrast, an ordinary increasing (marginal) returns profit curve, such as curved line TVR', will at least indicate the direction of the global maximum point when we get close enough to it—at point V, going uphill takes us toward global optimum T, even if we were to start further to the right the "go-uphill" rule would take us in the wrong direction.

It is, of course, only because we are dealing with a multi-branch firm that our problem is really difficult. As a result, even our graph is likely not to give us the right answer. Perhaps it is best not to close our branch B after all. Instead it might be better to close some other branch, C, and save the fixed charges at C, meanwhile serving C's former customers from B, for this increases the maximum demand for branch B's product and thus permits us to move higher along our profit curve to the right of point R'. With a large number of branches the problem of examining the possibilities case by case, to decide how many and which to choose, leads us into an enormous problem of permutations and combinations which rapidly grows astronomical. A more systematic computation procedure is required.

A similar problem arises in the search for optimal investment criteria. Suppose, for example, that a country has limited investment funds to be divided between two competing projects. The first yields a low rate of return but has low fixed costs of entry into production, and the reverse is true of the second project. Which of the projects should be chosen will clearly depend on the magnitude of the fixed costs.

The role of integer programming in such a problem is easily represented schematically. As in the nonconvex feasible region case, we introduce an artificial variable, A. In the three-dimensional diagram 2b point T of the original profit curve is placed where $A = 0$, while line RR' is moved to where $A = 1$. The three points T, R, and R' are then connected by the plane TRR' which can now serve as the feasible portion of an artificial *linear* programming objective function. But if we include the constraints $A \geq 0$ and $A \leq 1$ in the problem and require that A take only integer values, it is clear that we can only have either $A = 0$ or $A = 1$. We can end up only at point T or on line segment RR', i.e., we must remain somewhere on the original profit curve TRR' of Figure 2a. Thus by use of integer programming we have been able to substitute for our original fixed charges problem another ordinary linear programming problem which gives the same answers.

In principle, this translation can be made for all of the company's branches at once, so the entire problem can be transformed into one large linear integer programming problem and thus be solved. Unfortunately, in practice this has not, so far, proved practical for even moderately large-scale problems; the number of artificial variables which must be added can make the computation prohibitively time-consuming and expensive.

4. The Method of Solution

A geometric picture of the integer programming problem will give the reader an intuitive grasp of the method of solution. In Figure 3 we rep-

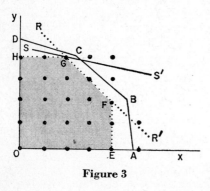

Figure 3

resent the feasible region, $OABCD$, of an ordinary linear programming problem. The dots within this region represent all feasible points both of whose coordinates are integers (called the *integer lattice points*). Solutions to the ordinary programming problem occur on the boundary of the feasible region, and in the diagram none of the boundary (other than the origin) passes through an integer lattice point. Suppose, however, that the feasible region could somehow be shrunk to the *convex hull* of the feasible lattice points (the shaded region) where the convex hull is defined as the smallest convex region which contains all of the lattice points. It is to be noted that this revised figure is also the diagram of an ordinary linear programming problem—in fact, of the original problem modified by the addition of several supplementary linear constraints such as RR'. This new programming problem has two other important features: (1) it includes every integer feasible solution to the original program, and (2) every basic (corner) solution of the new problem is an integer solution, for the boundary of the convex hull consists of linear segments which join lattice points. It follows at once that a (basic) optimal solution to the new programming problem must be an optimal integer solution to the original problem.

In practice it is difficult to cut the feasible region down to the convex hull of the feasible integer lattice points. The method of solution which will be described does consist of a sequence of steps involving the automatic generation of additional constraints to the original linear program from the results of the previous computational steps and the subsequent solution of this expanded linear program.[5] These Gomory constraints are chosen in a way which gives them the following properties: (1) they normally reduce the feasible region; (2) their graph (e.g., SS') ordinarily goes through at least one lattice point (point G in the figure) but it must be emphasized that *this lattice point need not lie in the feasible region;* (3) they never exclude from the new feasible region a lattice point which was originally feasible; and (4) they produce, in a finite number of steps, a new linear program whose solution is in integers and which is therefore the optimal integer solution of the original programming problem (if any such solution exists). It is to be noted that the feasible region of this final programming problem will include $OEFGH$, the convex hull of the feasible lattice points, and will itself be included in the original feasible region, $OABCD$. In this diagram it is clear that, with a suitable objective function, an optimal integer solution will occur, e.g., at point G at the intersection of the additional constraint lines RR' and SS'.

It remains now to describe the construction of these additional Gomory constraints. Consider any equation which occurs in the course of the solution of the linear programming problem [compare Equations (3) of Chapter 5] which we write as

$$\Sigma\, a_{ij}x_j \leq a_{i0}$$

or in the standard slack variable form used in the simplex matrix,

$$(1) \qquad\qquad t_i = a_{i0} + \sum_{j=1}^{n} - a_{ij}x_j.$$

Note that, because of the transposition of the $a_{ij}x_j$ terms in (1) as compared to their positions on the left of the original inequality, minus signs have appeared before the coefficients a_{ij} of the x_j. Note also that (1) *may be the objective (profit) function* $z = a_{00} + \Sigma\, a_{0j}x_j$, where z is the variable whose value is to be maximized (total profit). In other words, (1) need not be a constraint equation.

Before we show how (1) can be used as the basis for one of the Gomory constraints, let us first take care of a matter of terminology. Consider the two numbers 2.7 and -5.1. There are at least two ways in which one can break the first number 2.7 into an integer and a fractional part. We may write either $2.7 = 2 + 0.7$ or, alternatively, $2.7 = 3 - 0.3$. Similarly, this

[5] The method was developed by Ralph E. Gomory. See his "Outline of an Algorithm for Integer Solutions to Linear Programs," *Bulletin of the American Mathematical Society,* Vol. 64, September 1958.

may be done for the second number -5.1, for which we obtain either $-5.1 = -5 - 0.1$ or $-5.1 = -6 + 0.9$. Let us ignore the ways of splitting up the numbers which yield negative fractional parts $(-0.3$ and $-0.1)$ and refer to 0.7 and 0.9 as the respective *non-negative fractional parts* of the numbers 2.7 and -5.1.

Using this terminology we can now state the following theorem: The additional constraint which corresponds to a line such as SS' in Figure 3 is given by

$$\text{(2)} \qquad\qquad \Sigma f_{ij} x_j \geq f_{i0}$$

or alternatively by

$$\text{(3)} \qquad\qquad s_i = -f_{i0} + \Sigma f_{ij} x_j$$

where s_i is a slack variable which is required to take a non-negative integer value, and the f_{ij} are the non-negative fractional parts of the constants a_{ij} in Equation (1).

An economic interpretation of the Gomory constraint (2) is easily given. We may rewrite the inequality (1) in the form

$$\Sigma \ (k_{ij} + f_{ij}) x_j \leq k_{i0} + f_{i0}$$

where the k's are all integers and the f's are all non-negative fractions. If we interpret this as a warehouse space constraint, so that a_{i0} is the total number of cubic feet of warehouse space available, e.g., suppose $a_{i0} = 1260.7$, k_{i0} is then the approximating whole number of cubic feet of warehouse space obtained by slicing away any fraction of a square foot of warehouse space (in our example $k_{i0} = 1260$), and f_{i0} ($= 0.7$) is the fractional amount that is rounded away in the process. Similarly, f_{ij} is the amount which must be sliced off one crate of item j to get the dimensions down to a whole number of cubic feet, and k_{ij} is the resulting (whole number) size of the remainder of the crate. Thus $f_{ij} x_j$ is the total amount shaved off all x_j crates of size j, etc.

We are now readily able to interpret the Gomory constraint (2) as the assertion that the fractional cubic footage which is shaved off the warehouse space in this integerizing process must not exceed the sum of the fractional amounts sliced off all of the crates stored in the warehouse.

The logic of the derivation of this constraint can now also be illustrated. For this purpose let us confine ourselves to the case in which $\Sigma \ a_{ij} x_j = a_{i0}$, i.e., in which the warehouse space is completely filled up. The derivation for the general case is a simple extension of this argument. We note that f_{i0}, the amount rounded off the warehouse space, must be a fraction, but $\Sigma f_{ij} x_j$, the *total* of all the fractional amounts cut off the crates in the warehouse, may conceivably add up to a number greater than unity. Consider now two possible cases:

Case 1. If $\Sigma\, k_{ij}x_j = k_{i0}$, i.e., if the "integerized crates" still exactly fill up the integerized warehouse space, then, since they started out equal, the same amount must have been sliced from both the warehouse and its contents, and we must have $\Sigma\, f_{ij}x_j = f_{i0}$.

Case 2. If $\Sigma\, k_{ij}x_j \neq k_{i0}$ then, since all of these numbers are integers, the two sides of the inequality must differ by at least 1 (cubic foot). This means that the amounts shaved off the crates ($\Sigma\, f_{ij}x_j$) must differ by at least 1 foot from the amount shaved off the warehouse (f_{i0}). Since the latter is a fraction, this is only possible if no less than 1 foot was shaved off the crates, i.e., if

$$\Sigma\, f_{ij}x_j \geq 1 \; (>f_{i0}).$$

In either case, then, the Gomory constraint holds. This is the essence of the argument involved in its derivation.[6]

It is easily shown that the addition of this constraint always causes a change in the solution to the problem so that every Gomory constraint must in fact cut the feasible region down effectively.[7]

To illustrate the construction of such a Gomory constraint, consider the constraint equation

(1a) $$t = 3.8 - 2.7x_1 + 5.1x_2 - 6x_3.$$

[6] This also indicates that we must have $\Sigma\, k_{ij}x_j \leq k_{i0}$. Gomory has made this inequality the basis of a promising new dual integer method, all of whose trial solutions are integer lattice points. See Ralph E. Gomory, "An All-Integer Integer Programming Algorithm," IBM Research Report, RC-189, January 1960. For a derivation of the Gomory constraint (2) see Ralph E. Gomory and William J. Baumol, "Integer Programming and Pricing," *Econometrica*, Vol. 28, July 1960.

[7] *Proof:* The previous solution must have involved a positive fractional part in the constant term, $f_{i0} > 0$. Moreover, in the preceding basic solution we must, as usual, have had $x_1 = x_2 = \ldots = x_n = 0$. But this solution cannot possibly satisfy the Gomory constraint (2), for substituting in the zero value of the x's we obtain the requirement $f_{i0} \leq 0$, which, by hypothesis, cannot hold. This shows that the Gomory constraint line (*SS'* in Figure 3) must cut off the optimal point (*C*) of the preceding trial solution.

The proof that the Gomory method finds a solution (if one exists) in a finite number of steps is rather difficult. However, the following considerations are relevant: (1) By the argument above, the computational process will never bog down at any point at which there is not an integer solution. (2) Each additional Gomory constraint will, generally, cut down profit because it reduces the range of options available to the firm, and, in particular, always renders nonfeasible the solution which was most profitable in the preceding trial. (3) By the nature of its construction, the optimal integer solution cannot violate any Gomory constraint. (4) Hence, if at each step profits are cut *sufficiently*, the firm will ultimately be forced down to the profit level of the optimal integer solution, and the ordinary simplex method will then select that solution as the best one which remains open to the firm. For a rigorous argument see Ralph E. Gomory, "An Algorithm for Integer Solutions to Linear Programs," Princeton-IBM Mathematics Research Project Technical Report No. 1, November 17, 1958 (mimeographed).

Because of the minus signs in Equation (1) we have to change the signs of all but the first of the constants in (1a) to obtain $a_{i0} = 3.8$, $a_{i1} = 2.7$, $a_{i2} = -5.1$, and $a_{i3} = 6$. The non-negative fractional parts of these numbers are respectively 0.8, 0.7, 0.9, and 0. Hence the artificial Gomory constraint (2) is

(2a) $$0.7x_1 + 0.9x_2 + 0x_3 \geq 0.8$$

or, alternatively,

(3a) $$s_i = -0.8 + 0.7x_1 + 0.9x_2.$$

5. Illustrations of the Integer Programming Computation

Example 1: Finding a Gomory constraint. To find an integer optimal solution to a linear programming problem after the noninteger optimal solution has been determined, we must introduce additional constraints. To show how such a constraint is formed, we consider the following simplex tableau:

		s_1	s_2	s_3
R	$19\frac{4}{10}$	$-\frac{2}{10}$	$-\frac{4}{10}$	-1
$\longrightarrow$ x	$1\frac{8}{10}$	$-\frac{4}{10}$	$4\frac{2}{10}$	-2
y	$2\frac{3}{10}$	$\frac{1}{10}$	$-\frac{3}{10}$	-0
z	$\frac{7}{10}$	$\frac{9}{10}$	$-\frac{3}{10}$	-1

This is obviously the tableau corresponding to an optimal solution since the elements in the first column are all non-negative and the remaining elements in the first row are negative. (The solution is

$$R = 19\tfrac{4}{10}, \quad x = 1\tfrac{8}{10}, \quad y = 2\tfrac{3}{10}, \quad z = \tfrac{7}{10}, \quad s_1 = s_2 = s_3 = 0.)$$

The usual approach to the formation of the Gomory constraint is to select the element in the first column with the largest non-negative fractional part. This is clearly the second row (see arrow) where the fractional part of the first element is $\tfrac{8}{10}$. This choice means that the artificial constraint is to be based on the (non-negative) fractional parts of

$$x = 1\tfrac{8}{10} - \tfrac{4}{10}s_1 + 4\tfrac{2}{10}s_2 - 2s_3.$$

Adjusting for sign in accord with the notation of Equation (1), i.e., changing the signs of the coefficients of variables s_1, s_2, and s_3, we have

$$a_{i0} = 1\tfrac{8}{10}, \quad a_{i1} = \tfrac{4}{10}, \quad a_{i2} = -4\tfrac{2}{10}, \quad \text{and} \quad a_{i3} = 2.$$

The non-negative fractional parts of these elements are, respectively,

$$f_{i0} = \tfrac{8}{10}, \quad f_{i1} = \tfrac{4}{10}, \quad f_{i2} = \tfrac{8}{10} \quad \text{and} \quad f_{i3} = 0$$

(since $a_{i2} = -4\frac{2}{10}$ is negative we must rewrite it as $-4\frac{2}{10} = -5 + \frac{8}{10}$ to obtain its *non-negative* fractional part, $\frac{8}{10}$).

The Gomory constraint (3) is therefore

$$s_4^g = -\tfrac{8}{10} + \tfrac{4}{10}s_1 + \tfrac{8}{10}s_2 + 0s_3$$

where the superscript g is employed as a reminder that s_4^g is the slack variable of an artificial Gomory constraint. The coefficients of this constraint equation are now added to the preceding simplex tableau to form a new bottom row:

		$-s_1$	$-s_2$	$-s_3$
R	$19\frac{4}{10}$	$-\frac{2}{10}$	$-\frac{4}{10}$	-1
x	$1\frac{8}{10}$	$-\frac{4}{10}$	$4\frac{2}{10}$	-2
y	$2\frac{3}{10}$	$\frac{1}{10}$	$-\frac{3}{10}$	-0
z	$\frac{7}{10}$	$\frac{9}{10}$	$-\frac{3}{10}$	-1
s_4^g	$-\frac{8}{10}$	$\frac{4}{10}$	$\frac{8}{10}$	0

This augmented simplex tableau is now ready for the next computation and one continues the linear programming computation until the next optimum solution is found. There is only one complication. It will be noted that none of the elements of the first row (except the first) is positive (because the previous solution was optimal). However, one of the elements in the first column $(-\frac{8}{10})$ is negative. Hence, this is not the simplex matrix of a feasible solution (the usual type of basic solution,

$$x = 1\tfrac{8}{10}, \quad y = 2\tfrac{3}{10}, \quad z = \tfrac{7}{10}, \quad s_4^g = -\tfrac{8}{10}, \quad s_1 = s_2 = s_3 = 0$$

is not feasible because it has a negative value for one variable). As a result, the computational procedure must be modified slightly.

To deal with such a situation we simply reverse the role of the rows and the columns (and in effect, change the signs of the elements in the first and last columns) and then proceed as usual. The justification of this procedure is relatively simple. The reader can verify that if he were to write out the simplex tableau for the dual problem of the present problem he would obtain exactly the tableau which has just been described—this last tableau, only with rows and columns interchanged and with the signs of all elements (except the upper left-hand element) in the first row and column reversed. Thus, in effect, we proceed now by making our calculations for the dual problem (Section 12 of Chapter 5) rather than for the primal problem. This method of linear programming calculation is therefore called *the dual method* (invented by C. E. Lemke). It involves no real complications, as is shown in the next illustration.

Example 2: *Finding an optimal integer solution.* Find the maximizing integer solution for

$$R = 4x + y$$

subject to

$$x + 2y \leq 5$$

$$3x + 1y \leq 4$$

$$x \geq 0, \quad y \geq 0.$$

With the insertion of slack variables s_1 and s_2 the constraints become

$$s_1 = 5 - x - 2y$$
$$s_2 = 4 - 3x - 1y$$
$$x \geq 0, \quad y \geq 0, \quad s_1 \geq 0, \quad s_2 \geq 0.$$

The corresponding simplex tableau is then simply the table of the coefficients of the expressions for R, s_1, and s_2:

		x	y
R	0	4	1
s_1	5	-1	-2
s_2	4	$-3*$	-1

Our pivot element must come from the second column since this has the largest positive first element (4). Moreover, the pivot element must be the third element down in this column (the 3) because the ratio between the first element of the *third* row and the corresponding element in the pivot column, i.e., $-\frac{4}{3}$, is smaller in absolute value than the corresponding ratio for any other row. We therefore pivot on the starred element in our first tableau, so that by the rules of Chapter 5, Section 8, we obtain as our second simplex tableau:

		s_2	y
R	$5\frac{1}{3}$	$-1\frac{1}{3}$	$-\frac{1}{3}$
$\longrightarrow$ s_1	$3\frac{2}{3}$	$\frac{1}{3}$	$-1\frac{2}{3}$
x	$1\frac{1}{3}$	$-\frac{1}{3}$	$-\frac{1}{3}$

which (through no accident) is optimal after one pivot operation. We know it is optimal because it now contains no negative elements in the first column and no positive elements (other than the first) in the first row. Hence the optimal *noninteger* solution is $R = 5\frac{1}{3}$, $s_1 = 3\frac{2}{3}$, $x = 1\frac{1}{3}$, $s_2 = y = 0$.

To find an optimal integer solution we must now add a Gomory constraint. The second row (arrow) is the one whose first element, $3\frac{2}{3}$, has the largest fractional part ($\frac{2}{3}$). Adjusting signs of the elements of this row, we obtain in accord with (1), $a_{i0} = 3\frac{2}{3}$, $a_{i1} = -\frac{1}{3}(= -1 + \frac{2}{3})$ and $a_{i2} = 1\frac{2}{3}$, whose non-negative fractions are $\frac{2}{3}$, $\frac{2}{3}$, and $\frac{2}{3}$. Hence the simplex tableau involving this constraint is the same as the previous tableau with these elements constituting a new final row:

		s_2	y
R	$5\frac{1}{3}$	$-1\frac{1}{3}$	$-\frac{1}{3}$
s_1	$3\frac{2}{3}$	$\frac{1}{3}$	$-1\frac{2}{3}$
x	$1\frac{1}{3}$	$-\frac{1}{3}$	$-\frac{1}{3}$
s_3^0	$-\frac{2}{3}$	$\frac{2}{3}$	$\frac{2}{3}*$

To apply the *dual* simplex method to this tableau we note that the dual simplex computation differs from the ordinary simplex computation only in the method of determining the pivot element.

1. To obtain the dual simplex pivot element we first find the *row*, i, in which it will lie. This will be the row which has the largest *negative* first number. That is, the pivot row always has a negative first element, and if two rows, k and i, have first elements -3 and -7, respectively, the latter must be chosen as the pivot row.

2. The pivot element which is chosen from this row, i, must be a *positive* number.

3. The pivot element, a_{ii}^*, is selected from among the positive elements of pivot row, i, by forming the ratio $-a_{0k}/a_{ik}$ between each candidate element and the absolute value of the corresponding element in the first row. The element a_{ii}^* for which this ratio, $-a_{0i}/a_{ii}^*$ is the smallest must be chosen as the pivot.

Thus, in our present problem, the dual simplex method requires us to employ a *positive* pivot element from a *row* (here, the last row) whose first element is *negative*. Moreover, the pivot element must be the one in the last column because the ratio of the corresponding first row element and this element $\frac{1}{3}/\frac{2}{3} = \frac{1}{2}$ is smaller than any other such ratio.

Pivoting, therefore, on the starred element in the lower right-hand corner, we obtain, by the usual rules (which are unchanged for the dual simplex method):

	s_2	s_3^g
z	5	-1	$-\frac{1}{2}$
s_1	2	2	$-2\frac{1}{2}$
x	1	-0	$-\frac{1}{2}$
y	1	-1	$-1\frac{1}{2}$

This is an optimal integer solution $z = 5$, $s_1 = 2$, $x = 1$, $y = 1$, $s_2 = s_3^g = 0$.

A final comment: The last column of the simplex tableau still contains non-integer elements. These fractions, too, can be eliminated by the addition of more Gomory constraints. (Of course, we can no longer employ the rule-of-thumb criterion which tells us to form the next Gomory constraint from the row whose first element has the largest fractional part, since the first column now contains only integers. In any event, a recent computation has apparently shown that this rule of thumb is fallible.) In our present illustration any Gomory constraint must have the coefficients 0, 0, and $\frac{1}{2}$ so that the simplex tableau becomes:

	s_2	s_3^g
z	5	-1	$-\frac{1}{2}$
s_1	2	2	$-2\frac{1}{2}$
x	1	0	$-\frac{1}{2}$
y	1	-1	$-1\frac{1}{2}$
s_4^g	0	0	$\frac{1}{2}^*$

The reader should have no difficulty in showing that the next tableau contains only integer elements; in fact, that it differs from this tableau only in that every element in the last column is doubled. This result can be used to show that in an integer programming solution the imputed prices of the dual program (which turn out to be the elements of the first row with their signs reversed) are also integers.

PROBLEMS

Maximize[8]

1. $R = 3x + 2y + 15z$

subject to

$$x + y + \ z \leq 12$$
$$2x + y + 5z \leq 18.$$

2. $R = 12x + y$

subject to

$$2x + 2y \leq 6$$
$$7x + \ y \leq 8.$$

3. $R = 2x + 6y$

subject to

$$3x + \ y \leq 5$$
$$4x + 4y \leq 9.$$

6. *The Dual Prices and Marginal Valuation*

The solution to the integer programming problem which has just been described involves the solution to an ordinary linear programming problem which is identical with the original program except for the addition of several "artificial" constraints. For convenience we may refer to this new program as the *augmented linear program*. Clearly, as to any linear program, there is a dual program which corresponds to this augmented program. Moreover, if the augmented program has a solution, i.e., if the original program has any integer solution, the dual problem, too, will have a solution which consists of the imputed prices corresponding to the constraints of the primal problem (where the primal problem is interpreted as that of selecting the optimal levels of several activities). These dual prices are obtained just as they are in linear programming. The only difference is that it can be shown that the prices, too, will be integers.

Since these prices are the solution to an ordinary linear programming problem, they will possess the usual characteristics of ordinary dual prices. They will be non-negative; they will ordinarily impute zero profits to any activity which is included in an optimal solution and negative profits to all other activities; zero prices will be imputed to inputs which are not

---

[8] *Note:* All variables are also required to take non-negative values.

used to capacity; and they will make the total imputed cost of all "scarce inputs" equal to the value of the optimum output combination.

However, in several respects these integer programming prices will be peculiar. As just indicated, the prices will themselves be integers. More important, these prices will vary with the choice of additional constraints (2). Finally, we note that prices will be imputed not just to the scarce facilities of the original program—corresponding to each of the added constraints of the augmented program there will also be a shadow price. Before discussing the prices corresponding to these added constraints (call them the artificial capacity prices), let us see what happens to the prices of the original scarce facilities.

Some of these prices may have risen. For example, in Figure 4 suppose C is the optimal solution to the noninteger program, that T is the optimal integer solution and that SS' is the added constraint of the augmented program. Then the input associated with constraint AA' is not used to capacity at C but it is at T. Hence its price will be zero in the noninteger program and rise to some positive value in the integer program.

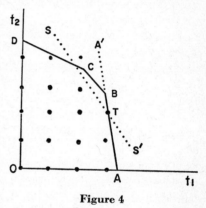

However, many prices which would be positive in a noninteger solution may be expected to fall to zero in the integer programming case. Thus the prices corresponding to constraint segments DC and CB are both positive

Figure 4

when C is optimal, but they are both zero at the integer optimum T. The economic interpretation of these zero prices is easily given. If a warehouse has a capacity to store 36,463.4 cases of some item, an integer solution requires that the last 0.4 storage capacity be left empty—cases just do not come in fractional batches. But, because this fraction of the warehouse's space is "idle," the computation will label warehouse space a free good—it is given a zero price[9] even though this does violence to our economic intuition—for it is clearly possible in this case that a considerably larger warehouse can be put to good use.

We see, then, that the requirement that the solution be in integers may increase some dual prices and will normally reduce others. However, if we know that the capacities, Q_i, of the scarce facilities, including the capacities associated with the additional inequalities, are all non-negative

---

[9] It is tempting to jump to the conclusion that "almost all" prices of original facilities will be driven to zero. In practice, however, this observation seems to be an exaggeration. Experience in problem-solving shows that nonzero dual prices occur frequently.

it is easy to show that the *arithmetic mean (average) price* of the original facilities (when each price is weighted by the capacity of the corresponding facility) must fall.[10]

There is a lower bound to this fall in average price. Suppose, of the various constraints that could have been added in the augmented linear program, we had chosen those which correspond to the boundary *EFGH* of the convex hull of the lattice points (Figure 3). Since no constraint line *SS'* of our original augmented program has any points interior to this convex hull, it can be added to the convex hull augmented program without affecting its solution. It follows that the convex hull augmented program consists of any other augmented program *plus some additional constraints*. It is then a direct consequence of the preceding theorem on average prices that the average dual price of the original capacities in any other augmented program will be greater than or equal to that of the convex hull augmented program.

It is tempting to consider the latter to be the "true" integer programming prices since the convex hull of the integer lattice points represents the smallest convex body containing the entire integer feasible region. We would then say that the computed dual prices are usually overvaluations of the "true" dual prices.

So much for the prices of the original facilities. There remains the problem of interpreting the prices which correspond to the additional Gomory constraints (2). These may be viewed as a measure of the opportunity cost of indivisibility—e.g., the loss imposed on the businessman by the lack of a unit of artificial capacity which prevents him from obtaining four-tenths of a case to fill up that last empty bit of space in his warehouse.

However, we must be careful here—the preceding interpretation amounts to our thinking of these dual prices as the marginal revenues of these inputs. In the integer programming case, this concept runs into difficulties. In integer programming, inputs clearly must be thought of as

---

[10] *Proof:* Let the augmented program have m original constraints and n additional constraints. Let the optimal noninteger prices be $P_1, \ldots, P_m$ and let the optimal integer prices be $P_1^*, \ldots, P_{m+n}^*$. Finally, let the capacities of the scarce facilities be $Q_1, \ldots, Q_{m+n}$. Then, since additional constraints can never increase the maximum value of an objective function, our added Gomory constraints can never increase the maximum profit from the total output (equals the total imputed cost, ΣPQ, of the scarce facilities), so that we have

$$\sum_{i=1}^{m} P_i Q_i \geq \sum_{i=1}^{m+n} P_i^* Q_i \geq \sum_{i=1}^{m} P_i^* Q_i.$$

Dividing through by $\sum_{i=1}^{m} Q_i$ we obtain the desired result. This argument assumes that all the artificial Q_i are non-negative, which can be shown to be true.

coming in indivisible units. For that reason we cannot speak, e.g., of the marginal profit contribution of a small change in input, i.e., we must deal with $\Delta R/\Delta X$ rather than dR/dX where ΔX is an indivisible unit of input X and R is total profit. But a dual price represents dR/dX, which may change over the range of a unit change in X, and hence it may well give an incorrect evaluation of the marginal revenue of input X.

PART II

Microeconomic Analysis

CHAPTER EIGHT

Theory of demand

1. Demand Curves

The demand curve is among those devices of economic theory which have found frequent employment in applied economics. In its traditional form, it sums up the response of consumer demand to alternative prices of a product—it can tell management what may be expected to happen to the demand for one of its outputs if the price of that item is changed.

This information is summarized in a graph (the demand curve itself) which shows how much will be demanded at every possible (hypothetical) price over the relevant range (Figure 1). For example, point D_0 on the de-

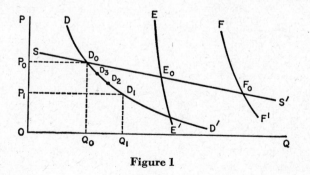

Figure 1

mand curve DD' indicates that at price OP_0 the consumer, or group of consumers, for whom the curve is drawn will wish to purchase OQ_0 units of the product.

Several features of the demand curve should be noted:

1. It is customary to represent the price level on the vertical axis and the quantity demanded on the horizontal axis.[1]

2. The graph depicts the situation at a single point in time, say 4:33 P.M. on June 12. Hence, all but one of the prices and quantities must be hypothetical—the curve must generally answer the "iffy" question: "If price were OP how much would this (these) consumer(s) buy?"

3. The curve is generally assumed to have a negative slope. In economic terms, this is the plausible assertion that, other things being equal, more of the commodity would be demanded (OQ_1 rather than OQ_0) if the price were lower (OP_1 instead of OP_0). However, two possible exceptions should be mentioned: cases of snob appeal and cases where consumers judge quality by price. Commodities like expensive jewelry may be purchased precisely because their price is high, and a fall in their price might reduce their snob appeal and therefore, perhaps, their sale (although enough poorer consumers might then be induced to buy the items to make up for the loss of affluent customers). Similarly, when consumers have no ability to judge the quality of a good directly and use price as an indicator of quality, as they probably often do, a reduction in its price may cut into the demand for a good. The negative slope of the usual demand curve will be discussed again later in this chapter.

2. Shifting Demand Curves: Demand Functions

The second demand-curve characteristic just listed, its temporary nature, implies that the shape and position of the curve is likely to change with the passage of time. At one moment DD' is the relevant demand curve, but at another instant the curve has the shape EE'. Such a change is described as a *shift* in the demand curve. This is contrasted with a *movement along* a demand curve, say from point D_0 to D_1.

A shift in a demand curve is normally accounted for by a change in the value of some of the other variables which affect demand. For example, a rise in consumer income can lead to an upward shift in the demand curve from DD' to FF'. This means that at *any given price* such as OP_0, the consumer(s) will demand more than before the shift. It should be noted, however, that if price happens to rise sufficiently at the same time, con-

---

[1] This arbitrary convention would seem to be an inappropriate arrangement because in the present discussion we treat quantity demanded as the dependent variable and price as the independent variable. The origin of this practice is that this curve together with a supply curve has traditionally been used in the analysis of price determination in a competitive industry as described in Chapter 11, Section 3. However, even here the price cannot be considered a dependent variable since, in the supply-demand analysis, price and quantity are determined simultaneously.

sumers may end up buying less despite an outward shift in the demand curve. In such a case, the shift in demand is accompanied by an offsetting movement *along* the curve.

Besides income, many other variables can affect the position of the curve. A change in the amount of advertising, a change in price or quality, or the advertising approach of a competing product—even a change in the weather—can shift a demand curve. Some of the relevant variables may even be intangible and unquantifiable—for example, a change in consumer tastes can cause a shift in a demand curve—although we may prefer to go behind this phenomenon and seek the variables which account for the taste change. To summarize, demand is a function of many variables such as price, advertising, and decisions relating to competing products. The relationship which describes this entire many-variable interconnection is called the *demand function*. By contrast, the demand curve deals only with two of these variables, price and quantity demanded, and ignores the others. Indeed, the distinction between a movement along and a shift in a demand curve may be described in terms of the variables involved. Any change in quantity demanded which results only from a variation in price is a movement along the curve, whereas a change in the value of any other variable in the demand *function* is likely to shift the demand *curve*.

Several concluding observations are relevant:

1. Phrases such as "a rise in demand" are ambiguous and should never be used, since it is not clear whether they refer to a shift in or a movement along the curve.

2. The distinction is relevant for a number of matters of applied economics. For example, the statement that a reduction in demand is deflationary is valid only if it refers to a downward shift in the demand curve, since a leftward movement (a decrease in quantity demanded) along a negatively sloping demand curve must, by definition, be concurrent with a rise in price. One can find cases where this has been misunderstood by legislators who thereupon have made nonsensical statements on inflation policy. Similarly, the sort of increase in demand which is most eagerly hoped for in a business firm will involve a shift in the demand curves for its products. In fact, it will normally result from autonomous changes in the values of the variables which are entirely outside management's control. There is usually some cost to the firm when the quantity of its products demanded increases as a result of a change in the firm's advertising expenditure, or in the incidental services which it provides to its customers, or in some other of its demand-raising activities. But an increase in demand which occurs because of a rise in national income or favorable weather comes to the company free.

3. The possibility that demand curves can frequently shift implies that a statistical investigation of the shape of such a curve requires the aid

of relatively subtle methods. There is a serious difficulty in the obvious approach, which involves our taking price quantity data for a number of months and plotting them on a graph. For example, if in October OQ_0 units were sold at (average) price OP_0 (point D_0 in Figure 1) whereas November and December sales were represented by points E_0 and F_0 respectively, this method would have us draw in the statistical "demand curve" SS' which, as we can see, really resembles *none* of the true demand curves (the DD' curve for October, the EE' curve for November, and the FF' December curve). The difficulty is that the true demand curve has shifted over this period. The naive statistical method which has just been described does not even indicate this fact and it certainly offers us no means of correcting for it.

More sophisticated methods have been developed for dealing with this so-called *identification* problem, but it is not appropriate to pursue the matter further in this book. For further details the reader is referred to the standard writings on econometrics.[2] It may be worth pointing out that the reason we are interested in the true demand curve rather than the statistical curve SS' is that only the former permits us to judge the effects of pricing decisions. Since, by definition, it is the true demand curve which shows how sales will vary with price, that is the curve which must be involved in optimal pricing-output policy calculations.

3. Elasticity: A Measure of Responsiveness

The most obvious piece of information we desire of a demand function (or from economic relationships of other varieties) is an indication of the effect on the "dependent" variable of a change in the value of one of the other variables. In the case of the demand curve, this involves measurement of the response in quantity demanded which can be expected to result from a given change in the price of the commodity.

The obvious measure of responsiveness is, of course, what we may call the marginal demand contribution of a price change, $\Delta Q/\Delta P$, or the corresponding derivative, dQ/dP, the change (fall) in quantity demanded caused by a unit change (rise) in price. It will be observed, incidentally, that this measure is the reciprocal of the slope of the demand curve $\Delta P/\Delta Q$ (or dP/dQ), so that the flatter the demand curve the greater will be the value of this measure of responsiveness to price change. This peculiarity results from the oddity in the conventional drawing of the demand curve which has already been noted—the fact that the value of the apparently

---

[2] See, e.g., Tjalling C. Koopmans, "Identification Problems in Economic Model Construction," in W. C. Hood and T. C. Koopmans, *Studies in Econometric Method*, Wiley, New York, 1953; and Lawrence R. Klein, *A Textbook of Econometrics*, Row Evanston, Ill., 1953, Chapter III.

dependent variable, quantity, is measured along the horizontal axis, and that of the independent variable, price, along the vertical axis. We might well get a better intuitive grasp of the degree of price responsiveness of a demand curve if the diagram were turned on its side.

In any event, the obvious measures of responsiveness, $\Delta Q/\Delta P$ and dQ/dP, are subject to a drawback which has led theorists to employ instead another measure—elasticity. The difficulty with, say, $\Delta Q/\Delta P$ is that it deals with the absolute changes in quantity and price, which makes it difficult to compare the responsiveness of different commodities. Commodities are measured in different units—labor in hours, land in acres, and whiskey in fifths or quarts. There is no simple way of comparing a 20,000-quart increase in the quantity of Scotch demanded with a 3000-acre rise in the demand for land. In economics it is difficult, because of the very nature of the animal, to impose uniform units on all of the relevant magnitudes as is done in physics.

But the problem extends beyond the dissimilarity of units, because, even in the measurement of price change, the magnitudes are not readily comparable. Consider a 1¢ fall in the price of a package of bubble gum and an equal fall in the price of an automatic dishwasher. We might not be surprised to find bubble gum sales booming when habitués discover the bargain in this brand of the confection, but it is difficult to believe that a one-penny reduction in dishwasher prices would even be noticed. Though the measure $\Delta Q/\Delta P$ would therefore almost certainly yield a much higher number in the case of chewing gum than in that of major household appliances (a much greater change in quantity demanded per penny price reduction), we would surely hesitate to conclude from this that the demand of the former was significantly more price-sensitive.

Theorists have concluded, from such considerations, that an appropriate measure of responsiveness of demand to price changes should employ percentage rather than absolute change figures. A one *per cent* (rather than a one penny) fall in price then becomes the standard of comparison, so that the change in dishwasher price in our illustration is discounted as an insignificant price fall in comparison with that of the bubble gum.

Employing these percentage terms we have the definition

price elasticity of demand for item x

$$= -\frac{\text{percentage change in quantity of } x \text{ demanded}}{\text{percentage change in the price of } x}.$$

The only peculiarity in the definition which remains to be explained is the presence of the minus sign before the fraction. This is inserted to make the elasticity number non-negative. When the demand curve is negatively inclined, a rise in price (ΔP positive) will lead to a fall in quantity (ΔQ negative) so that in our elasticity fraction the numerator and denominator will be of opposite sign. Therefore the fraction will be a negative number, and a minus sign is needed to make the number positive. The insertion of this sign in the elasticity formula is, then, just a matter of linguistic convenience.

For our purposes it is necessary to define the elasticity measure somewhat more specifically. The percentage change in any quantity, Q, is defined as 100 times the change in Q, i.e., as $100\Delta Q$, divided by Q. For example, if quantity rises from 10 to 15 we have $\Delta Q = 15 - 10 = 5$ and the percentage rise in $Q = 100\Delta Q/Q = 500/10 = 50$ per cent. Similarly, the percentage change in P is given by the expression $100\Delta P/P$. Therefore we have, by our definition of elasticity,

$$\text{price elasticity of demand} = -\frac{100\Delta Q/Q}{100\Delta P/P} = -\frac{\Delta Q/Q}{\Delta P/P}$$

(since we can divide both numerator and denominator by 100).

Moreover, since division by a fraction, $\Delta P/P$, is the same as multiplication by its reciprocal,[3] $P/\Delta P$, we obtain the expression

(1) $$\text{price elasticity of demand} = -\frac{\Delta Q}{Q} \cdot \frac{P}{\Delta P} = -\frac{\Delta Q}{\Delta P} \cdot \frac{P}{Q}.$$

This expression, which will be used throughout the remainder of the elasticity discussion, helps now to describe two different elasticity concepts: *point elasticity* and *arc elasticity*. Arc elasticity is a measure of the *average* responsiveness to price change exhibited by a demand curve over some finite stretch of the curve such as D_0D_1 in Figure 1. One complication is inherent in the concept. In the elasticity formula (1), when price changes from P_0 to P_1 it is clear that $\Delta Q = Q_1 - Q_0$, the change in quantity bought (Figure 1), and that $\Delta P = P_1 - P_0$. But what are the values of Q and P? Since a range of values of Q occurs along arc DD', no unique value of this variable is called for by the definition. It is customary for this purpose to use the average of the two end values of Q; that is, to set $Q = (Q_1 + Q_0)/2$, and to do the same for the percentage change in price. Hence the arc elasticity of demand is defined by the expression

$$-\frac{\Delta Q}{\Delta P} \cdot \frac{P}{Q} = -\frac{Q_1 - Q_0}{P_1 - P_0} \cdot \frac{(P_1 + P_0)/2}{(Q_1 + Q_0)/2}$$

so that, multiplying both numerator and denominator by 2, we have

(2) $$\text{arc (price) elasticity of demand} = -\frac{Q_1 - Q_0}{P_1 - P_0} \frac{P_1 + P_0}{Q_1 + Q_0}.$$

[3] *Proof:* If we divide any number, k, by the fraction a/b we have (multiplying top and bottom of the resulting fraction by b/a)

$$\frac{k}{a/b} = \frac{k(b/a)}{(a/b)(b/a)} = \frac{k(b/a)}{1} = k\frac{b}{a}.$$

Point elasticity of demand is the corresponding concept for each particular point on the demand curve. But, at any such point there is no change in price ($\Delta P = 0$) or in quantity. We therefore define point elasticity in much the same way as the derivative concept in Chapter 4, above. That is, we take point elasticity to be the limit of the arc elasticity figure as the arc $D_0 D_1$ is made smaller and smaller, first being cut down to $D_0 D_2$, then to $D_0 D_3$, etc. We thereby arrive at the definition

$$(3) \qquad \text{point price elasticity of demand} = -\frac{dQ}{dP} \cdot \frac{P}{Q}$$

where the derivative dQ/dP has been substituted for $\Delta Q/\Delta P$ in the elasticity definition (1).

Before leaving the question of definitions, it is well to point out that the elasticity concept can be (and has been) adapted to measure responsiveness in variables other than quantity and price. For example, we may measure the responsiveness of the supply, S, of some commodity to a change in interest rate, i, as

$$\text{interest elasticity of supply} = -\frac{\text{percentage change in supply}}{\text{percentage change in interest rate}}$$

$$= -\frac{\Delta S}{\Delta i} \cdot \frac{i}{S}.$$

Similarly, when the price, P_x, of one commodity x, affects the quantity demanded, Q_y, of another commodity y, it is customary to define

$$\text{cross elasticity of demand} = \frac{\Delta Q_y}{\Delta P_x} \cdot \frac{P_x}{Q_y}.$$

The reader should try defining such concepts as the income elasticity of imports and the interest elasticity of investment.

4. Properties of the Elasticity Measure

The basic elasticity formula (1) permits us to see a relationship between an elasticity measure and the corresponding marginal measure of responsiveness, $\Delta Q/\Delta P$, with which the elasticity discussion began. Elasticity is the rejected marginal measure multiplied by the fraction $-P/Q$.

This observation, in turn, helps us to see one of the peculiarities of the elasticity measure. Consider a straight line demand curve like that in Figure 2. It is tempting to guess that the elasticity of such a demand curve is the same throughout the length of the curve. Such constancy does hold for the marginal measure of price responsiveness, $\Delta Q/\Delta P$, since it is the reciprocal of the slope of the demand curve which does not change along a straight line. There are two cases in which the elasticity measure also behaves in this way: If a demand curve is vertical (a fixed quantity demanded no matter what the price, so that $\Delta Q/\Delta P = 0$), its elasticity is zero throughout, and at the other extreme, a horizontal demand curve has "infinite elasticity." But in any other straight line case such as DD' in Figure 2, *elasticity* is not constant. Indeed, it varies continuously from zero

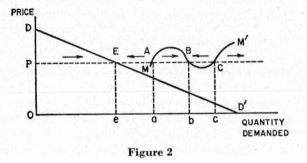

Figure 2

at point D' on the horizontal axis, to any number as high as we like when we get close to the vertical axis (so that elasticity is said to approach infinity as we move toward point D)!

The reason for the variability in the elasticity of a straight line is readily seen from our last elasticity formula. We have just noted that the first fraction in this expression, $\Delta Q/\Delta P$, retains the same value throughout the graph. But that is not true of the second fraction, P/Q. At point D', we have $Q = OD'$ and $P = O$ so that $P/Q = 0$ and hence the price elasticity of demand is zero also. As we move toward the left along the demand curve, the numerator of P/Q increases while the denominator, Q, approaches zero. Hence the value of the fraction grows larger and larger without limit and the same is consequently true of the price elasticity of demand.[4] We conclude that, except in the zero elastic vertical case and the infinite elastic horizontal case, elasticity of demand is certainly not constant along a straight line demand curve. This complication is a price which we pay for using percentage figures instead of absolute figures in the elasticity measure.

However, even here there is an important compensation as will be seen when we get to see the type of curve whose elasticity *is* constant. Though

[4] Note that I have avoided speaking of the elasticity being infinite at point D, where $Q = 0$. Here the elasticity is not even defined because an attempt to evaluate the fraction P/Q at that point forces us to commit the sin of dividing by zero. The reader who has forgotten why division by zero is immoral may recall that division is the reverse operation of multiplication. Hence, in seeking the quotient $c = a/b$ we look for a number, c, which when multiplied by b gives us the number a, i.e., for which $cb = a$. But if a is not zero, say $a = 5$, and b is zero, there is no such number because there is no c such that $c \times 0 = 5$.

the connection may at first not be obvious, the following important theorem will lead us to a type of curve whose elasticity *is* constant throughout.

ELASTICITY THEOREM I. Given any segment of the demand curve, a change in price within that segment will have no effect on the product PQ if and only if the elasticity of demand throughout the range is exactly equal to unity. More specifically, a change in price from P_0 to P_1 will yield $P_0Q_0 = P_1Q_1$ if and only if the elasticity of the arc D_0D_1 is unity, and each and every intermediate price change will also leave PQ unaffected if and only if point elasticity is unity at *every* point along this arc.[5]

The product PQ (price multiplied by quantity demanded) represents the amount which the consumer would spend and which the seller would therefore receive if quantity Q were bought at price P. This theorem therefore states that if the price elasticity of his demand is unity, a fall in price will induce the consumer to increase his purchases by exactly the amount needed to keep his total outlay the same as it was initially. This is certainly plausible intuitively, for we may view a price reduction as having

---

[5] *Partial Proofs:* If the arc elasticity is equal to unity, we prove that $P_0Q_0 = P_1Q_1$ as follows: By Equation (2) we have arc elasticity of demand equals

$$-\frac{Q_1 - Q_0}{P_1 - P_0} \cdot \frac{P_1 + P_0}{Q_1 + Q_0} = 1.$$

Multiplying both sides by $(Q_1 + Q_0)(P_1 - P_0)$,

$$-(Q_1 - Q_0)(P_1 + P_0) = (Q_1 + Q_0)(P_1 - P_0).$$

Now multiply out to obtain

$$-Q_1P_1 + Q_0P_0 - Q_1P_0 + Q_0P_1 = Q_1P_1 - Q_0P_0 - Q_1P_0 + Q_0P_1.$$

The last two terms, $-Q_1P_0 + Q_0P_1$, can be subtracted from both sides to leave us with

$$-Q_1P_1 + Q_0P_0 = Q_1P_1 - Q_0P_0.$$

Therefore, transposing all Q_0P_0 terms to the left-hand side of the equation and the Q_1P_1's to the right,

$$2Q_0P_0 = 2Q_1P_1 \quad \text{or} \quad Q_0P_0 = Q_1P_1. \qquad \text{Q.E.D.}$$

The reader should have no difficulty in proving the converse, i.e., that if $Q_1P_1 = Q_0P_0$ the relevant arc elasticity must be unity.

The part of the theorem relating to point elasticity follows from the preceding result by treating a point as the limit of an arc as the length of the arc approaches zero, or it can be proved directly by calculus methods. For example, we can prove that if PQ is a constant, then point elasticity, E, equals unity as follows: Given $PQ = K$, a constant, then

$$Q = K/P \quad \text{so that} \quad dQ/dP = -K/P^2.$$

Substituting these last two equations into the point elasticity formula we obtain

$$E = -\frac{dQ}{dP} \cdot \frac{P}{Q} = \frac{K}{P^2}\frac{P}{K/P} = \frac{K}{P^2} \cdot \frac{P^2}{K} = 1.$$

The proof of the converse involves only slightly more difficult bits of the differential (or integral) calculus.

an expenditure-increasing effect (more demanded) and an expenditure reducing effect (a lower price paid for each unit purchased). When the elasticity of demand is unity, the percentage fall in price is, by definition, exactly equal to the percentage rise in quantity demanded, and it is therefore believable that these two effects will then exactly offset one another as the theorem asserts.

The theorem describes, implicitly, one type of demand curve along which elasticity of demand is constant. Specifically, it tells us that the elasticity will take the constant value unity along any curve characterized by the equation $PQ = K$ (any constant). Such a curve is called a *rectangular hyperbola* and has the shape of one of the curves depicted in Figure 3a (where different curves correspond to different values of K).

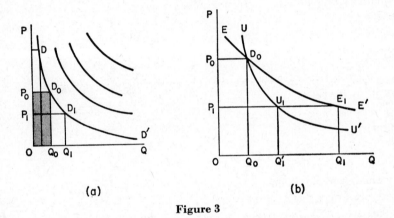

(a)   (b)

Figure 3

That a curve $PQ = K$ is of such a shape can be seen by noting that if our demand curve is DD', then, e.g., at price OP_0, consumer expenditure $OQ_0 \times OP_0$ is represented by the area of the shaded rectangle $OQ_0D_0P_0$ (= height OP_0 multiplied by width OQ_0). Similarly, at price OP_1 expenditure is depicted by area $OQ_1D_1P_1$. Since expenditure is constant along a demand curve of unit elasticity, it follows that all such rectangles must be equal in area. Hence the unit elastic demand curve must approach the axes of the diagram asymptotically, for as such a rectangle gets taller it must become narrower in order for its area to remain equal to that of its fellow expenditure rectangles. Moreover, such a demand curve must not touch either axis for at a point of intersection with an axis either P or Q is zero so that PQ must equal zero rather than K. It can be shown, incidentally, that demand curves of constant elasticity 2 or $\frac{3}{4}$ or any other number are asymmetrical but roughly similar in shape.

We may use a geometric argument to extend our first elasticity theorem as follows:

ELASTICITY THEOREM II. If a demand curve has elasticity less than unity (it is *inelastic*), a *rise* in price will *increase* consumer expenditure, *PQ*, and *vice versa*. If the curve has any elasticity greater than unity (it is *elastic*), a *fall* in price will increase consumer expenditure and *vice versa*.

Only the argument in the elastic case will be described but the inelastic case is completely and obviously parallel. First draw any elastic demand curve, EE' (Figure 3b). Now find the point, D_0, on the demand curve which corresponds to the initial price, OP_0, and by picking an appropriate value of K in its formula $PQ = K$, draw the unit elastic demand curve UU' which goes through point D_0. At this point, with price and quantity the same for both curves, the elastic demand curve, EE', must be the flatter of the two curves (since, in an elastic curve, the percentage rise in quantity demanded, $\% \, \Delta Q$, exceeds the percentage fall in price so that the reciprocal, $-\% \, \Delta P / \% \, \Delta Q$, and therefore the corresponding slope, $-\Delta P / \Delta Q$, will be smaller than in the unit elastic case).

Now consider a fall in price from OP_0 to OP_1. By Elasticity Theorem I, along the unit elastic curve expenditure remains unchanged, i.e., we have area $OQ_1'U_1P_1$ = area $OQ_0D_0P_0$. But it is obvious that the new expenditure along the elastic curve, area $OQ_1E_1P_1$, includes, and hence exceeds, the area representing the corresponding unit elastic expenditure, $OQ_1'U_1P_1$. Summarizing, we have

$$OQ_0D_0P_0 = OQ_1'U_1P_1 < OQ_1E_1P_1$$

i.e., when demand is elastic, and price falls from OP_0 to OP_1, consumer outlay *rises* from $OQ_0D_0P_0$ to $OQ_1E_1P_1$ as was to be proved.

The two elasticity theorems just given lie behind much of the use of the elasticity concept in applied economics. They are met, for example, in the analysis of problems of taxation, international trade, and pricing by private business. As a simple illustration, note that it will not ordinarily pay a firm to reduce the price of a product whose demand is inelastic, because this price reduction will tend to increase the number of units sold and hence the firm's total raw material, labor, and other costs, but, by Elasticity Theorem II, *it will also decrease the firm's revenue PQ*—clearly a losing proposition! As a second illustration, consider a country suffering from a "dollar shortage." In such a case, popular writers often recommend that the country devalue its currency, thus making its products cheaper and hence leading Americans to import more. There are a number of complications to be considered but the one which is relevant for our purposes is the possibility that the elasticity of the United States' demand for that country's exports may be less than unity. Thus the country may find, after devaluing, that though it is shipping more to America, it is actually obtaining fewer dollars than before!

5. *Utility Analysis of Demand*

Economic theory has long sought to go behind the obvious and observable demand phenomena which are summed up in the demand function in an attempt to explain these observations in terms of the structure of consumer desires. It seemed immediately apparent that there is some connection between demand and the *utility* of the commodity, i.e., the subjective benefit which the consumer obtains from its possession. But to classical economists this connection appeared to be limited largely to the fact that items totally without utility would not be demanded at all. To show that there is little or no connection with price, they called attention to the fact that water, which is essential to life and therefore to be considered of very great utility, commands only a very low and often no more than a zero price, whereas diamonds, whose utility is presumably less than that of water, are notoriously expensive.

This "diamond-water" paradox was explained by an analysis which was the focal point of the economic literature at the turn of the century. It was argued that the price of a commodity was determined not by its *total* but by its *marginal* utility. For this discussion it is convenient to evaluate the marginal utility of a commodity, X, in money terms (the amount of money the consumer is just willing to give up for another unit). The connection between price and marginal utility is that if to some rational consumer the marginal utility of some item, X, when he holds A units of X, is more than its price, he can increase his welfare by purchasing more than A units of X. This is because, by definition, he receives more value than he gives up in such an exchange. Similarly, if the marginal utility of an Lth unit of the commodity is less than its price, the consumer can benefit by buying less than L units. He should, therefore, always buy such an amount of X that its marginal utility is equal to its price.[6]

The marginal utility theorists carried their analysis considerably further. For one thing, they argued, largely on introspective grounds, the more we possess of a commodity the less we value an additional unit—the famous "law" of *diminishing marginal utility*. Partly, it was stated, this is so because we give priority to more highly valued uses—if we have only one piece of cake we feed it to our child; if we have two we give the second to our wife, a third we keep for ourself, and a fourth we give to our mother-in-law.

---

[6] More formally, if Q is the amount of X purchased, and if $U(Q)$ is the total utility of the purchase (measured in dollars), the consumer presumably seeks to maximize the difference between this total utility and his expenditure, PQ, i.e., he seeks to maximize $U(Q) - PQ$. Differentiating with respect to Q and setting the result equal to zero, we obtain $dU/dQ - P = 0$, i.e., $P = dU/dQ$, the marginal utility of Q.

The marginal utility analysis of pricing and the diminishing marginal utility proposition can quickly dispose of the diamond-water paradox. With the aid of this analysis we can now explain that the relative scarcity of diamonds results in their having a high *marginal* utility and, therefore, a high price, while the relative abundance of water means that its *marginal* utility and, consequently, its price will be low despite its high *total* utility.

This law of diminishing marginal utility was also used as an explanation of the negative slope which is alleged to characterize most simple demand curves. The argument is that if the marginal utility of a commodity falls when the consumer purchases more of the item, he can only be induced to buy more of a good by a fall in its price.

Another important function of the law of diminishing marginal utility arises out of the need for *second-order* equilibrium conditions. It will be recalled (Section 5 of Chapter 4) that a marginal equation such as "price equals marginal utility" is not enough to guarantee that the consumer is getting the maximum possible utility for his money. There may be several purchase levels at which the equation holds. For example, referring back to Figure 2, we see that if the marginal utility curve has the peculiar shape of curve MM' and price is OP, then there are three purchase levels, Oa, Ob, and Oc at which marginal utility equals price. However, these are not all optimal purchase levels. In fact, two of these, Oa and Oc, are extremely *dis*advantageous to the consumer! If, for example, the consumer increases his purchase quantity from Oa (direction of an arrow) he enters a region where marginal utility exceeds price, and it will pay him to increase the amount he buys even more. Only when he gets to the true equilibrium point B (where marginal utility is diminishing—the curve MM' has a negative slope) does it pay him to stop increasing his purchases. Similarly, from quantity Oc it pays the consumer either to increase or decrease his purchases—not to stay at Oc (direction of the arrows). In sum, even if price equals marginal utility but marginal utility is *increasing* (points A and C) the consumer is at a point of *minimum*, not maximum net gain. The "price equals marginal utility" condition only assures us that the consumer is on neither the uphill nor the downhill side of a total utility hill, but this means that he may be either at the top of the hill or the bottom of the valley (see Figure 4 of Chapter 4). Only if marginal utility is diminishing (as at point B) do we know that he must be at a point of *maximum* net gain. From B it pays him to move neither to the right nor to the left (see arrows at point b). Finally, if the law of diminishing marginal utility is valid, the entire marginal utility curve will have a negative slope (curve DD' in Figure 2). There will then be only one point, E, where marginal utility is equal to price and it will always pay the consumer to move toward the corresponding purchase level, Oe (arrows). The law of diminishing marginal utility thus guarantees that there will be only one possible equilibrium level, *Oe*, and that it will possess an element of stability— consumers will always be motivated to move toward that point.

At the beginning of this section we employed a monetary measure of marginal utility to make our comparison between the price of a commodity and its marginal utility. The marginal utility of X in money terms was defined as the maximum amount of money which a consumer is willing to pay for an additional unit of X. But the marginal utility theorists were generally dissatisfied with such a measure. For when money becomes scarcer, they maintained, its subjective marginal value will increase, like that of any commodity. Hence, measurement of the marginal utility of X by asking the person how much *money* an additional unit is worth to him is like calculating length with a rubber ruler which stretches as we measure. Marginal utility must, according to this view, be measured in its own, subjective, units—we may call them utils. Some noted economists believe that subjective introspective experiments can be conducted successfully, and that marginal utility, measured in utils rather than some directly observable unit (like money), can be known to diminish. That is, by thinking about our own feelings about additions to our holdings of, say, packages of spaghetti, we can come to be sure that additional packages are worth less and less to us in these absolute units (which correspond to no objective experience that any of us has ever had). This view can be referred to as the *neoclassical cardinal utility* position.[7]

6. Indifference Maps: Ordinal and Cardinal Utility

Many theorists, who classify themselves as *ordinalists*, believe that measurement of subjective utility on an absolute scale is neither possible nor necessary. They question the validity of the introspective data of neoclassical cardinal utility and maintain that all consumer behavior can be described in terms of preferences, or rankings, in which the consumer need only state which of two collections of goods he prefers, without reporting on the magnitude of any numerical index of the strength of this preference.

The geometric device employed to represent this sort of ordinal preference information is the indifference map (Figure 4a). In this diagram quantities of different commodities are measured along the axes, so that, for example, point A on indifference curve II' represents a collection of

---

[7] That view is briefly discussed again in Chapter 17, where it is contrasted with Neumann-Morgenstern cardinal utility, an entirely different sort of construct despite the similarity in nomenclature. Neoclassical cardinalism is also mentioned in the next section, where it is contrasted with the ordinalist position.

commodities consisting of one serving of zabaglione and four cummerbunds. It represents no more than this, and this datum, by itself, contains no information about the consumer in question. In particular, *it does not mean that he is indifferent between the four cummerbunds and the serving of Italian dessert.* We note also that every possible combination of these two items can be represented by a point in this diagram.

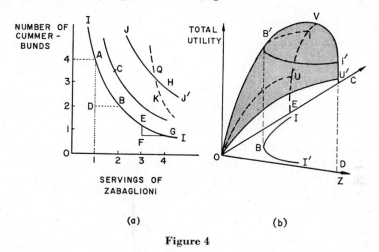

Figure 4

We may now define an indifference curve as the locus of points each of which represents a collection of commodities such that the consumer is indifferent among any of these combinations. For example, the presence of point B on curve II' means that the consumer is indifferent between *collections A* and *B*, that is between the combination of four cummerbunds and one serving of zabaglione (point A) and the combination which consists of two units of each of these items (point B). The indifference map consists of the infinite set of indifference curves such as II' and JJ' (there is, by assumption, one through every point in the diagram) of which only a few can be shown in any actual drawing.

If, for reasons which will be discussed presently, we go along with the assumption that the consumer prefers combinations represented by points on higher indifference curves (e.g., he prefers collection C to A), the indifference map provides us with a complete and simple report on the consumer's ordering of all possible combinations of the two items. For if two combinations are represented by points on the same indifference curve, the consumer is indifferent between them, and in any other case he prefers that collection which is represented by a point on a higher indifference curve.

Let us now see how the indifference map is related to the neoclassical cardinal utility representation of the consumer's tastes. The three-dimensional Figure 4b shows the same consumer's utility surface which is constructed as follows: Lay Figure 4a on a horizontal surface to constitute the floor of the diagram. Any point, such as B, on this floor again represents a collection of these two items. Now suppose we have somehow found out the number of utils which this collection, B, can yield to the consumer. We erect over point B a flagpole BB', whose length is equal to the number of utils. Similarly, such a flagpole is erected above every point on the floor of the diagram representing the utility of every possible combination of the two items. For example, DU' is the utility of the collection of OD servings of zabaglione (and zero cummerbunds) whereas EU is the utility of OE cummerbunds. If we now stretch a canvas over the top of the collection of flagpoles, this canvas is the consumer's utility surface, $OUVU'$ (shaded surface).

Since all combinations of consumer goods represented by points on an indifference curve II' have equal utility, the flagpoles above such a curve must all be of equal height, i.e., the portion of the utility surface which lies directly above an indifference curve (such as IBI') must all be of a single height (line $iB'i'$). In other words, the consumer's indifference curves are the contour lines (iso utility lines) of his utility surface. They are the loci of commodity combinations of equal utility, just as the contour lines on an ordinary geographic map are loci of combinations of latitude and longitude of equal height above sea level.

There is, however, one respect in which this geographic analogy does not hold. A contour line on an ordinary map is labeled by a number which indicates the height of its points above sea level. But an indifference curve bears no number to indicate the corresponding height of the utility surface—no cardinal utility number is attached to the curve. Hence indifference curves do not contain cardinal utility information—they only record preferences—the order in which the consumer ranks the various commodity combinations. From utility information we can deduce preferences; the consumer prefers the item whose utility is highest—but the converse is not true: the statement that the consumer prefers A to B gives us no numerical utility magnitudes.[8]

---

[8] This statement has the following geometric counterpart: We have seen that indifference curves can be deduced from the consumer's utility surface. But the indifference map does not give us enough information to draw the utility surface. We know that above any indifference curve the utility surface is level and that the surface gets higher as we move to higher indifference curves, but no more. The actual height of the utility surface above any indifference curve is left completely unspecified, so that any of an infinite number of utility surfaces is usually consistent with any given indifference map—that is, all of the surfaces in the set will give us the same indifference map.

7. Properties of Indifference Curves

The slope of an indifference curve has a significant economic interpretation. For example, in Figure 4a we see that the arc AB has the slope AD/DB. But in moving from point A to B the consumer loses AD (2) cummerbunds and gains DB (1) serving of zabaglione. Since A and B are indifferent, it must mean that the DB unit gain in his zabaglione holdings just compensates him for his AD unit cummerbund loss. Thus the absolute (i.e., positive) value of the slope, $AD/DB = \frac{2}{1} = 2$, indicates that it takes one serving of zabaglione to supply heart balm to the consumer for the loss of two cummerbunds. This absolute value of the slope, called the consumer's *marginal rate of substitution of zabaglione for cummerbunds*, therefore represents the number of units of the latter whose loss can be made up by a unit gain in the former. It is the consumer's psychological rate of exchange between the two commodities.

It is also possible to show that this slope is equal (in absolute value) to the fraction (marginal utility of zabaglione/marginal utility of cummerbunds),[9] that is, the marginal rate of substitution of z for c equals

$$\text{slope of } II' \left(= \frac{\Delta C}{\Delta Z} \right) = \frac{\text{marginal utility of } z}{\text{marginal utility of } c}$$

where Z and C represent respectively the quantities of zabaglione and cummerbunds.

Two features of this result bear some discussion:

1. In the equation

$$\frac{\Delta C}{\Delta Z} = \frac{\text{marginal utility of } z}{\text{marginal utility of } c}$$

it is noteworthy that C appears in the *numerator* of the left-hand fraction but in the *denominator* of the fraction on the right-hand side of the equation, and that the reverse holds for Z. This inverse relationship between ΔC and the marginal utility of C is easily explained. $\Delta C = AD$ units of C is the amount of C which the consumer is willing to give up for $\Delta Z = DB$ units of z. But the more valuable c is to him (the greater the marginal utility of c), obviously the less the consumer will be willing to give up in exchange for ΔZ; i.e., the smaller will be ΔC; hence the inverse relationship.

---

[9] *Proof:* If arc AB is sufficiently small, the utility loss involved in giving up AD units of cummerbunds is the marginal utility of such a unit (MU_c) multiplied by AD, the number of units involved, i.e., the loss in giving up $AD = (AD) \times (MU_c)$. Similarly, the utility gain involved in acquiring DB units of z is $(DB) \times (MU_z)$ where MU_z represents the marginal utility of zabaglione. Since the gain and the loss just offset one another (points A and B are indifferent) we have $AD \times MU_c = DB \times MU_z$. Dividing both sides of the equation by $MU_c \times DB$ we obtain the required result

$$MU_z/MU_c = AD/DB = \text{the slope of } II'.$$

2. A second thing to be noted is that marginal *utility* seems to have sneaked back into the analysis despite the ordinal nature of the indifference map. However, its return is not as serious as it may appear from the point of view of the ordinalist. Only the *ratio* of two marginal utilities ever occurs in indifference analysis. In such a ratio we measure the marginal utility of one commodity not in terms of utils, but in terms of the other commodity. We ask how much of c an additional unit of z is worth (the marginal rate of substitution of c for z). Thus we are, in effect, back to measuring marginal utility in terms of money, or some other commodity, and that is perfectly satisfactory to the ordinalist.

In indifference curve analysis it is customary (at least implicitly) to make these assumptions about the psychology of the consumer:

Assumption 1 (*nonsatiety*): The consumer is not oversupplied with either commodity, i.e., he prefers to have more of c and/or z.

Assumption 2 (*transitivity*): If A, B, and D are any three commodity combinations and if A is indifferent with B and B is indifferent with D, then the consumer is also indifferent between A and D. This condition simply requires that the consumer's tastes possess a conceptually simple type of consistency.

Assumption 3 (*diminishing marginal rate of substitution*): Consider two collections represented by points along the same indifference curve (e.g., A and E in Figure 4a). Then if at one of these points, E, the consumer has a relatively small supply of one commodity, c, and a relatively large supply of the other, then at E the marginal utility of the relatively scarcer c will be large in comparison to that of z, i.e., the consumer will there be willing to give up only a relatively small amount of c in exchange for an additional unit of z. Thus, in Figure 4a, at point A the consumer is willing to give up AD units of c for an additional unit of z. But at point E, where c is scarcer, he is only willing to pay EF units of c for the same increment in his holdings of z.

These assumptions permit us to deduce four properties of indifference curves which normally characterize their drawings:

PROPERTY A (*by Assumption* 1): An indifference curve which lies above and to the right of another represents preferred combinations of commodities.

Proof: Consider the indifference curves II' and JJ' in Figure 4a, and combination B on II' and Q on JJ'. Since point Q is above and to the right of point B, it involves more of both commodities c and z. Hence, by Assumption 1, the consumer must prefer Q to B, and therefore he must prefer every point on JJ' (all of which are indifferent with Q) to any point on II'.

PROPERTY B: Indifference curves have a negative slope (by Assumption 1).

Proof: Start, e.g., at point A in Figure 4a, and move along it to the right so that the consumer holds more of commodity z as a result. By Assumption 1 the consumer must prefer this new point (he cannot be indifferent between it and A) unless at the same time it involves his having less of the other commodity, c. In other words, if he is to be indifferent between the new point and A, it must lie below A as well as to its right, as does point B.

PROPERTY C: Indifference curves can never meet or intersect, so that only one indifference curve will pass through any one point in the map (by Assumptions 1 and 2).

Proof: Suppose on the contrary that two indifference curves, JJ' and the dotted curve, were to intersect at point Q. Pick point K on the dotted indifference curve and point H on JJ' where H lies above and to the right of K. By Property A (Assumption 1) H must be preferred to K. But H is indifferent with Q, and Q is, in turn, indifferent with K. Hence, by Assumption 2, H must be indifferent with K. Since H cannot be both indifferent with and preferred to K the intersection of the two curves which led to this self-contradictory result cannot possibly occur.

PROPERTY D: The absolute slope of an indifference curve diminishes toward the right (the curve is flatter at point E than it is at point A) so that the curve is said to be *convex to the origin* (by contrast with SS' in Figure 5 which is said to be concave to the origin). This theorem is a direct consequence of Assumption 3 which states that the marginal rate of substitution of z for c [which, it will be remembered, is represented by the slope of the curve (neglecting minus signs)] is smaller at E than at A (Figure 4a).

8. Price Lines: Consumer Income and Prices

By itself, an indifference map cannot possibly predict consumer behavior because it leaves out two vital types of information—the income of the consumer and the prices of the commodities. The indifference curves do not ask the consumer which combination he believes will give him the most for his money. It is merely a hypothetical ranking of various commodity combinations—perhaps castles in Spain against yachts in Portugal—regardless of which the consumer can afford.

Price and income information is supplied in an indifference diagram by another curve which is called the *price line* or, sometimes, the *budget line*. Since the axes of the diagram represent only quantities of commodities rather than amounts of money, dollar prices and incomes cannot be shown directly. Instead, the price line does the next best thing and indicates what amounts of the commodities a given amount of money can buy.

For example (Figure 5), suppose \$50 spent exclusively on commodity z will, at its current price, buy OP' units of that commodity, whereas the same amount spent entirely on c will purchase exactly OP units of that item. Suppose, moreover, that every point such as A on line PP' represents

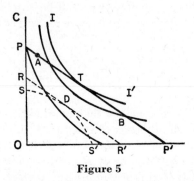

Figure 5

a combination of the two commodities which sells for \$50 (e. g., \$10 worth of z plus \$40 of c). Then line PP' is a price or budget line. Such a line is defined as the locus of all combinations of commodities which cost some fixed amount of money (e.g., our illustrative \$50).

If the prices of both commodities are fixed, that is, they do not vary with the amounts of the goods which are purchased, the price line will possess the following properties:

1. It will be a straight line.
2. It will have a negative slope.
3. Its slope will be equal to the *negative inverse* of the ratio of the prices of the two commodities, i.e., we will have $\Delta C/\Delta Z = -P_z/P_c$ where P_z and P_c are the unit prices of z and c respectively.
4. Suppose two price lines involve the same commodity prices but represent the expenditure of different amounts of money (say \$50 for PP' and \$30 for RR'). Then the two lines will be parallel.

The equation of the price line is, in the fixed price case, given by a simple expression. If the consumer buys Z units of commodity z, his total expenditure on this item will be P_zZ (the price per unit, P_z, multiplied by the number of units purchased). Similarly, expenditure on the other commodity is given by P_cC so that total expenditure is given by

(4) $$P_zZ + P_cC = M$$

where M is the amount of money spent (our illustrative \$50 for line PP')

and is therefore constant along a price line. This, then, is the equation of a price line.[10]

The four properties can readily be generalized to take account of price variability. There are two possibilities: either that buying in quantity will make the commodities scarce relative to the quantities demanded and so raise their prices to the purchaser (as wages go up when the demand for labor increases) or, on the other hand, that he will be offered discounts if he buys in larger quantities (special today: One elephant, $200, or two for $325). The former possibility, which can be interpreted as a case of diminishing returns to an increased number of dollars spent on a given commodity, will yield a curved price line which, like SS', is concave to the origin (Figure 5). The reason is that as one moves toward the axes from an interior point such as D, a greater proportion of the consumer's fixed amount of money, say $30, is spent on one of the commodities; thus near S almost all of it is spent on commodity c. This raises the price of c against the consumer so that his $30 will buy only OS—which is less than the OR units he could obtain for $30 if the price of c were fixed at the level it is at point P.

For a completely analogous reason, quantity discounts (increasing returns to increased expenditure on any one item) will result in a budget line which, like II', is convex to the origin.

There remains one point to discuss about price lines. What do they tell us about the consumer's income and the prices of the various products? First, to deal with the information on consumer income which is conveyed by a price line, it is convenient to define the multi-commodity analogue of a price line [Equation (4)]—the algebraic budget relationship for all of the (say, 1257) different commodities which the consumer buys or considers buying:

$$P_1X_1 + P_2X_2 + \ldots + P_{1257}X_{1257} = M$$

where, e.g., X_2 is the quantity of commodity number 2 purchased and P_2 is its unit price. In such a multi-commodity budget equation it is convenient to consider savings to be one of the 1257 goods which he buys or can buy for his money. On this interpretation, the consumer has no choice but

---

[10] The four properties of the price line are readily derived from this equation. Dividing both sides by P_c and rearranging terms the equation becomes

$$C = -\frac{P_z}{P_c} Z + \frac{M}{P_c}.$$

If we now change our notation, writing y for C, x for Z, a for $-P_z/P_c$, and b for M/P_c, this becomes the standard *linear* equation of Chapter 2, $y = ax + b$, with (*negative*) *slope* $a = -P_z/P_c$. The four price-line properties follow directly from this result as the reader should verify.

to spend all his money (either on savings or on some other commodity) and the only relevant price line is the one which uses up all of the funds which he has available to him. This price line, then, specifies the consumer's *real income* (or wealth). It tells us just what combinations of commodities he can afford to buy.

So much for the income information supplied by a price line. Let us now see what the price line tells us about prices.

Property 3 states that the slope of such a line tells us the *ratio* of the prices of the commodities. If the slope is -2 we know that the price of z must be twice the price of a unit of c (note again the inverse relationship, $-P_z/P_c = \Delta C/\Delta Z$).

To summarize, the price line specifies the real purchasing power which is available to the consumer and the ratio of the prices of the two commodities. But since monetary quantities are not shown anywhere on the diagram, it is impossible for the price line by itself to specify either the level of the consumer's liquid assets or the money price of any commodity.[11]

9. Equilibrium of the Consumer

The consumer who wants to get the most for his money will want to land on as high an indifference curve as his purchasing power permits— the highest indifference curve which can be reached from his budget line. This optimum purchase combination is given by the point of tangency, T, between the price line and indifference curve II' (Figure 5). For it is clear, by inspection of the diagram, that any other point on the price line, such as B, will be intersected by an indifference curve which lies below II'. In this way, the indifference map together with the price line permit us to predict the demand pattern of the "rational" consumer—the consumer who spends his money efficiently in the pursuit of his needs and interests. We say that T is a *point of equilibrium* because once he arrives at the decision to purchase the combination of commodities represented by that point, the consumer has no motivation to revise his purchase plans.

The tangency condition of equilibrium immediately yields another equilibrium condition. At their point of tangency the slope of the price line and that of the indifference curve must, by definition, be equal. But we know that the (absolute value of the) slope of the budget line is equal to the (inverse) ratio of the two prices, whereas the slope of the indifference curve is equal to the (inverse) ratio of the two marginal utilities or to the

---

[11] However, if we know any one of these values, the others follow at once. For example, if the price of c is known to be $10 and the price line shows z to be twice as expensive as c, then the price of z must obviously be $20. Similarly, since his money buys OP units of c at $10 per unit, his expendable money must be OP times $10.

marginal rate of substitution of z for c. Therefore, in equilibrium we must have

$$\frac{P_z}{P_c} = \frac{MU_z}{MU_c} = \text{marginal rate of substitution of } z \text{ for } c.$$

This is the marginal condition of equilibrium of the consumer. Note the close resemblance to the neoclassical equilibrium condition that price must equal the marginal utility of a commodity. The condition just given states, instead, that the *ratio* of the marginal utilities of two commodities must equal the *ratio* of their prices.

The logic of this condition is easily demonstrated. Suppose the condition is violated so that, e.g., the first of these fractions is greater than the second. Then, multiplying both sides by the presumably positive number MU_c/P_z, we obtain the inequality $MU_c/P_c > MU_z/P_z$. But if item c costs, e.g., $P_c = \$5$ per unit, we can for \$1 obtain $1/5 = 1/P_c$ units of this item, and $(1/5)MU_c = (1/P_c)MU_c$ therefore represents the utility which can be obtained spending an additional dollar on c. The last inequality therefore states that the consumer can acquire more utility out of an additional dollar spent on c than from another dollar spent on z. If this is so he cannot possibly be getting the most for his money—he can get more by reallocating his funds, spending less on z and more on c. This is illustrated in Figure 5 where we note that at point B the absolute value of the slope of the indifference curve is less than that of the price line (the indifference curve is flatter) so that we have $MU_z/MU_c < P_z/P_c$ and so, as before, $MU_z/P_z < MU_c/P_c$. It therefore pays the consumer to plan to buy less of z and more of c, i.e., for him to move upward and to the left along the price line from B toward the point of tangency T. We see then that B violates our equilibrium condition and *that it does so in a way which motivates the consumer to move toward the equilibrium point* T. Thus with curves of the usual shape (as in the diagram), the equilibrium point possesses an element of stability. From any other point on the price line the consumer is motivated to move in the direction of the point of tangency.

Indeed, the shape we have assumed for the indifference curves plays an important role in our tangency solution. If any one of the four properties of indifference curves (listed in Section 7, above) were violated, consumer equilibrium would not occur at a point of tangency. Thus, if Property A were violated so that the consumer wished, say, to be on the lowest attainable indifference curve, his optimum point would be P rather than T, i.e., he would end up spending his money exclusively on one commodity. If Property B were violated so that the slope of the indifference curves was not negative, there could be no point of tangency with the negatively sloping price line. If Property C (nonintersectability of indifference curves) were violated, a number of points of tangency might occur (Figure 6a), and if the indifference curves were concave to the origin, in violation of Property D, the point of tangency would yield the lowest attainable indifference curve, whereas the highest indifference curve would lie at one of the endpoints of the indifference curve (P' in Figure 6b), so the rational

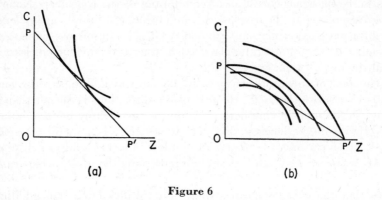

Figure 6

consumer would again end up spending all of his money on just one commodity!

10. Responses to Price and Income Changes

If the income of the consumer increases, his budget line will retain its slope (relative prices remain unchanged) but the budget line will shift upward (he can get more goods for his increased money supply). In other

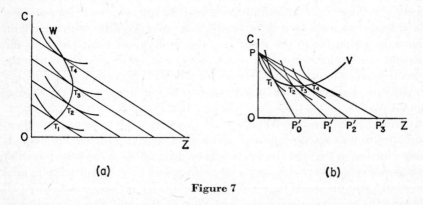

Figure 7

words, income changes cause parallel shifts in the budget line, and a set of parallel budget lines (Figure 7a) shows how the consumer's possible purchases will vary with changes in his income. On each such line we can find the equilibrium point of tangency (points T_1, T_2, etc.). The line OW, which is the locus of all such points, shows how the consumer's purchases of the two commodities will vary when his income changes. Such a curve is called an *income-consumption* curve or, sometimes, an Engel curve (named after an early student of the effects of income changes on consumer expenditure patterns).

Normally, consumers may be expected to increase their purchases of commodities as their incomes rise. But sometimes, if an item is of low quality, demand for it will drop as the consumer's financial position improves, and more desirable commodities are substituted for it. Such an item is called an *inferior good*. Plausible examples of inferior goods are recapped automobile tires, poorly made clothing, poor cuts of meat, etc., any of which the consumer may be buying only because he can afford no better. In Figure 7a commodity z is taken to be an inferior good. This is shown by the relative positions of points T_3 and T_4 (the negatively sloping segment of OW). The latter point lies to the left of the former (it represents a lower quantity of z) despite the fact that it (T_4) is on a higher budget line and therefore involves a higher income for the consumer.

Next, we can investigate the effects on the consumer's purchases of changes in the price of one of the commodities. Suppose the price of z falls, other things remaining equal. This means that the buyer can get more of this commodity for his money (e.g., OP_1' instead of OP_0' in Figure 7b) though he can only obtain the same amount of c (OP) as before. We see, then, that a fall in the price of the item on the horizontal axis leads the price line to flatten out by swinging to the right. Figure 7b represents a number of such price lines and the corresponding equilibrium tangency points. Curve PV, the locus of these points of tangency, shows how changes in the price of z affect the purchases of *both* commodities. PV is called a *price-consumption curve* or sometimes, particularly in international trade theory, an *offer curve*.

It will be noted that the *income-consumption* curve, OW, begins at the origin (point O) because with zero income the consumer can buy none of either commodity. By contrast, the *price*-consumption curve, PV, characteristically begins at point P, the pivot point of the swinging price line in Figure 7b. The reason is that, as the price line approaches the vertical axis (the price of z increases further and further), the consumer finds that he gets less and less of z for his money. Eventually, when its price goes high enough, the consumer will be forced out of buying z altogether and he will therefore spend all his money on the remaining commodity, c, i.e., he will buy OP units of c and no z (point P).

The offer curve construction can readily be translated into an ordinary demand curve for the consumer if one of the commodities represented in the diagram is M, the money held by the consumer (Figure 8a). By this device money values are inserted into the indifference map. As before, let PV be the offer curve so that if the consumer buys zero units of the commodity he will have \$30 for himself (point P). Now consider point A on the offer curve which represents the consumer possessing $Z = 1$ unit of commodity z and $M = \$12$. Since in moving from P to A he acquired 1 unit of the good but gave up $18 = 30 - 12$ dollars, the price per unit at A must be \$18. Thus, point A states that the consumer will buy 1 unit of the commodity if its price is \$18. This information is recorded by point a in Figure 8b. Similarly, point B on his offer curve involves the buyer's

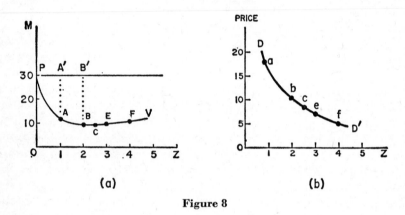

(a)   (b)

Figure 8

spending $20 = 30 - 10$ dollars on *two* units of the good so the price *per unit* must be $\$20/2 = \$10$. Hence (point b in Figure 8b) the offer curve tells us that he is prepared to buy 2 units if the price is \$10. Points c, e, and f in Figure 8b are derived similarly. These are clearly points on the consumer's demand curve since they indicate how many units he is prepared to buy at different prices. DD', the locus of all such points, is the demand curve for this consumer.

It is noteworthy that the *offer* curve gives us information about the elasticity of the *demand* curve. For example, inspection of PV tells us that to the left of point c the demand curve DD' must be elastic. To see why this is so, note that the unit price at point B (\$10) is lower than that at A (\$18) but that total consumer expenditure on the commodity at B ($BB' = \$20$) is greater than that at A ($AA' = \$18$). Thus a fall in price has produced a rise in total expenditure (the price-consumption curve has a negative slope). By Elasticity Theorem II in Section 4 of this chapter, expenditure will rise when price falls only if the demand curve is elastic. The reader should have no difficulty showing that DD' is unit elastic at point c and inelastic to the right of point c.

11. Income and Substitution Effects:
The Slutsky Theorem

It is customary to analyze somewhat further the effect on purchases of a change in the price of one of the commodities. The effect, e.g., of a fall in the price of z is classified into categories: the income and the substitution effect. Its lower price makes z a better buy relative to c than it was before, and, as will be shown presently, that consequence by itself would always induce the consumer to increase his purchase of z (the Slutsky theorem). This price-ratio portion of the effect of a price change on purchases is called the *substitution* effect. Purchases of z will be substituted for those of c because z is *relatively* more price-attractive than it was initially.

But the fall in price of z also affects the purchases of both commodities in another way—it increases the purchasing power of the consumer's income. This will, in turn, tend to increase the purchases of *both* commodities provided that neither of them is an inferior good, the demand for which is reduced by an increase in real income. The income effect, then, is the effect *on the consumer's purchases* of the rise in real income which results from a fall in the price of commodity z. Note that the income effect refers to the resulting change in his purchases and *not* to the change in his real income.

To summarize, a fall in the price of any commodity, x, will affect the consumer's demand for x. This effect may be subdivided into two parts: the substitution effect, which always increases the demand for x, and the income effect, which will increase the demand for x unless x is an inferior good. Thus, ignoring this exceptional possibility, *the demand curve for x must have a negative slope*, i.e., a fall in the price of x must increase the demand for that commodity. Even if x is an inferior good its demand curve will still have a negative slope unless the income effect is stronger than the substitution effect, for, as will soon be shown, the substitution effect of a lower price of x is always a rise in the demand for x. In addition, in practice, the income effect for most consumers' goods is likely to be small because a buyer's outlay on any one commodity constitutes a relatively small proportion of his budget, so a fall in the price of that item alone will not increase his real income significantly.[12]

[12] But, at least as a remote possibility, we see that a very inferior good for which the income effect is very high provides another possible case of a positively sloping demand curve. The other two cases which were mentioned in Section 1 of this chapter (snob appeal and quality judged by price) do not show up in the usual indifference map analysis because each of these involves the consumer's preference structure being changed by the price change. He values platinum collar stays or a brand of frozen chop suey more highly when its price rises. In other words, the consumer's indifference curves shift when there is a swing in the price line—a possibility which has not been considered in the text.

Two different graphic depictions of the income and substitution effects have been employed in the literature. In Figures 9a and 9b let PP' and PP'' be two price lines involving different prices of commodity z, and let A and B represent the (tangency) equilibrium points on the two price lines.

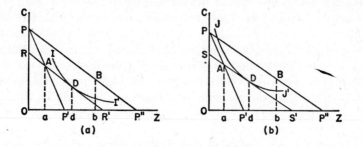

Figure 9

The total effect of the price change on the amount of z purchased is, therefore, ab. Our object is to divide ab into two parts—the income effect and the substitution effect. For this purpose the change in position of the price line is divided artificially into two parts: a parallel shift (a change in real income with no change in relative prices) and a pivot or twisting (change in slope) of the price line (a change in relative prices with no change in real income). To accomplish this division we employ an imaginary price line RR' in Figure 9a (or SS' in Figure 9b) which is parallel to one of the price lines (they have the same relative prices) and is, in some sense, at the same real income level as the other. Here is where the ambiguity in interpretation occurs (the source of difference between the two diagrams). When do two price lines, which are not identical, represent the same real income? One highly persuasive solution is to say that this occurs when they both yield the same satisfaction to the consumer, i.e., they are both tangent to the same indifference curve, as are PP' and SS' in Figure 9b (they are tangent, at points A and D respectively, to indifference curve JJ'). There is another solution, which is perhaps less satisfying intuitively, but which is very useful, and which we will need presently. This is to say that RR' (Figure 9a) yields the same income as PP' if RR' passes through point A so that it just gives the consumer enough money to buy combination A, the combination he would buy if PP' were in fact the prevailing price line. In this case, the point of equilibrium, D, on the imaginary price line RR' lies on an indifference curve II' which is not tangent to PP'. Indeed, since line RR' in Figure 9a is higher than SS' in 9b, the indifference curve II' to which RR' is tangent must lie above indifference curve JJ' in 9b which is tangent to both SS' and the original price line, PP'.

The income and substitution effects can now be read off from the diagrams. The substitution effect is *ad*, the change in purchase of *z* which results from the twisting of the imaginary price line, whereas the income effect is *db*, the effect of the parallel shift in the price line.

In this two-commodity analysis, Figure 9b can be used to show that when the price of *z* falls (the price line flattens out), the substitution effect must lead to a rise in the demand for *z*. For *SS'* and *PP'* are both tangent to the same indifference curve. But since *SS'* is the flatter price line, its point of tangency, *D*, must occur to the right of *A*, the point of tangency of *PP'* (because the slope of an indifference curve gets smaller toward the right). Hence, with the lower relative price of *z* (*SS'*) the demand for *z* (*d*) will be greater than the demand for *z* when the price line is *PP'*. Unfortunately this argument is not valid when there are more than two commodities so that the consumer's preferences cannot be summed up in a two-dimensional indifference map. Presently, a more general proof of this result, *Slutsky's theorem*, will be presented.

12. *Revealed Preference*[13]

As we have seen the indifference analysis requires fewer data about the consumer than does neoclassical cardinal utility theory. But even so, the construction of an indifference map may require quite a bit of introspective information from the consumer—he must be able to state his preferences among *all possible* combinations of commodities.

Professor Samuelson has invented an alternative approach to the theory of the consumer which, in principle, does not require the consumer to supply any information about himself. If his tastes do not change, this revealed-preference theory permits us to find out all we need to know just by observing his market behavior—by seeing what he buys at different prices—assuming that his acquisitions and his buying experiences do not change his preference patterns or his purchase desires. Given enough such information, it is even theoretically possible to reconstruct the consumer's indifference map, as we shall see.

The entire revealed-preference analysis is based on a rather simple idea. A consumer will decide to buy some particular set of items either because he likes them more than the other goods that are available to him, or because they happen to be cheap. Suppose we observe that of two collections of commodities offered for sale the consumer chooses to buy *A* but not *B*. We are, then, *not* entitled to conclude that he *prefers A* to *B*, because it is also possible that his decision just reflects the fact that *A* is the cheaper collection and he may even be most regretful about not buying *B*. But price information may be able to remove this uncertainty. If their price

---

[13] This section involves somewhat more advanced material and the reader may therefore prefer to omit it.

tags tell us that A is not cheaper than B then there is only one plausible explanation of the consumer's choice—he bought A because he likes it better. More generally, if a consumer buys some collection of goods A, rather than any of the alternative collections B, C, D, etc., and it turns out that none of the latter is more expensive than A, we say that A has been *revealed preferred* to the others (or that the others have been revealed to be inferior to A).

The complete set of combinations which are revealed inferior to A by one purchase can be found with the aid of the price line. In Figure 10a, let A represent the collection of commodities which is bought when the price line is PP'. By definition, any other point on PP', such as B, is equally expensive with A. Moreover, since every point, such as D, which is below and to the left of the price line, represents smaller amounts of both commodities than do some points on PP', it follows that such lower points are cheaper than A. Therefore, because the consumer bought A rather than any of these other no more expensive collections, it follows that every point on or below PP' is revealed inferior to A. Finally, since it should be clear that any point above PP' is more expensive than A, we see that none of these can be revealed inferior to A by the consumer's purchase of A.

We can now state the basic assumption of the revealed-preference theory, which asserts that the consumer will never behave in a manner which is so inconsistent that some collection, A, will be revealed preferred to B, and that B will simultaneously be revealed preferred to A. Violation of this assumption must involve the consumer's buying A if it were the more expensive, and then being induced by a relative *rise* in B's price *to above the price of* A to switch his allegiance to B! A Cadillac buyer who could be induced to switch to a Chevrolet by a rise in its price to $50,000 would violate the revealed-preference assumption. We would not normally expect consumers to behave in this apparently peculiar manner. However, both snob appeal and the judging of quality by price can, clearly, be inconsistent with this revealed-preference assumption.

We shall also employ a second assumption:

> Given any collection of goods, the consumer can be induced to buy it if its price is made sufficiently attractive, i.e., for any point in Figure 10a there exists some price line which will lead the consumer to buy it.

These assumptions are all that is needed to derive any of the standard results of the theory of consumer behavior.[14]

---

[14] There is a single exception involving what is called the problem of *integrability*. Earlier in this chapter we saw that it is possible to derive the consumer's indifference map from his utility surface. Conversely, from a two-commodity (two-dimensional) in-

As an illustration let us see how revealed-preference theory can be used to prove the Slutsky theorem, which states that if the income effect is ignored, the demand curve must have a negative slope. Although a two-dimensional diagram is employed for expository purposes, every step of the argument carries over to a situation involving any number of commodities.

In Figure 10a let A represent the combination of commodities bought when the price line is PP'. We want to show, once again, that a fall in the price of commodity z from PP' will increase purchases of z if we consider only the substitution effect. Using the substitution-effect construction of Figure 9a, we insert the imaginary price line RR' which passes through point A. RR' is again flatter than PP' because z has, by hypothesis, fallen in price. We want to prove that the new equilibrium point on RR' (if it is different from A) must be a point like E which lies to the right of A (an increased demand for z). To prove that this must be so, we show that any point on RR', such as D, which lies to the left of A, is ruled out by the revealed-preference axiom. We know that, since D lies below PP', A is revealed to be preferred to D. But if D were chosen when the price line was RR', then since A is no more expensive than D at those prices (they lie on the same price line), D would be revealed preferred to A. Hence A would be revealed preferred to D and vice versa, which is precisely what the revealed-preference assumption prohibits. Thus, no point on RR' which, like D, lies to the left of A can be chosen. The substitution effect of a fall in the price of z will generally increase the demand for z, as was to be proved.

The revealed-preference assumptions also permit us, in principle, to construct the consumer's indifference map on the basis of enough observations on his market behavior. Going back to Figure 10a, suppose this time that B is observed to be the combination which is chosen by the consumer when the price line is PP', and let us try to find the indifference curve through point B. We already know from our first observation that B is revealed preferred to every point on or below PP'. Moreover, it is easily

difference map we can always derive utility surfaces which are consistent with that map. However, when more than two commodities are involved when we try to derive a utility function from an indifference map, we may run into trouble. There may arise pathological (n-dimensional) indifference maps which cannot be derived from any conceivable utility function. Such an indifference map is said not to satisfy the integrability conditions (the term *integrability* occurs because indifference curves can be described by differential equations, and integration of these equations, if it is possible, yields the equation of the corresponding utility surfaces). It is considered desirable to exclude this queer possibility, but Houthakker has shown that an assumption somewhat stronger than the basic assumption of revealed-preference theory is required to assure integrability. See H. S. Houthakker, "Revealed Preference and the Utility Function," *Economica*, Vol. XVII, May 1950.

shown that every point such as M, which lies in the region above and to the right of point B (the shaded region above KBL), is revealed preferred to B. It is, of course, highly plausible that M is preferred to B, for M contains more of one or both commodities than does B (it is above and to the right of B).[15]

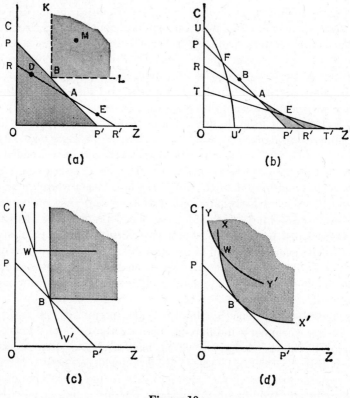

(a)

(b)

(c)

(d)

Figure 10

It follows that the remainder of the indifference curve through B must lie below area KBL and above price line PP', i.e., that it must lie somewhere in the unshaded region in the diagram. This proves at once that, at least near B, the indifference curve must have a negative slope (otherwise it would enter area KBL) and that it must be convex to the origin (it must be above PP' both to the right and to the left of B). Since this argument can be repeated for any other point in the diagram, we see how the revealed-

---

[15] M is revealed preferred to B by the fact that it is always at least as expensive as B since it contains more of at least one commodity (and no less of either good). And since, by the second assumption of revealed-preference theory, some prices can induce the consumer to buy M, those prices must reveal that he prefers M to B.

preference theory can be used to prove that all indifference curves must be of negative slope and convex to the origin throughout their length.

However, we still have quite a way to go before we find the precise shape of the indifference curve through B, since all we have seen so far is that it can lie anywhere in the unshaded region of the diagram (which has been called the *zone of ignorance*). But further observations of the consumer's behavior can, as will be shown now, permit us to extend the shaded regions by chipping away at the zone of ignorance, and thus to get closer and closer to finding the precise location of the indifference curve through B.

First let us see how we can extend the region OPP' which is revealed inferior to B. Consider any point other than B on PP', e.g., point A which has, therefore, been revealed inferior to B. By the second assumption of revealed-preference theory, there is some price line, RR', which will lead the consumer to purchase A. We find RR' by watching the consumer and recording his income and the prices he pays when we see him buy A. Any point on or below RR' is now revealed inferior to A, and since A has, in turn, been revealed inferior to B, everything on or below RR' is revealed inferior to B.[16] Thus triangle $AP'R'$ is revealed inferior to B—it has been chopped off from the region of ignorance. We can repeat this procedure as many times as we wish. For example, we can take any other point, such as F, on PP' (Figure 10b), find its price line UU', and thereby show that triangle PFU is revealed inferior to B and thus remove this triangle from our zone of ignorance. Or we can take a point *on one of the added price lines*, such as point E on RR', and observe the price line TT' at which E is bought. Since every point on or below TT' is revealed to be inferior to E, and E is inferior to A which is, in turn, inferior to B, all of these points are revealed inferior to B. Hence, triangle $R'ET'$ is now removed from the zone of ignorance, etc. In this way we can go on chopping away at the under-belly of the zone of ignorance indefinitely, getting closer and closer to the indifference curve through point B which we seek.

Moreover, the upper portion of the zone of ignorance can also be hacked away bit by bit. Thus, in Figure 10c draw *any* new price line, VV', through B. We observe the consumer when prices and his income happen to correspond to budget line VV'. Let W be the point which is chosen with these prices and income. At these prices B is no more expensive than W, so that W (and, consequently, all of the shaded region above and to the right of W) is revealed to be preferred to B. This procedure can be repeated with other price lines through point B, each of which yields a point like W that is revealed to be preferred to B. The locus of all such points, the curve XX'

---

[16] Note that this argument sneaks in an assumption of transitivity. If E is revealed inferior to A and A is revealed inferior to B, we assume that E is thereby revealed inferior to B.

in Figure 10d, and all points above and to the right of XX' are, then, revealed preferred to B. XX' is called the *offer curve* through point B.[17] We can chop away still more of the zone of ignorance by choosing any point W on offer curve XX', observing what the consumer buys with various price lines through W, and so constructing the offer curve YY' through W. Since any point on or above YY' is revealed preferred to W which is in turn preferred to B, these points are all shown to be preferred to B. Proceeding as long as we wish in this way, we can narrow down the region of possible location of the indifference curve through B (the zone of ignorance) as far as we like.

Unfortunately, the proof that the upper and lower chopping-away sequences converge, and so *exactly* narrow the zone of ignorance down to a single indifference curve, is rather difficult, and involves more advanced theorems in differential equations.[18] However, the basic idea of the revealed-preference approach to indifference-curve construction should be clear from the foregoing discussion.

13. Revealed Preference and Index Numbers of Real Income

An index number formula for the measurement of real income undertakes to employ price and quantity information for each of two periods, and to determine on the basis of these data alone whether real income has risen, fallen, or remained unchanged. One of the major difficulties in the construction of an index number formula lies in the problem of evaluating a real income change which involves many individuals, since it may be an improvement from the point of view of some people but an unfortunate development in the opinion of some others. But even though we will deal with only *one* person in order to evade this problem, we will see that the construction of an index number formula still runs into fundamental difficulties.

Suppose that the consumer receives some collection of goods, B, in one period and some other collection, Q, in the next. In some ultimate psychological sense we can say that his real income will have risen if and only if Q lies above his indifference curve through B; his real income is unchanged if and only if B and Q are on the same indifference curve, and his real income will have fallen if point Q lies below the indifference curve which passes through point B. Thus, to accomplish its purpose the index number

---

[17] That is because XX' shows the various commodity combinations, such as W, which the consumer will buy at different relative prices (different price lines) any of which enable the consumer to buy combination B with no money left over.

[18] See H. S. Houthakker, *op. cit.*

formula must somehow be able to indicate on the basis of two sets of price-quantity observations where the indifference curve through B lies in relation to point Q.

But we have just seen that such a small amount of price and quantity information must leave us with a considerable zone of ignorance as to the location of any indifference curve. Hence it is impossible to develop any index number formula which *always* tells us whether real income has risen, fallen, or remained unchanged. In some cases, depending on the prices or quantities involved, it is possible to determine whether B or Q represents the larger income. For example, in Figure 10a if PP' represents the price situation when B is purchased, then if Q lies below PP' we know that B is revealed preferred to Q so that the change from B to Q represents a fall in real income. Similarly, if Q lies in region KBL, we know that real income must have risen. But if Q lies in the unshaded zone of ignorance we may well lack information sufficient to determine what has happened to real income, and no formula can supply these missing data.

There are two cases in which we can be sure of what has happened to real income: If Q lies below B's price line, real income must have fallen, whereas if B lies below the price line when Q is purchased, so that Q is revealed preferred to B, then real income has risen. That is as far as the data will carry us—if neither of these situations happens to hold, no index number formula can determine what has really happened to real income.

Yet any one of the standard index number formulas is set up as a test of the direction of change of real income. The price and quantity data for points B and Q are inserted into the formula, and if the resulting index number turns out to be greater than 100, real income has allegedly risen; if it is equal to 100, it is supposed to be unchanged; and so on. It is natural to ask about the basis on which these judgments are made when the required indifference-curve information is not available. The answer is that any index number formula implicitly sets up an imaginary and arbitrary indifference map and then treats it as though it were the consumer's true indifference map, using this arbitrary map to determine what has happened to his real income. Of course, if the individual's true indifference map differs from the artificial map implicit in the index number formula, the index number may well imply that real income has gone up, when it has in fact decreased, and vice versa.

This can be illustrated by a brief analysis of that index number of real income which uses base-period prices as weights (the Laspeyres index). Let us, for simplicity, suppose there are only our two commodities, c and z, and let P_{bc} and P_{bz} be their respective base-period prices. If the quantities held by the consumer in the base period were C_b and Z_b, and if C and Z are his current possessions of the commodities, the expression for the Laspeyres index of current real income is

$$100 \frac{P_{bc}C + P_{bz}Z}{P_{bc}C_b + P_{bz}Z_b}$$

i.e., the value of current purchases C and Z at base-year prices $(P_{bc}C + P_{bz}Z)$ divided by the actual base-year expenditure on the two commodities $(P_{bc}C_b + P_{bz}Z_b)$, all multiplied by 100. Suppose, then, that we know the four base-year numbers P_{bc}, P_{bz}, C_b, and Z_b, and that we want to find which possible combinations of C and Z will, according to this expression, leave our consumer's real income unchanged. Income will remain constant on this Laspeyres index calculation whenever we have

(5) $$100 \frac{P_{bc}C + P_{bz}Z}{P_{bc}C_b + P_{bz}Z_b} = 100$$

where the reader should remember that the four base-year magnitudes, P_{bc}, P_{bz}, C_b, and Z_b are given, fixed numbers, not variables. Now divide both sides of the equation by 100 to cancel it out, and use M_b to designate the given (constant) total base-year expenditure on both commodities together, that is,

(6) $$M_b = P_{bc}C_b + P_{bz}Z_b.$$

The indifference-curve Equation (5) then becomes, substituting the symbol M_b in the denominator of the fraction,

$$\frac{P_{bc}C + P_{bz}Z}{M_b} = 1$$

that is,

(7) $$P_{bc}C + P_{bz}Z = M_b.$$

This Equation (7) is just another version of the formula (5) for any combination of goods c and z which the Laspeyres index considers indifferent with that of the base year (real income unchanged). It is the equation of a

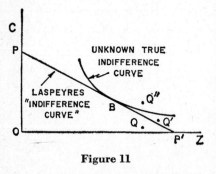

Figure 11

Laspeyres index indifference curve. But the reader will note by comparison with Equation (4) of Section 8 of this chapter, that (7) is the equation of the price line with base-period prices P_{bc} and P_{bz}, and base-period income (expenditure) M_b. In other words, the Laspeyres indifference curve is the base-period price line! Thus it is the very lowest edge (PP') of the zone of ignorance (Figure 10a) —any points below it are necessarily revealed inferior to the base-period point. This result helps us to evaluate the Laspeyres index number, for we know that the true indifference curve through point B (which represents the combination of c and z consumed during the base period) must lie above this price line PP' (Figure 11). This shows that if the point representing current consumption is located below PP' (point Q) so that the Laspeyres index number says real income has fallen, this must actually be the case. But if the Laspeyres index number indicates that real income has risen, it may (point Q'') or may not (point Q') in fact have done so (for point Q'' also lies above the true indifference curve but point Q' lies *below* it). In sum, the Laspeyres indifference curve may charitably be considered the lowest possible curve in the zone of ignorance and, whenever it is wrong, it must overvalue current real income. In other words, it is the most sanguine of all admissible indices of real income, since any index which is more biased in this direction (e.g., if it says Q is also better than B) must imply that the consumer's base-period indifference curve actually cuts below the base-period price line, into the region which is revealed inferior to B!

Although it is possible to conduct a similar analysis of the concealed implications of any other index number formula, such an investigation, is usually somewhat more difficult and yields less clear-cut results than does that of the Laspeyres case.

REFERENCES

American Economic Association, *Readings in Price Theory* (George J. Stigler and Kenneth E. Boulding, eds.), Irwin, Homewood, Ill., 1952, Articles 1–4.

Henderson, James M., and Quandt, Richard E., *Microeconomic Theory*, McGraw-Hill, New York, 1958, Chapter 2.

Hicks, J. R., *Value and Capital*, 2nd edition, Oxford University Press, New York, 1946, Part I and Mathematical Appendix to these chapters. (Rather difficult reading.)

Marshall, Alfred, *Principles of Economics*, 8th edition, Macmillan, London, 1922, Book III and pp. 838–840.

Samuelson, Paul A., *Foundations of Economic Analysis*, Harvard, Cambridge, Mass., 1947, Chapters V and VI. (Highly mathematical.)

———, "Consumption Theorems in Terms of Overcompensation Rather Than Indifference Comparisons," *Economica*, Vol. XX, February 1953. (More on revealed preference.)

CHAPTER NINE

Production and cost

1. Production, Inputs and Outputs

The standard economic discussions of production classify the firm's decision variables into only two categories, *inputs* and *outputs*. An input is simply anything which the firm buys for use in its production or other processes. An output is any commodity which the firm produces or processes for sale.

The term "processing," as it is used here, may denote an act of transportation or storage and does not necessarily imply a manufacturing activity. To an economist, all of these may be equally productive acts. For example, transportation increases the usefulness of the product by bringing it to the location where the consumer needs it—without transportation the item may be just as useless to him as it would be if it were still just a collection of raw materials. Similarly, storage gets the item to the consumer *when* he needs it, just as transportation gets it to him *where* he needs it. The terms "production" and "processing," then, are used in this more general sense which does not necessarily involve the literal, physical transformation of raw materials.

Management's production decision problems may be considered to fall into four types:

1. How much, in total, shall be spent on the purchase of inputs?
2. How shall this amount be divided among the various types of input?
3. How much of each type of input will be allocated to each type of output?
4. How much of each final product (output) shall the firm produce?

The answer to the last question is determined by decision 3, for once it is determined how much labor, machine time, raw material, and other input is to be allocated to the production of, say, railroad cars, the planned railroad cars' output level is automatically settled—for we must assume that the firm wishes to produce as many railroad cars as is technologically feasible with these input quantities. If it wishes to produce a smaller number of cars, it can save money simply by buying correspondingly smaller amounts of inputs.

Question 3, how to divide the inputs among the firm's various outputs, is obviously relevant only for a multi-product firm. Of course, most firms in our economy do turn out a large variety of products, but in most of this chapter it will simplify matters to deal only with the single-product firm. The analysis of question 3 will, therefore, be postponed until the next chapter with the comment that its analysis is almost identical in form with that of question 2, the determination of the relative amounts of the various inputs to be hired or purchased. The determination of the scale of the firm's operations, and hence its total input budget (question 1), will also be left for the next few chapters.

2. The Production Function

Decisions on inputs and outputs cannot, of course, be taken independently. There are technological relationships which restrict the options available to management and tell him that he cannot produce Q units of output q with a combination involving less than I units of input i, J units of input j, etc. This technological information is summarized in the *production function*

$$Q = g(I, J, K, \ldots)$$

which states that Q is the maximum amount of output q which the firm can produce if it uses exactly I units of i, J units of input j, etc. The existence of such a function already presupposes a set of optimality calculations on the part of the company's engineers or production managers. They must be taken to have examined the many alternative ways in which the combination of inputs $I, J, K, \ldots$ can be used to produce output q in the different technological processes available for use in its manufacture. From their optimality calculation we may assume they have decided that Q is the *maximum* output possible with this set of inputs.[1]

[1] It is noteworthy that the standard mathematical-programming analysis of the production process begins further back and includes even this optimality calculation. That is, it considers not only how much of each output ought to be produced, but also at what level each available technological process should be employed. This is handled by a simple device. Suppose there are two processes for producing shoes. Instead of using one variable, S, to represent shoe output, we employ two variables, S_1 and S_2, to

Confining our discussion to two inputs, for the sake of simplicity, the production function can be represented in a three-dimensional diagram very much like the graph of the utility function in the preceding chapter. In Figure 1a any point R just represents a combination of two inputs—

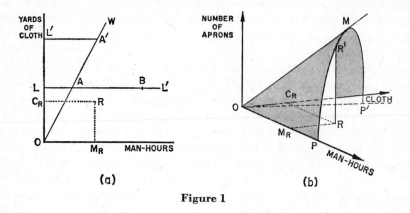

Figure 1

quantity OM_R of labor and quantity OC_R of cloth. Suppose we know that with that combination of inputs we can produce some maximum quantity of our output, aprons. Call this amount RR'. We represent this information in the three-dimensional diagram, Figure 1b, as follows: We place diagram 1a flat on the floor, and erect over point R a vertical line of length RR' (the output permitted by input combination R). The top of this vertical line, point R', is one point on the *production surface*. The locus of all such points is a roughly (split) conical surface, a portion of which is shown in Figure 1b as $OPMP'$.

3. Relative Input Levels and Production

We note that, as it is drawn, the production surface does not extend beyond the labor and cloth axes. The reason for this is that at a point such as M_R, which lies on one of the axes, we have a positive quantity of only one input. At point M_R we have OM_R labor and no cloth. We know that with such a combination of inputs it is not possible to produce any aprons, i.e., output at point M_R must be zero. Hence the production surface at that point must be of zero height. That is what also gives the production function the roughly upside-down U-shaped cross section PMP'. This shape indicates that output cannot be produced with only cloth alone or

represent the quantities produced by the first and second processes, respectively. Then the optimal values of S_1 and S_2 can both be calculated by the standard programming techniques and these values obviously determine, implicitly, the optimal combination of use of shoe manufacturing processes 1 and 2 for that level of output.

only labor alone and that positive outputs can only be produced by combinations of the two (intermediate points in the diagram). Note that by more careful cutting and workmanship it is possible to save on cloth by increased use of labor so that aprons can indeed be produced with varying proportions of cloth and labor, as the diagram shows.

There are several respects in which the diagram may be misleading on these matters:

1. The cross section PMP' need not be symmetrical, for the two inputs need not make similar contributions to output, particularly since the choice of units to measure inputs—man-hours and yards—is completely arbitrary and the shape of the diagram will change when the unit of measure is varied—a square meter of cloth can be used to produce more aprons than can a yard of cloth because a meter is slightly longer than a yard.

2. The cross section PMP' need not be smooth—it may have dents, kinks, or even sharp breaks. For example, consider what happens when we move from point R in the direction of P'. This involves a reduction in the firm's use of labor and an increased use of cloth. At some point along this line the labor/cloth ratio may become so low that it is necessary to switch to labor-saving equipment, and this switch may produce a sharp rise in output—a break (a sudden rise) in the production surface.

3. Point M, the highest point on the cross section PMP', will *not* normally represent an optimum arrangement. True, it represents a technologically productive combination of inputs, but whether it will pay to employ that input combination depends on relative prices which we have not yet brought into the picture. That is, whether it will pay to use 10 minutes or 15 minutes of labor per yard of cloth will depend in part on the level of wages, no matter what the physical productivity of labor.

4. Diminishing Returns

A standard economic assumption affecting the shape of the production function is the "law" of diminishing returns which is interpreted here to mean (eventually) diminishing marginal productivity. This highly plausible empirical allegation (which seems to be fairly well supported by experience) states that:

> As more and more of some input, i, is employed, *all other input quantities being held constant*, eventually a point will be reached where additional quantities of input i will yield diminishing marginal contributions to total product.

The plausibility argument is that, eventually, other inputs will grow short relative to input i, and so additional units of i will be at a growing disadvantage in adding to production. As we hire more and more labor but do not supply the increased labor force with additional workroom equipment or raw material, further additions to the labor force may well be expected to grow less helpful.

The effect of this assumption on the shape of the production surface is readily shown. Consider line LL' in Figure 1a. Point B on this line involves more labor than does point A. But, because LL is parallel to the horizontal labor axis, both A and B involve the same quantities of cloth input. We see, then, that a line parallel to either axis represents the conditions necessary to test for the presence of diminishing returns—by moving along such a line we can increase the use of one input *while holding the quantity of the other input constant.*

To see now whether the production surface exhibits diminishing returns we must investigate what happens to the production level as we make such a move (from A toward B on LL'). For this purpose we examine the cross section, $LSTB$, of the production surface taken above line LL' (Figure 2a). This curve, which is reproduced by itself in Figure 2b, is a total product curve for labor, given the fixed quantity of cloth, OL. We

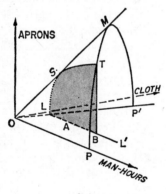

(a)

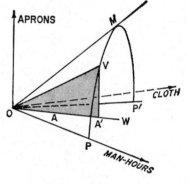

(c)

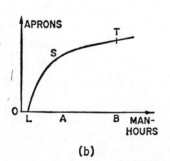

(b)

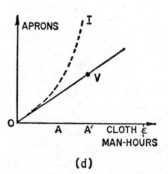

(d)

Figure 2

note that as it is drawn it flattens out as we move toward the right (its slope diminishes with increasing quantities of labor input). But we know (Chapter 3, Section 4) that the marginal product of labor is represented by the slope of the total product curve. It follows that as we move to the right along LL', the marginal product of labor (the slope of LST) is declining, as the diminishing-marginal-returns assumption requires. To summarize, if (and only if) the production function involves diminishing marginal returns, any cross section taken parallel to *either* input axis will have the gradually flattening shape shown in Figure 2b, and not a constant slope (as does OV in Figure 2d) or an increasing slope (OI in Figure 2d).

5. Returns to Scale

So far we have examined what happens when any one input is increased by itself. This leads naturally to our next question, what happens when all inputs are increased together, that is, when the production process is expanded exactly *to scale?* For this purpose, let us return again to the floor of our production diagram (Figure 1a). Suppose we begin with some input combination, A, and ask how a doubling of both of the input quantities at A will be represented. We then have the following theorem:

Draw any straight line OW which goes through both the origin and point A. Pick point A' on this line OW so that length OA' = twice (k times) length OA. Then point A' represents an exact doubling (multiplication by k) of all of the inputs at point A.[2]

Moreover, it is simple to extend this result to obtain the converse proposition that any proportionate increase (decrease) in all of a firm's inputs must be represented by a movement along some straight line, OW, from the origin on the floor of the three-dimensional production diagram (Figure 2c). Note that this straight line need not bisect the angle formed by the axes. For example, in Figure 1a curve OW is relatively close to the cloth axis because it represents what looks like a large (constant) cloth-to-labor ratio (in this case a two-to-one ratio—two yards of cloth per man-hour).

This, then, is how we ask our question: To find out what happens to production when all inputs increase in the same proportion (an increase to scale) we take a cross section $OA'V$ of our production diagram (Figure

---

[2] *Proof:* Triangles LOA and $L'OA'$ are similar because they are both right triangles and they have angle LOA in common. Therefore their sides are proportional, i.e., we have $L'A'/LA = OL'/OL = OA'/OA = k$. But OL and OL' are the cloth input at points A and A' respectively and LA and $L'A'$ are the respective labor inputs at A and A'. The result then follows at once.

An alternative proof which is even simpler is that the equation of a straight line through the origin is $y = ax$ (see Chapter 2, Section 3) so that $y/x = a$ (a constant), i.e., along such a line the ratio of the values of the variables is always equal to a constant.

2c) cutting along the straight line on the floor from the origin, and examine the shape of this cross section. There are three possibilities:

1. *Diminishing returns to scale:* The curve representing the top of the cross section has the shape of *LT* in Figures 2a and 2b, in which the slope decreases toward the right.

2. *Increasing returns to scale:* The top of the cross section has an increasing slope, as does *OI* in Figure 2d.

3. *Constant returns to scale:* The cross section line is straight (*OV* in Figures 2c and 2d).[3]

This last possibility, which is called the case of a *linear homogeneous production function,*[4] has received a great deal of attention in the literature. It turns out that such a relationship has extremely convenient mathematical properties, which make it very useful for purposes of analysis. Whenever we are fortunate enough to encounter a production function which (at least approximately) exhibits constant returns to scale, we can at once bring to bear a number of special theorems, one of which will be described presently. It has already been noted in Chapter 5, Section 3, how important a role this type of production relationship plays in the linear programming analysis of production. We will also discuss some more properties of this type of production function in the Chapter 14, "Theory of Distribution," and Chapter 15, "Input-Output Analysis."

There is also some empirical evidence that the production function for the economy as a whole is not too far from being linear and homogeneous.[5]

Finally, it is almost tempting to argue that production functions will *necessarily* exhibit constant returns to scale. The view is that if, in some sense, all inputs are, say, tripled, what is there to prevent all outputs from being tripled? After all, if we build three identical factories with identical work forces, equipment, and raw materials, will we not obtain three times the output of a single factory? In this view, given constant prices, there are only two reasons why costs (input use) should not vary in exact proportion with output:

[3] Note that the "spine" of the diagram, *OM*, which is one such cross section, is also a straight line in this case.

[4] This is the mathematical terminology for the constant-returns-to-scale case and refers to the form of the algebraic equation of such a production function. Incidentally, the reader would do well to convince himself that a production function can satisfy the "law of diminishing returns" and yet, simultaneously, exhibit constant returns to scale. It should be noted that both of these phenomena occur in linear programming problems.

[5] See Paul H. Douglas, "Are There Laws of Production?" *American Economic Review,* Vol. XXXVIII, March 1948, and Robert M. Solow, "Technical Change and the Aggregate Production Function," *Review of Economics and Statistics,* Vol. XXXIX, August 1957.

1. *Limited input quantities:* If we increase outputs, but there are some factors whose use cannot expand in proportion because their supplies are limited, costs per unit will be driven up because there will be diminishing returns to those inputs whose use is increased.

2. *Indivisibilities:* Some inputs just do not come in small units. We cannot install half a blast furnace or half a locomotive (a small locomotive is not the same as a fraction of a large locomotive). As a result, only if operations are carried on on a sufficiently large scale will it pay to employ such indivisible items. This, it is said, is the only source of economies of large-scale production. In other words, from this point of view all production functions are linear and homogeneous, only, unfortunately, it is not always possible to increase or diminish all input uses in exactly the same proportion.

This position has been criticized on several grounds. First of all, it has been maintained that one cannot even meaningfully speak of duplicating all of the elements in a given situation. A pair of factories in close proximity simply is not the same as a duplication of one factory in isolation. The existence of another nearby factory affects labor morale, air pollution, the cost of labor-force training, etc.

More important, suppose one larger factory is more efficient than two small factories of similar total capacity. Then there is no motivation for a businessman to expand by duplicating his original facilities even if this option is open to him. In other words, if he can obtain increasing returns to scale he can be expected to take advantage of such opportunities when he expands his output.

There are standard examples of the manner in which such economies can arise. For example, it was shown in Chapter 1 that the optimal inventory level is likely to increase less than in proportion with the scale of a firm's output. In other words, when the firm doubles its sales, it may be foolish to double its inventory expenditures. Here is an increasing-return case—an economy of large-scale production. Another standard example is the warehouse construction case. Suppose the work in building a rectangular warehouse is in proportion to the number of bricks used in its construction and that, within limits, the number of bricks depends strictly on the wall area of the building. It is a matter of elementary geometry that the wall area will increase as the *square* of the perimeter of the warehouse but the volume of the building (the storage area) will increase as the *cube* of the perimeter. In other words, double both the bricks and the bricklaying labor and one more than doubles warehouse capacity. Here is another case of economies of large-scale production.

One must conclude that whether or not the production function of a particular plant is linear and homogeneous or even approximately so is a matter of empirical investigation and cannot be settled by *a priori* considerations.[6]

6. Production Indifference-Curve Analysis

Continuing with our illustrative two-input, one-output case, it is convenient at this point to leave the three-dimensional production surface and turn to a two-dimensional diagram which contains exactly the same information. This is done, as in the case of consumer preference analysis, by use of the indifference-curve device. A production indifference curve is defined as a locus of input combinations all of which are capable of producing the same output level. It is a contour line on the floor of the three-dimensional diagram representing the "latitudes and longitudes" of points of equal height on the production surface. Thus, in Figure 3a, all points

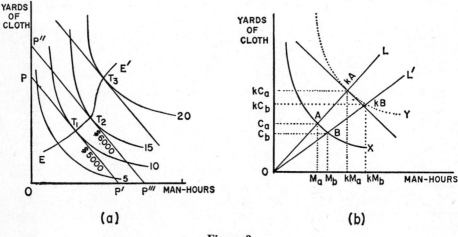

(a)   **(b)**

Figure 3

on the curve marked "10" represent input combinations capable of producing the same number of aprons (say 10,000 aprons as indicated by the 10 next to that indifference curve). These production indifference curves

[6] Some of the standard references on this discussion are Nicholas Kaldor, "The Equilibrium of the Firm," *Economic Journal*, Vol. XLIV, March 1934; Paul A. Samuelson, *Foundations of Economic Analysis*, Harvard University Press, Cambridge, Mass., 1947, pp. 81–87; Edward H. Chamberlin, "Proportionality, Divisibility, and Economies of Scale," *Quarterly Journal of Economics*, Vol. LXII, February 1948; "Comments" by A. N. McLeod and F. H. Hahn and "Reply" by Chamberlin, same journal, Vol. LXIII, February 1949; "Random Variations, Risk and Returns to Scale," Thompson M. Whitin and Maurice H. Peston, same journal, Vol. LXVIII, November 1954; and Harvey Leibenstein, "The Proportionality Controversy and the Theory of Production," same journal, Vol. LXIX, November 1955.

will normally possess properties which are the same as (or analogous with) those usually assumed for consumer indifference curves (see Section 7 of Chapter 8):

1. They have a negative slope;
2. If one indifference curve, X, lies above and to the right of another indifference curve, Y, then X will normally correspond to a higher output level than Y;
3. No two indifference curves intersect;
4. The curves are convex to the origin.

The rationale of each of these properties is so closely analogous with that involved in the theory of the consumer that its investigation is left entirely as an exercise for the interested reader.

Only one new feature arises in production indifference-curve analysis. A *consumer* indifference curve can be defined as a line of constant utility. But since the entire idea of utility measurement (in this sense) is under suspicion, no attempt was made to put numbers next to each consumer indifference curve to specify the utility level which it represents. Production indifference curves present no analogous problem for the finicky. The output level of a single commodity is a meaningful concept and we need feel no compunction about labeling the curves 5, 10, 15, etc., as is done in Figure 3a to indicate the production level to which each curve corresponds.

7. Price Line and Expansion Path

As previously indicated, the production indifference map (or the production surface) represents only technological information. Such data alone ordinarily do not permit us to determine the firm's optimal decisions, for we lack price information which can tell us what each input gives us *for our money*. This information is supplied to us by the price line (e.g., PP' in Figure 3a). The price line in our production analysis is exactly the same as the price or budget line in consumer theory—it is not even a matter of analogy. The price line is again a line of constant expenditure—it represents all combinations of labor and cloth which can be bought for a fixed amount of money. Thus, for example, PP' in Figure 3a represents all possible combinations of these two inputs which together cost exactly $5000. Here there is not even any point in repeating the properties of the price line which were discussed in Section 8 of the previous chapter.

It will clearly be in the interests of the profit-maximizing (or the revenue-maximizing) firm to obtain as high a level of production for its money as possible. If management is going to spend $5000, the firm will obtain one of the input combinations represented by the points on line PP'. Management will want to end up on the highest possible production indifference curve consistent with this expenditure. This optimum point will be the point of tangency, T_1, between PP' and indifference curve 10. For any other point on PP', such as K, must lie on a lower indifference curve. Point T_1, then, represents the optimum input combination for the firm if it should decide to spend \$5000.

But suppose the firm considers also what will happen if it spends some other amount of money, say \$6000. This will involve a parallel shift in the price line, say to $P''P'''$. The optimum input combination (the maximum output for the firm's \$6000 outlay) here is given by the point of tangency, T_2. Thus, if we draw in curve EE', the locus of all such points of tangency, we obtain what is called the company's *expansion path*. For the given relative prices of the two inputs (the slope of the price line), the expansion path tells us how the firm's optimum input combination will vary when the size of the company input budget changes.

Our condition that optimum input combinations occur at points of tangency between a price line and a production indifference curve is a geometric representation of the following basic optimality rule (which we will encounter again in this book):

> An optimum combination of any two inputs, I and J, requires that the ratio of their marginal products be equal to the ratio of their prices. Symbolically, we must thus have
>
> $$MP_i/MP_j = P_i/P_j.$$

The reader can readily prove by an argument analogous to that of footnote 9 of the preceding chapter that the slope of the production indifference curves of Figure 3a equals the marginal product of labor over the marginal product of cloth (MP_L/MP_C). Moreover, since the slope of the price line equals the ratio of the two prices (Section 8 of Chapter 8), the preceding rule follows at once. Since two tangent curves have the same slope, at a point like T_1 in Figure 3a we must have $MP_L/MP_C = P_L/P_C$.

The rationale of the rule is also readily explained. Rewrite the equation as $MP_L/P_L = MP_C/P_C$. Now, if one added man-hour of labor produces 3 aprons ($MP_L = 3$) and costs \$2 ($P_L = 2$), the ratio $MP_L/P_L = 3/2 = 1\frac{1}{2}$ tells us that every additional dollar spent on labor yields $1\frac{1}{2}$ aprons. In other words MP_L/P_L is the measure of what the firm gets by putting an additional dollar into labor. Similarly, MP_C/P_C is the corresponding measure of the yield of a dollar spent on cloth. If the two happen to be unequal, say if $MP_C/P_C = 2$, this means that a reallocation of the company budget must be profitable—one dollar taken out of labor outlay and transferred to cloth purchasing will yield a net increase in output of one-half apron. Obviously, then, if MP_C/P_C exceeds MP_L/P_L the firm must not be buying enough cloth to keep the men busy—the firm's cloth-labor combination cannot be optimal. Only if the two ratios are equal can the firm be allocating its input expenditures optimally.

8. Linear Homogeneous Production Functions

We can now come back to the constant-returns-to-scale case to derive the following theorem:

> The expansion path of a linear homogeneous production function is always a straight line through the origin. This means that, given the prices of its inputs, the optimal proportion of the inputs of the firm will not change with the size of the firm's input budget.

This will be shown diagrammatically with the aid of Figure 3b. First it must be noted that all of the production indifference curves of such a production function are exactly similar in shape. If one such curve, Y, is further from the origin than another indifference curve, X, then Y is simply a magnified version of curve X.

More explicitly, let OL be any straight line from the origin, and let points A and kA be the respective points of intersection of curves X and Y with line OL. Then in a linear homogeneous production function the slope of curve X at point A must be exactly equal to the slope of curve Y at point kA.[7] In this sense, then, the curves must be parallel when viewed from the origin.

The rest of the theorem of this section now follows readily. For sup-

[7] *Proof:* Consider another straight line, OL', through the origin, and let B be its point of intersection with indifference curve X. The average slope of curve X between points A and B is

$$\frac{\Delta Y}{\Delta X} = \frac{C_a - C_b}{M_a - M_b}.$$

Now let the length of line segment OkA be k times as great as the length of line segment OA. Find point kB on line OL' such that segment OkB is k times as great as OB. We observe:

1. The coordinates of kA and kB are, respectively, k times as large as those of A and B (because OL and OL' are straight lines through the origin—see the proof in footnote 2 of this chapter).

2. kB is on the same indifference curve as is kA, for we have constant returns to scale, and since A and B yield the same outputs (X), then kA and kB must yield the same outputs ($kX = Y$).

The result now follows at once, for the average slope of indifference curve Y between points kA and kB is

$$\frac{kC_a - kC_b}{kM_a - kM_b} = \frac{k(C_a - C_b)}{k(M_a - M_b)} = \frac{C_a - C_b}{M_a - M_b}$$

which is exactly the same as the average slope of curve X between points A and B.

pose point A on OL is a point of tangency between a price line and indifference curve X. Then any other point, kA, on line OL must also be such a point of tangency, because all price lines are parallel (if input prices do not change) and the slope of indifference curve Y at kA is the same as that of curve X at point A, as was just shown. Thus, if any point on line OL lies on the expansion path, so will any other point on this line.

Hence, the expansion path of a linear homogeneous production function will always be a straight line. But, as was shown in Section 5, above, all points on such a line involve the same input proportions. We conclude that with constant returns to scale and fixed input prices there will be just one optimum input proportion (say, 8 yards of cloth per man-hour) which does not change no matter what the level of the firm's output.

This result is quite convenient. For the businessman it means that he need only compute one such figure, and as long as input prices do not change he has no further input-proportion decision problems. The theorem can also be useful for economic analysis, as we shall see in our input-output discussion.

9. Derivation of Cost Curves

From the firm's expansion path it is fairly easy to find the firm's *total* and *average cost curves*. The total cost curve is, as we know, defined as a curve which shows how total company outlays vary with its level of production, and the average (per unit) cost curve is defined analogously.

It will be recalled that price line PP' in Figure 3a was taken to represent an outlay of $5000. Thus, point of tangency T_1 on this price line tells us that the maximum output obtainable for that outlay is 10,000 aprons.

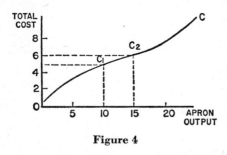

Figure 4

This information is represented by point C_1 in Figure 4. Similarly, point C_2 in Figure 4 tells us that it will cost $6000 to produce 15,000 aprons, which is the information given by point T_2 in Figure 3a, and so on. The curve OC in Figure 4, which is the locus of all points like C_1 and C_2, is the company's total cost curve.

It is also possible to find the firm's average cost curve directly with the aid of Figure 3a. For example, point T_1 tells us that the unit cost of producing 10,000 aprons is $5000/10,000 = 50 cents. We can find the same information for every other point on the expansion path, EE', and by recording these data on another graph (not shown) we obtain the firm's average cost curve.

Alternatively, we can use the methods of Chapter 3 to obtain the firm's average and marginal costs from its total cost curve in Figure 4.

10. *Long Run and Short Run: Definitions*

Before we go any further, it is necessary to define a bit of economists' jargon: the terms *long run* and *short run*. These do *not* refer to any fixed units of calendar time—we cannot say in advance and without reference to a specific problem that a two-month period lies in the short run and that a five-year period extends into the long run.

Rather, these concepts are defined flexibly in terms of the period over which the company's commitments extend. The very long run is a period so long that all of the firm's present contracts will have run out, its present plant and equipment will have been worn out or rendered obsolete and will therefore need replacement, etc. In other words, the long run is a period of sufficient duration for the company to become completely free in its decisions from its present policies, possessions, and commitments. Thus the long run is a sufficiently distant period in which the firm can be free to reconsider all of its policies. For example, if the company finds that the demand for its product has increased substantially, it may be ten years before it can afford to redesign its plant and equipment completely in accord with the requirements of this development.

The other extreme case, the very short run, is that where the firm has a minimum of free choice. In the very short run a firm will not even be able to increase its output in response to increased consumer demand. To do this it must acquire more raw materials, perhaps it must arrange for some of its labor force to work overtime, and it may also have to hire more labor. Even after all of this is arranged, it will take time for the increased production flow to begin rolling off the assembly line. In the very short run, then, the firm can only supply increased demands out of inventory.

In between these extreme cases, the very short and the very long run, there are all sorts of intermediate time periods in which the firm can make partial adjustments to any changes in the situation. But in any such in-between period it will find its options circumscribed to some extent by previous commitments.

11. *Long-Run and Short-Run Average Costs*

These concepts enable us to examine somewhat further the nature of the data which lie behind the firm's cost relationships.

Imagine a firm which is considering renting one of four factories where the owners of these factories all insist on, say, two-year leases. Call these four factories, arranged in increasing order of size, S, T, V, and W. If our firm decides to lease factory S, its average cost curve for the next two years will (other things remaining unchanged) then be given, say, by curve SS' in Figure 5a. The other U-shaped curves in Figure 5a can be interpreted similarly. We see that if, for example, the firm expects to produce and sell output OV_m it will pay its management to rent factory V, the third largest of the available factories. For although factories T and W are also both capable of producing that output, it can be done in plant V at lower unit cost than in either of the other facilities.

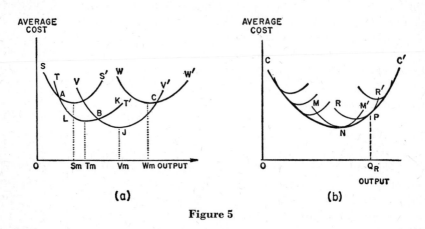

Figure 5

Suppose that the firm decides to lease plant T. TT' in Figure 5 will then be its average cost curve for the two-year lease period—its short-run average cost curve. Once it has committed itself to T, if the firm ends up producing output OV_m, it will for the next two years have no choice but to incur average cost V_mK. In other words, the U-shaped curves in the diagram are the alternative *short-run cost curves* available to the firm.

The corresponding long-run cost curve is also apparent from the diagram. For before the firm has made its commitment it will be free to choose the plant size most appropriate for its anticipated output—it will be able to lease that plant which produces its output at the lowest possible cost. Thus with output OS_m it will want to use plant T and produce at unit cost S_mL; with output OV_m it will want to use plant V so that its unit costs will be V_mJ; etc. In sum, the firm's long-run average cost curve will be the heavy scalloped curve $SALBJCW'$. This curve consists of the lowest segments of all of the short-run average cost curves.

Sometimes the firm has an unlimited number of alternatives in picking its plant capacity. This would be the case if it were having an architect draw up plans for a new factory (rather than looking for an existing property to rent). In such a situation there would be an infinite number of possible short-run cost curves, some of which are represented in Figure 5b.

Here it is to be noted that the scallops can be smoothed out of the long-run cost curve, CNC'. The smooth long-run curve consists, as before, of the "bottom" of the set of the short-run curves. For obvious geometric reasons it is called the "envelope" of the short-run curves.

One interesting theorem follows from these drawings: It will not always pay to use a plant at an input level where it operates at minimum unit costs! For example, in Figure 5a it will pay to rent plant S if it is expected that very low outputs will be called for. But suppose the firm anticipates turning out output OS_m at which plant S is at its "most efficient" (its point of minimum unit costs). At this output, plant T is even more efficient so that it will pay to use T rather than S to produce OS_m. In other words, if it pays to rent plant S, it will only be for the production of outputs well below the technical "capacity" of that plant! A somewhat similar conclusion holds for plant W, as an examination of the cost situation at output OW_m will readily show.

Indeed, in the smooth long-run average-cost-curve case in Figure 5b there will be almost no plant which should be used at its point of minimum cost. For example, consider plant R whose short-run cost curve touches the long-run curve only at point P (output OQ_r). This, then, is the only output at which it pays to use plant R. But at P curve RR' is tangent to the long-run average cost curve which happens to have a positive slope at that point. Therefore, at P, curve RR' must also have a positive slope, i.e., P cannot possibly be the minimum point of short-run average curve RR'.

The only exception is plant M whose short-run cost curve MM' touches the long-run curve at its minimum point N. For there both these curves will be level and so they will both be at their minimum points.

Appendix: Derivation of the Optimum-Input-Combination Rules

The results of Section 7 on the optimum combinations of inputs for the firm are easily derived with the aid of the Lagrange multiplier methods of Chapter 4, Section 8. Let the firm's production function be represented by

$$Q = f(X_1, X_2, \ldots, X_n)$$

where X_1 is the quantity of x_1 (say labor) used by the firm, X_2 is the quantity of input 2 (say leather). Given any output level, Q^*, the firm will try to produce Q^* as cheaply as it can. This means that it is trying to minimize its expenditure, M, on the inputs used to produce Q^*, where this expenditure is given by

$$M = P_1 X_1 + P_2 X_2 + \ldots + P_n X_n.$$

Here P_1 is the price of input 1, etc. The firm is trying to minimize M subject to the constraint on its operations given by the production function.

To obtain the Lagrangian expression for this constrained maximization problem, we rewrite the constraint into the standard form

$$f(X_1, X_2, \ldots, X_n) - Q^* = 0$$

and multiply it by the artificial variable, λ. Adding this to the expression for M, which we are trying to minimize, we have our Lagrangian expression

$$M_\lambda = P_1 X_1 + P_2 X_2 + \ldots + P_n X_n + \lambda[f(X_1, X_2, \ldots, X_n) - Q^*].$$

It is minimized by setting each of its partial derivatives equal to zero, in turn, to obtain

$$\frac{\partial M_\lambda}{\partial X_1} = P_1 + \lambda \frac{\partial f}{\partial X_1} \qquad\qquad = 0$$

$$\frac{\partial M_\lambda}{\partial X_2} = P_2 + \lambda \frac{\partial f}{\partial X_2} \qquad\qquad = 0$$

$$\cdots \cdots \cdots \cdots \cdots \cdots \cdots$$

$$\frac{\partial M_\lambda}{\partial X_n} = P_n + \lambda \frac{\partial f}{\partial X_n} \qquad\qquad = 0$$

$$\frac{\partial M_\lambda}{\lambda} = f(X_1, X_2, \ldots, X_n) - Q^* = 0.$$

This is a system of $n + 1$ simultaneous equations which can presumably be solved for the optimal values of our n input variables, $X_1, X_2, \ldots, X_n$ as well as the value of the Lagrangian variable, λ.

In particular, to derive the rule of Section 7 we rewrite the first two of these partial derivative equations as

$$P_1 = -\lambda \frac{\partial f}{\partial X_1} \quad \text{and} \quad P_2 = -\lambda \frac{\partial f}{\partial X_2}$$

and dividing one equation by the other, we obtain, canceling out the $-\lambda$'s,

$$\frac{P_1}{P_2} = \frac{\partial f/\partial X_1}{\partial f/\partial X_2}$$

which, noting that $\partial f/\partial X_1$ is the marginal product of X_1, etc., gives us our result of Section 7. The reader should also convince himself that the first n of the partial derivative equations $\partial M_\lambda/\partial X_i = 0$ determine the firm's expansion path. Exactly the same method can be used to derive the results of Sections 4 and 7 of the next chapter.

REFERENCES

Traditional Production Analysis

American Economic Association, *Readings in Price Theory* (George J. Stigler and Kenneth E. Boulding, eds.), Irwin, Homewood, Ill., 1952, Articles 5–13 (especially Article 10, "Cost Curves and Supply Curves," by Jacob Viner, also reprinted in R. V. Clemence, *Readings in Economic Analysis*, Addison-Wesley, Cambridge, Mass., 1950, and in Jacob Viner, *The Long View and the Short*, Free Press, Glencoe, Ill., 1958).

Carlson, Sune, *A Study on the Pure Theory of Production*, P. S. King, London, 1939.

Cassels, John M., "On the Law of Variable Proportions," *Explorations in Economics*, McGraw-Hill, 1936, reprinted in American Economic Association, *Readings in the Theory of Income Distribution*, Blakiston, Philadelphia, 1946.

Henderson, James M., and Quandt, Richard E., *Microeconomic Theory*, McGraw-Hill, 1958, Chapter 3.

Programming Analysis of Production

Dorfman, Robert, *Application of Linear Programming to the Theory of the Firm*, University of California Press, Berkeley, 1951.

————, "Mathematical or 'Linear' Programming: A Nonmathematical Exposition," *American Economic Review*, Vol. XLIII, December 1953.

————, Samuelson, Paul A., and Solow, Robert M., *Linear Programming and Economic Analysis*, McGraw-Hill, New York, 1958, Chapters 6 and 7.

CHAPTER TEN

The firm and its objectives

We have now discussed the data which the firm needs for its decision-making—the demand for its products and the cost of supplying them. But, even with this information, in order to determine what decisions are optimal it is still necessary to find out the businessman's aims. The decision which best serves one set of goals will not usually be appropriate for some other set of aims.

1. Alternative Objectives of the Firm

There is no simple method for determining the goals of the firm (or of its executives). One thing, however, is clear. Very often the last person to ask about any individual's motivation is the person himself (as the psycho-analysts have so clearly shown). In fact, it is common experience when interviewing executives to find that they will agree to every plausible goal about which they are asked. They say they want to maximize sales and also to maximize profits; that they wish, in the bargain, to minimize costs; and so on. Unfortunately, it is normally impossible to serve all of such a multiplicity of goals at once.

For example, suppose an advertising outlay of half a million dollars minimizes unit costs, an outlay of 1.2 million maximizes total profits, whereas an outlay of 1.8 million maximizes the firm's sales volume. We cannot have all three decisions at once. The firm must settle on one of the three objectives or some compromise among them.

Of course, the businessman is not the only one who suffers from the desire to pursue a number of incompatible objectives. It is all too easy to try to embrace at one time all of the attractive-sounding goals one can muster and difficult to reject any one of them. Even the most learned have suffered from this difficulty. It is precisely on these grounds that one great economist was led to remark that the much-discussed objective of the greatest good for the greatest number contains one "greatest" too many.

It is most frequently assumed in economic analysis that the firm is trying to maximize its total profits. However, there is no reason to believe that all businessmen pursue the same objectives. For example, a small firm which is run by its owner may seek to maximize the proprietor's free time subject to the constraint that his earnings exceed some minimum level, and, indeed, there have been cases of overworked businessmen who, on medical advice, have turned down profitable business opportunities.

It has also been suggested, on the basis of some observation, that firms often seek to maximize the money value of their sales (their total revenue) subject to a constraint that their profits do not fall short of some minimum level which is just on the borderline of acceptability. That is, so long as profits are at a satisfactory level, management will devote the bulk of its energy and resources to the expansion of sales. Such a goal may, perhaps, be explained by the businessman's desire to maintain his competitive position, which is partly dependent on the sheer size of his enterprise, or it may be a matter of the interests of management (as distinguished from shareholders), since management's salaries may be related more closely to the size of the firm's operations than to its profits, or it may simply be a matter of prestige.

In any event, though they may help him to formulate his own aims and sometimes be able to show him that more ambitious goals are possible and relevant, it is not the job of the operations researcher or the economist to tell the businessman what his goals should be. Management's aims must be taken to be whatever they are, and the job of the analyst is to find the conclusions which follow from these objectives—that is, to describe what businessmen do to achieve these goals, and perhaps to prescribe methods for pursuing them more efficiently.

The major point, both in economic analysis and in operations-research investigation of business problems, is that the nature of the firm's objectives cannot be assumed in advance. It is important to determine the nature of the firm's objectives before proceeding to the formal model-building and the computations based on it. As is obviously to be expected, many of the conclusions of the analysis will vary with the choice of objective function. However, as some of the later discussion in this chapter will show, a change in objectives can, sometimes surprisingly, leave some significant relationships invariant. Where this is true, it is very convenient to find it out in advance before embarking on the investigation of a specific problem. For if there are some problems for which the optimum decision will be the same, no matter which of a number of objectives the firm happens to adopt, it is legitimate to avoid altogether the difficult job of determining company goals before undertaking an analysis.

2. *The Profit-Maximizing Firm*

Let us first examine some of the conventional theory of the profit-maximizing firm. In the chapter on the differential calculus, the basic marginal condition for profit maximization was derived as an illustration. Let us now rederive this marginal-cost-equals-marginal-revenue condition with the aid of a verbal and a geometric argument.

The proposition is that no firm can be earning maximum profits unless its marginal cost and its marginal revenue are (at least approximately) equal, i.e., unless an additional unit of output will bring in as much money as it costs to produce, so that its marginal profitability is zero.[1]

It is easy to show why this must be so. Suppose a firm is producing 200 thousand units of some item, x, and that at that output level, the marginal revenue from x production is \$1.10 whereas its marginal cost is only 96¢. Additional units of x will, therefore, each bring the firm some 14 cents = \$1.10 − 0.96 more than they cost, and so the firm cannot be maximizing its profits by sticking to its 200 thousand production level. Similarly, if the marginal cost of x exceeds its marginal revenue, the firm cannot be maximizing its profits, for it is neglecting to take advantage of its opportunity to save money—by reducing its output it would reduce its income, but it would reduce its costs by an even greater amount.

We can also derive the marginal-cost-equals-marginal-revenue proposition with the aid of Figure 1. At any output, OQ, total revenue is represented by the area $OQPR$ under the marginal revenue curve (see Rule 9 of Chapter 3). Similarly, total cost is represented by the area $OQKC$ immediately below the marginal cost curve. Total profit, which is the difference between total revenue and total cost is, therefore, represented by the difference between the two areas—that is, total profits are given by the lightly shaded area TKP minus the small, heavily shaded area, RTC. Now, it is clear that from point Q a move to the right will increase the size of the profit area TKP. In fact, only at output OQ_m will this area have reached its maximum size—profits will encompass the entire area $TKMP$. But at output OQ_m marginal cost equals marginal revenue—indeed, it is the crossing of the marginal cost and marginal revenue curves at that point which

---

[1] The word "approximately" is inserted because, in practice, a precise adjustment may be impossible to achieve. A 230,773rd car may bring in \$2 more than it costs to produce but the production of a 230,774th auto may cost somewhat more than the revenue it yields, so that perhaps only at something like an (impossible) $230,773\frac{3}{4}$ automobile output level would marginal cost and revenue be equal.

prevents further moves to the right (further output increases) from adding still more to the total profit area. Thus, we have once again established that at the point of maximum profits, marginal costs and marginal revenues must be equal.

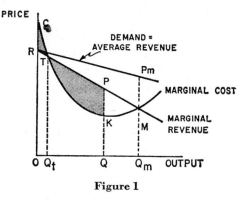

Figure 1

Before leaving the discussion of this proposition, it is well to distinguish explicitly between it and its invalid converse. It is *not* generally true that any output level at which marginal cost and marginal revenue happen to be equal (i.e., where marginal profit is zero) will be a profit-maximizing level. There may be several levels of production at which marginal cost and marginal revenue are equal, and some of these output quantities may be far from advantageous for the firm. In Figure 1 this condition is satisfied at output OQ_t as well as at OQ_m. But at OQ_t the firm obtains only the net loss (negative profit) represented by heavily shaded area RTC. A move in either direction from point Q_t will help the firm either by reducing its costs more than it cuts its revenues (a move to the left) or by adding to its revenues more than to its costs. Output OQ_t is thus a point of *minimum* profits even though it meets the marginal profit-maximization condition, "marginal revenue equals marginal cost."

This peculiar result is explained by recalling that the condition, "marginal profitability equals zero," implies only that neither a small increase nor a small decrease in quantity will add to profits. In other words, it means that we are at an output at which the total profit curve (not shown) is level—going neither uphill nor downhill. But while the top of a hill (the maximum profit output) is such a level spot, plateaus and valleys (minimum profit outputs) also have the same characteristic—they are level. That is, they are points of zero marginal profit, where marginal cost equals marginal revenue.[2]

---

[2] Again, this problem arises because our marginal maximum condition must be supplemented by a second-order condition—that the second derivative of profits be nega-

We conclude that while at a profit-maximizing output marginal cost must equal marginal revenue, the converse is not correct—it is not true that at an output at which marginal cost equals marginal revenue the firm can be sure of maximizing its profits.

3. Application: Pricing and Cost Changes

The preceding theorem permits us to make a number of predictions about the behavior of the profit-maximizing firm and to set up some normative "operations research" rules for its operation. We can determine not only the optimum output, but also the profit-maximizing price with the aid of the demand curve for the product of the firm. For, given the optimum output, we can find out from the demand curve what price will permit the company to sell this quantity, and that is necessarily the optimum price. In Figure 1, where the optimum output is OQ_m we see that the corresponding price is Q_mP_m where point P_m is the point on the demand curve above Q_m (note that P_m is *not* the point of intersection of the marginal cost and the marginal revenue curves).

It was shown in the last section of Chapter 4 how our theorem can also enable us to predict the effect of a change in tax rates or some other change in cost on the firm's output and pricing. We need merely determine how this change shifts the marginal cost curve to find the new profit-maximizing price-output combination by finding the new point of intersection of the marginal cost and marginal revenue curves. Let us recall one particular result for use later in this chapter—the theorem about the effects of a change in fixed costs. It will be remembered that a change in fixed costs never has any effect on the firm's marginal cost curve (Chapter 3, Section 6) because marginal fixed cost is always zero (by definition, an additional unit of output adds nothing to *fixed* costs). Hence, if the profit-maximizing firm's rents, its total assessed taxes, or some other fixed cost increases, there will be no change in the output-price level at which its marginal cost equals its marginal revenue. In other words, the profit-maximizing firm will make no price or output changes in response to any increase or decrease in its fixed costs! This rather unexpected result is certainly not in accord with common business practice and requires some further comment which will be supplied presently.

---

tive, which means, in the present context, that the marginal revenue curve must cut the marginal cost curve from above (going from left to right). The reader should verify that this condition is satisfied at the profit-maximizing output OQ_m in Figure 1 but that it is violated at OQ_t. He should also give an economic interpretation of the condition. Compare Section 5 of Chapter 4.

4. *Extension: Multiple Products and Inputs*

The firm's output decisions are normally more complicated, even in principle, than the preceding decisions suggest. Almost all companies produce a variety of products and these various commodities typically compete for the firm's investment funds and its productive capacity. At any given time there are limits to what the company can produce, and often, if it decides to increase its production of product x, this must be done at the expense of product y. In other words, such a company cannot simply expand the output of x to its optimum level without taking into account the effects of this decision on the output of y.

For a profit-maximizing decision which takes both commodities into account we have a marginal rule which is a special case of Rule 2 of Chapter 3:

> Any limited input (including investment funds) should be allocated between the two outputs x and y in such a way that the marginal profit yield of the input, i, in the production of x equals the marginal profit yield of the input in the production of y.

The reasoning behind this result is straightforward. If the condition is violated the firm cannot be maximizing its profits, because the firm can add to its earnings simply by shifting some of i out of the product where it obtains the lower return and into the manufacture of the other.

Stated another way, this last theorem asserts that if the firm is maximizing its profits, a reduction in its output of x by an amount which is worth, say, $5, should release just exactly enough productive capacity, C, to permit the output of y to be increased $5 worth. For this means that the marginal return of the released capacity is exactly the same in the production of either x or y, which is what the previous version of this rule asserted.[3]

Still another version of this result is worth describing: Suppose the price of each product is fixed and independent of output levels. Then we require that the marginal cost of each output be proportionate to its price, i.e., that $MC_x/P_x = MC_y/P_y$, where P_x and MC_x are, respectively, the price and the marginal cost of x, etc.[4]

---

[3] The earlier rule states that the marginal *profitability* must be the same in both uses, whereas now we have the marginal *revenue* of the input the same in the production of either x or y. But if a unit of resources costs D dollars, the marginal profit of i in the production of x (MP_{ix}) equals its marginal revenue minus its cost, so that if marginal profitability is the same in both uses we have

$$MP_{ix} = MR_{ix} - D = MR_{iy} - D = MP_{iy}$$

so that we must also have $MR_{ix} = MR_{iy}$, and conversely.

[4] To see how this follows from the preceding version of our rule, suppose that $1 in inputs produces K dollars worth of x and K dollars worth of y. Then if one unit of x

In this discussion we have considered only the output decisions of a profit-maximizing firm. Of course, the firm has other decisions to make. In particular, it must decide on the amounts of its inputs including its marketing inputs (advertising, sales force, etc.). There are similar rules for these decisions, as discussed in the preceding chapter and in Chapter 14, Section 6. The main result here is that profit maximization requires for any inputs i and j

$$MP_i/P_i = MP_j/P_j$$

where MP_i represents the marginal profit contribution of input i and P_i is its price, etc.

Having discussed the consequences of profit maximization, let us see now what difference it makes if the firm adopts an alternative objective, one to which we have already alluded—the maximization of the value of its sales (total revenue) under the requirement that the firm's profits not fall short of some given minimum level.

5. Price-Output Determination: Sales Maximization

Sales maximization under a profit constraint does not mean an attempt to obtain the largest possible physical volume (which is hardly easy to define in the modern multi-product firm). Rather, it refers to maximization of total revenue (dollar sales) which, to the businessman, is the obvious measure of the amount he has sold. Maximum sales in this sense need not require very large physical outputs. To take an extreme case, at a zero price physical volume may be high but dollar sales volume will be zero. There will normally be a well-determined output level which maximizes dollar sales. This level can ordinarily be fixed with the aid of the well-known rule that maximum revenue will be obtained only at an output at which the elasticity of demand is unity, i.e., at which *marginal revenue is zero*. This is the condition which replaces the "marginal cost equals marginal revenue" *profit*-maximizing rule.

But this rule does not take into account the profit constraint. That is, if at the revenue-maximizing output the firm does, in fact, earn enough or more than enough profits to meet the competitive requirements, then it will want to produce the sales-maximizing quantity. But if at this output profits are too low, the firm's output must be changed to a level which, though it fails to maximize sales, does meet the profit requirement.

We see, then, that two types of equilibrium appear to be possible: one

---

requires, say, \$5 in inputs (marginal cost \$5), one unit of x must be worth (approximately) $5K$ dollars. Similarly, if it costs \$9 to produce a unit of y, that unit must be worth $9K$ dollars. Hence we must have

$$MC_x/P_x = 5/5K = 9/9K = MC_y/P_y.$$

in which the profit constraint does not provide an effective barrier to sales maximization, and one in which it does. This is illustrated in Figure 2, which shows the firm's total revenue, cost, and profit curves as indicated.

The profit- and sales-maximizing outputs are, respectively, OQ_p and OQ_s. Now if, for example, the minimum required profit level is OP_1, then the sales-maximizing output OQ_s will provide plenty of profit, and that is the amount it will pay the sales maximizer to produce. His selling price will then be set at Q_sR_s/OQ_s. But if the producer's required profit level is OP_2, output OQ_s, which yields only profit Q_sP_s, clearly will not do. Instead, his output will be reduced to level OQ_c, which is just compatible with his profit constraint.

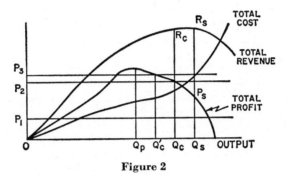

Figure 2

It will be argued presently that in fact only equilibrium points in which the constraint is effective (OQ_c rather than OQ_s) can normally be expected to occur when other decisions of the firm are taken into account.

The profit-maximizing output, OQ_p, will usually be smaller than the one which yields either type of sales maximum, OQ_s or OQ_c. This can be proved with the aid of the standard rule that at the point of maximum profit marginal cost must equal marginal revenue. For marginal cost is normally a positive number (we can't usually produce more of a good for nothing). Hence *marginal revenue will also be positive when profits are at a maximum*, i.e., a further increase in output will increase total sales (revenue). Therefore, if at the point of maximum profit the firm earns more profit than the required minimum,[5] it will pay the sales maximizer to lower his price and increase his physical output.

6. *Advertising*

The decision as to how far to carry advertising expenditure can also be influenced profoundly by the firm's choice of objectives—whether it chooses

[5] If it earns less than the required minimum at this output, there is obviously no output which will satisfy the profit constraint.

to maximize sales or profits. The relevant diagram for the advertising decision is completely elementary. The horizontal axis in Figure 3 represents the magnitude of advertising expenditure and the vertical axis total sales (revenue) and total profit. The drawing of the total revenue curve assumes, as most businessmen seem to do, that increased advertising expenditure

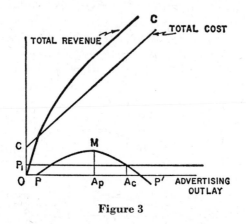

Figure 3

can always increase physical volume, though after a point sharply diminishing returns may be expected to set in.[6] This means that total revenue must vary with advertising expenditure in precisely the same manner. For, unlike a price reduction, a *ceteris paribus* rise in advertising expenditure involves no change in the market value of the items sold. Hence, whereas an increase in physical volume produced by a price reduction may or may not increase dollar sales, depending on whether demand is elastic or inelastic, an increase in volume brought about by added advertising outlay must always be accompanied by a proportionate increase in total revenue.

If all other costs are added to advertising cost, we get the line which depicts the firm's total (production, distribution, and selling) costs as a function of advertising outlay. Subtracting these total costs from the level of dollar sales at each level of advertising outlay, we obtain a total profits curve, PP'.

We see that the profit-maximizing expenditure is OA_p, at which PP' attains its maximum, M. If, on the other hand, the sales maximizer's minimum acceptable profit level is OP_1, the constrained sales-maximizing advertising budget level is OA_c. It is to be noted that there is no possibility

[6] Of course, this is not necessarily true—potential customers may perhaps be repelled by excessive advertising.

Incidentally, it should be noted that a more comprehensive analysis would take into account the interdependence between pricing and advertising decisions. This could be done with the aid of a three-dimensional diagram, with the axes representing price, advertising outlay, and revenue (and costs).

of an unconstrained sales maximum which is analogous to output OQ_s in Figure 2. For, by assumption, unlike a price reduction, increased advertising always increases total revenue. As a result, it will always pay the sales maximizer to increase his advertising outlay until he is stopped by the profit constraint—until profits have been reduced to the minimum acceptable level. This means that sales maximizers will normally advertise no less than, and usually more than, do profit maximizers. For unless the maximum profit level A_pM is no greater than the required minimum OP_1, it will be possible to increase advertising somewhat beyond the profit-maximizing level OA_p without violating the profit constraint. Moreover, this increase will be desired since, by assumption, it will increase physical sales, and with them, dollar sales will rise proportionately.

The interrelationship between output and advertising decisions now permits us to see the reason for the earlier assertion that an unconstrained sales-maximizing output OQ_s (Figure 2) will ordinarily not occur. For if price is set at a level which yields such an output, profits will be above their minimum level and it will pay to increase sales by raising expenditure on advertising, service, or product specifications. This is an immediate implication of the theorem that there will ordinarily be no unconstrained sales-maximizing advertising level. Since its marginal revenue is always positive, advertising can always be used to increase sales up to a point where profits are driven to their minimum level.

7. Choice of Input and Output Combinations

The typical firm is a multi-product enterprise (frequently the number of distinct items runs easily into the hundreds or even thousands) and, of course, it employs a large variety of inputs. This section examines briefly the effect of sales (rather than profit) maximization on the amounts and allocation of the firm's various inputs and outputs.

We obtain the following result which may at first appear rather surprising: Given the level of expenditure, the sales-maximizing firm will produce the same quantity of each output, and market it in the same ways as does the profit maximizer. Similarly, given the level of their total revenues, the two types of firm will optimally use the same inputs in identical quantities and will allocate them in exactly the same way. This result may be somewhat implausible because one is tempted to think of some products or some markets as higher-profit, lower-revenue producers than others and one would expect the profit-maximizing firm to concentrate more on the one variety and the sales-maximizing firm to specialize more in the other. But we shall see in a moment why this is not so.

It is easy to illustrate our result geometrically. In Figure 4 let x and y represent the quantities sold of two different products (or sales of one prod-

uct in two different markets) or the quantities bought of two different inputs. The curves labeled R_1, R_2, etc. are iso revenue curves, i.e., any such

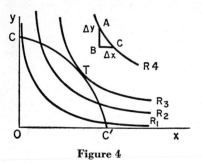

Figure 4

curve is the locus of all combinations
of x and y yielding some fixed amount
of revenue. Similarly, curve CC' represents all combinations of x and y
which can be produced with a fixed outlay (total cost). The standard analysis tells us that the point of tangency,
T, between CC' and one of the R
curves, is the point of profit maximization. But it is also the point of revenue maximization because it lies on
the highest revenue curve attainable with this outlay. This demonstrates
our result.

A little reflection should now render the result quite plausible. The
point is simply that, *given the level of costs*, since profit equals revenue minus
costs, whatever maximizes profits must maximize revenues. Hence, differences between the profit and the sales maximizer's output composition or
resource allocation must be attributed not to a reallocation of a given level
of costs (or revenues) but to the larger outputs (and hence total costs and
revenues) which, we have seen, are to be expected to accompany sales
maximization.[7]

Explained in this way, our theorem is completely trivial. But when
the sales maximizer's profit constraint is taken into account a more interesting but closely related conclusion can be drawn.

We may view the difference between maximum attainable profits and
the minimum profit level expected by the sales maximizer as a fund of
sacrificeable profits which is to be devoted to increasing revenues as much
as possible. Since each output is produced beyond the point of maximum
profits, *its marginal profit yield will be negative.* In other words, each time
it increases the output of some product in order to increase its total revenue the firm must use up more of its fund of sacrificeable profits. This
fund of sacrificeable profits must be allocated among the different outputs,
markets, inputs, etc., in a way which maximizes total dollar sales. The
usual reasoning indicates that this requires the marginal revenue yield of

[7] We conclude that when the operations researcher encounters the problem of allo-
cating optimally some *fixed* quantity of a firm's resources, the values of all other decision
variables being given, his answer will be exactly the same whether he is dealing with a
sales- or a profit-maximizing firm. Such analytically derived equivalences can clearly
permit significant economies in research. In this case, for example, it means that the
operations researcher may be able, when dealing with allocation problems, to avoid
wasting effort in determining the order in which the company ranks sales and profit
objectives.

a dollar of profit sacrificed, e.g., by product x to be the same as that obtained from a dollar of profit lost to any other product, y; i.e., we must have

$$\frac{\text{marginal revenue product of } x}{\text{marginal profit yield of } x} = \frac{\text{marginal revenue product of } y}{\text{marginal profit yield of } y}.$$

This relationship indicates that, even in the sales-maximizing firm, relatively unprofitable inputs and outputs are to be avoided, whatever the level of outlay and total revenue.

8. Pricing and Changes in Fixed Costs and Taxes

Students consistently find one of the most surprising conclusions of the theory of the firm to be the assertion that fixed costs do not matter to pricing and output decisions.[8] This piece of received doctrine is certainly at variance with business practice, where an increase in fixed costs is usually the occasion for serious consideration of a price increase. It is easy to show, however, that this is precisely the sort of response one would expect of the firm which seeks to maximize sales and treats its profits as a constraint rather than as an ultimate objective. For if, in equilibrium, the firm always earns only enough to satisfy its profit constraint, then a rise in overhead cost must mean that earnings fall below the acceptable minimum. Outputs and/or advertising expenditures must then be reduced in order to make up the required profits. The purpose of any such decrease in production is, of course, to permit an increase in selling price.

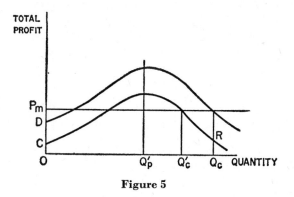

Figure 5

This is very easily restated in terms of Figure 5. An increase in overhead costs means, geometrically, a uniform downward shift in the total profit curve by the amount of the overhead expenses. Hence, if overheads

---

[8] Cf. Chapter 4, Section 9. However, it was shown in Chapter 7, Section 3, that the fixed charges can determine how many and which of the firm's *plants* or other facilities to use in a given operation.

rise by amount CD, output will fall from OQ_c to OQ'_c, for at OQ_c profits will now be Q_cR, which is less than the minimum acceptable level OP_m. By contrast, the change in overhead costs will leave the profit-maximizing output unchanged at OQ'_p. For the added costs reduce the height of the "profit hill" uniformly, but they do not change the location of its peak. This result also has implications for tax policy. It has sometimes been held that there is nothing a company can do to shift any part of the corporation income tax on to the consumer or its employees. The profit-maximizing firm can gain nothing by raising its prices or changing its outputs in response to a change in corporation tax rates, provided that these rates are so structured that the higher the firm's earnings are before taxes the more it gets to keep after taxes. The argument is almost exactly the same as the fixed cost analysis. The corporation tax reduces the height of the total profit curve, but it moves the peak of the curve neither to the right nor to the left.

But, once again, if the firm wishes to maximize sales subject to a profit requirement, rather than maximizing profits, this conclusion loses its validity. When taxes are raised, the firm will be motivated to increase its price (and, therefore, to reduce its output) in order to make up its lost profits. The explanation of the shiftability of this apparently unshiftable tax is simple—the sales-maximizing firm will, in effect, have a reserve of profits which it has not claimed (it has not maximized profit) but which it can fall back on when driven to do so by a rise in tax costs, though it can get back to its old profits only by some sacrifice in its sales.

This concludes the discussion of the implications of a sales-maximization objective. In the present context the analysis is important primarily as an illustration of the effects of alternative objectives on the optimum decisions of the firm. It is designed to indicate the seriousness of the errors which can arise unless care is exercised in investigating the goals of a company before undertaking an analysis of its behavior and its policies. Let us return now to some of the traditional (profit-maximization) analysis of the theory of the firm.

REFERENCES

Baumol, William J., *Business Behavior, Value and Growth*, Macmillan, New York, 1959, Chapters 6–8.

Hall, R. L., and Hitch, C. J., "Price Theory and Business Behavior," *Oxford Economic Papers,* No. 2, 1939.

Lester, Richard A., "Shortcomings of Marginal Analysis for Wage-Employment Problems," *American Economic Review,* Vol. XXXVI, March 1946.

Machlup, Fritz, "Marginal Analysis and Empirical Research," *American Economic Review,* Vol. XXXVI, September 1946. Reprinted (together with further comments by Lester and Machlup) in Richard V. Clemence, *Readings in Economic Analysis*, Vol. 2, Addison-Wesley, Cambridge, Mass., 1950.

Scitovsky, Tibor, "A Note on Profit Maximization and Its Implications," *Review of Economic Studies*, Vol. XI, 1943. Reprinted in American Economic Association, *Readings in Price Theory* (George J. Stigler and Kenneth E. Boulding, eds.), Irwin, Homewood, Ill., 1952.

Simon, Herbert A., "Theories of Decision Making in Economics," *American Economic Review*, Vol. XLIX, June 1959.

————, *Models of Man*, Wiley, New York, 1957, Chapter 14.

CHAPTER ELEVEN

Market structure, pricing, and output

The determination of prices and output levels is very much affected by the competitive structure of the market. Here, "competitive structure" is a phrase which refers to the nature and extent of the monopolistic elements, if any, that are present in any particular market situation. There exists a large body of literature which discusses various types of competitive conditions running the range from perfect competition to pure monopoly, and which seeks to analyze their effects on prices and output. It is convenient to begin our discussion with a listing of some of the market categories which have been investigated.

1. Classification of Market Structures

The economist has classified industries or groups of firms into several categories, depending on the nature of competitive conditions. The following are fairly standard definitions:

1. *Pure competition:* An industry is said to be operating under conditions of pure competition when the following requirements are met:

(a) *Many firms.* There must be a large number of firms in the industry, each of which controls so small a proportion of total output that its addition to or removal from the market has little or no effect on market price;

(b) *Homogeneity of products.* All firms must be known by buyers to produce identical products (cf. the definition of monopolistic competition below);

(c) *Freedom of entry and exit.* Any individual or company with the funds and inclination must be able to enter (start or buy a firm in) the industry without artificial hindrances being erected against him, and any owner of a firm in the industry who can find a buyer may freely sell his company;

(d) *Independent decision-making.* There must be no collusion.

2. *Pure monopoly:* A firm is classed as a pure monopolist if it is the sole producer of some commodity for which there are no close substitutes and if it faces no imminent threat of competitors.

3. *Monopolistic competition with product differentiation:* This is a market arrangement very similar to pure competition except for feature 1(b)—product standardization. Under product differentiation each firm produces goods which are different or which customers believe to be different from competitive products. The "product differences" may in fact not involve characteristics of the products themselves. More attractive wrapping, more convenient location, or special sales features such as better service or free gift coupons may be the basis for customer preferences and loyalties.

4. *Monopsony:* A buyer's monopoly.

5. *Discriminating monopoly:* A firm which charges different prices to different customers for the same commodity.

6. *Bilateral monopoly:* A single purchaser without competitors buying from a monopolist seller.

7. *Duopoly:* A two-firm industry. This is a special case of

8. *Oligopoly:* An industry with a small number of large firms producing the bulk of its output.

Pure monopolies have always been rare if they ever existed at all. Pure competition also is rare although there exist a number of commodities which, for many purposes, provide a good approximation: grains and the stock market are two outstanding examples.

Illustrations of the other market forms are readily found. For the defense industries the Government is a monopsonistic buyer, and wage negotiation between unions and industry representatives sometimes closely resembles bilateral monopoly. Doctors are well-known price discriminators.

However, the bulk of our enterprises seems to fall into the two remaining classifications, monopolistic competition and oligopoly. Competing neighborhood retailers of all sorts are typically monopolistic competitors, each with his corps of more or less loyal customers and locational and personality differences which make his products and services at least somewhat different from those of his competitors. The lion's share of manufacturing is in the hands of oligopoly firms—steel, autos, tobacco—almost any present-day large industry, and it is in these industries that most privately sponsored operations research work occurs.

Let us now discuss the price and output determination process in some of these market situations. The tools which have been described in earlier chapters will permit us to deal with these cases fairly briefly.

2. The Profit-Maximizing Competitive Firm

The bulk of the analytic literature on price-output determination has traditionally been devoted to the case of pure competition. The reason is at least partly that such a case is more readily amenable to analysis so that it is possible to develop a far richer theoretical structure for this situation than for other market firms.

First, let us examine some immediate consequences of the definition of pure competition. Under pure competition the demand curve of the firm is always horizontal (perfectly elastic). This follows from the first feature of the definition of pure competition—the relative insignificance of each firm so that no one of them can affect price noticeably. The single wheat farmer can do nothing about the day's price in Chicago. If he raises the price of his wheat above the going price, he will be unable to sell anything, whereas he can gain nothing by cutting his price below the market price for at the prevailing price he can sell any amount he can be expected to produce. For him, then, there is no price decision to be made—the price figure is simply handed to him.

In the short run the firm may, of course, end up making either profit or loss. But in the long run the free entry and exit feature of pure competition assures us that these profits or losses will disappear altogether! If the industry is profitable, new firms will be induced to enter it and compete with the already established concerns. The resulting increase in demand for inputs may bid up their prices and hence raise costs. Certainly the increased product supply can be expected to reduce its market price. Thus, profits will tend to be squeezed down toward zero or at least until no additional firms find it worth moving in.

Similarly, if there is initially a net loss to firms in the industry, the exit of concerns will raise profits and ultimately it will eliminate the loss.

Of course, this conclusion holds only if there are no autonomous changes in demands or costs during the period of adjustment. A foreign crop failure or the invention of more efficient equipment may suddenly restore high profits to wheat farming and so offset the influence of new entrants. Since, to some extent, such changes are always taking place, the adjustment toward zero profits will always be imperfect. However, the forces working in that direction will nevertheless be there.

Let us now examine in somewhat greater detail the nature of this competitive equilibrium towards which the market tends to adjust. Such a situation is depicted in Figures 1a and 1b. In these diagrams the horizontal line DD' is the firm's demand curve. The curve is horizontal because, as already stated, no change in the firm's output is a sufficiently significant contribution to total market supply to affect the price.

So long as there is no price discrimination, any firm's demand curve will also be its average revenue curve. The reason is that if all units of a commodity are sold at the same price, the revenue brought in by an average unit must be its price. Hence DD' is also the marginal revenue curve. Also, we know that where an average curve is neither rising nor falling it will coincide with the corresponding marginal curve. Here, since the average revenue curve is horizontal throughout its length, it must everywhere coincide with the marginal revenue curve (Chapter 3, Section 5).

Figure 1a represents the situation of a competitive profit-maximizing firm in short-run equilibrium. Its profit-maximizing output is OQ_p where its marginal cost curve, CMC, intersects the marginal revenue (demand) curve DD'.[1] At that point it is earning a profit, for on each unit it produces it obtains VW (= unit revenue minus unit cost). Thus its total profit (= unit profit multiplied by the number of units produced) is represented by area $UVWD$.

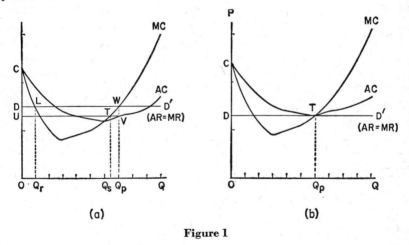

(a)   (b)

Figure 1

Figure 1b represents a long-run equilibrium situation. Here the average cost curve must be tangent to the demand curve, DD'. The reason is that if the unit costs were everywhere higher than price, every output would be unprofitable, and firms would leave the industry, thus shifting the curves toward tangency by raising DD' (price) and, possibly, lowering the cost

[1] Why is OQ_r not an equilibrium output in view of the fact that there, also, we have marginal cost = marginal revenue?

curves as well. Similarly, if the average cost curve were to intersect the demand curve, there would be some outputs at which profits could be earned and an influx of new firms would soon shift the cost and revenue curves sufficiently to wipe out these profits. Only when there is tangency will the "no-profit, no-loss" position of long-run equilibrium be the best the firm can do, and no firms will be tempted to enter or leave the field if this is the typical situation of all firms in the area.

Since the demand curve is horizontal, the point of tangency, T, of the average cost curve with the demand curve must occur at an output at which the average cost curve is also horizontal, i.e., it will be at an output where unit costs are at a minimum. For that reason the marginal cost curve will also intersect the average cost curve at that point. In sum, at the point of equilibrium we have the impressive set of equalities, marginal cost equals marginal revenue equals average cost equals average revenue equals price (Figure 1b).

It is to be noted that in equilibrium every firm in the industry must have the same costs, for the product price will be the same for all such companies, and both marginal and average costs will equal price for all firms. This may appear to smack of the miraculous. Firms with dissimilar resources, production techniques, and operating procedures all end up with the same costs. But this is another work of the competitive mechanism. More efficient firms must have lower costs because some of their resources are better—items such as more convenient location, purer raw materials, or more skilled managers must account for the difference. But competition guarantees that if manager A can run a firm at $10,000 more cheaply per year than can B, then A's salary will tend to be bid up until it is $10,000 per annum higher than B's. For if A's firm pays him only $8000 more, it will be in B's firm's interests to try to bid A away with an offer of $9000 and it will pay A's firm to hold him with a $9500 counteroffer, etc. (Of course, if A is the owner of the firm he will simply gather these wages of his special skills in the form of profit in the noneconomist's sense of the word.) In this way all cost savings will tend to be paid out to the more efficient inputs that make them possible. Hence, since we must include these bonus payments, the costs of the more efficient firms will tend to be driven toward equality with those of the less efficient.

One more point needs to be made here—the zero-profit rule may seem implausible at first glance. Why should anyone stay in business if it yields him no returns? But the term "profits" is used here in a rather strict sense. A small businessman may earn a comfortable living. But if his earnings are no more than he could get by spending the same amount of time working for someone else plus the return he could get by investing his money elsewhere, the economist states that he is receiving just the wages for his labor and interest on his capital. Only if he receives any more than this sum is the excess counted as profit. It is surely true that many a small businessman has shown himself willing to work for even negative profits when the term is interpreted in this sense.

3. Equilibrium in the Competitive Industry

The standard and well-known analysis of pricing and output determination in the competitive *industry* (as contrasted with the single firm) involves the drawing of an industry supply curve and an industry demand curve with price and output determined by the intersection of the two curves.

The supply curve can be given an interpretation in terms of costs. In fact, in the long run it tends to approximate a curve of average costs for the industry. This, again, is a consequence of the free-entry-and-exit assumption and its zero-profit result. If the industry were to supply its commodity at a price which exceeded its average cost, some firms would necessarily be making a profit. We have seen how the entry of new firms could make short work of that profit.

One must examine the stability of this industry equilibrium in order to see whether this equilibrium point can be expected to be of direct relevance to any real market situations, i.e., whether there is any mechanism which pulls competitive prices and outputs into line with their equilibrium levels. It is not appropriate here to go into a full dynamic analysis of this stability question, but we will at least examine the outlines of the mechanism which can work in the direction of stability. Figure 2a shows the usual supply-

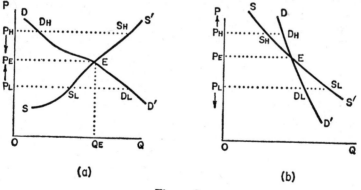

(a)   (b)

Figure 2

demand diagram for the competitive industry. The equilibrium occurs at the point of intersection, E, of the two curves, and P_E and Q_E constitute the equilibrium industry price-quantity combination.

Suppose now that, for some reason, the market price falls below the equilibrium price, say to P_L. In this case the quantity demanded will exceed the quantity supplied by quantity $D_L - S_L$, and we may expect price to be pushed back up toward the equilibrium price. In the same way, a price like P_H, which is above the equilibrium level, will be pushed back down. In this situation, then, the equilibrium at least gives an appearance of stability which dynamic analysis can rationalize.

But it does not follow that the supply-demand equilibrium point will always be stable. On the contrary, it is easy to find a case where the machinery works in the wrong direction. Figure 2b depicts such a situation. Here, when the price falls to P_L, below the equilibrium price, supply will exceed demand (by quantity $S_L - D_L$). Hence price will be driven down even further. Similarly, we have instability on the upward side. Doubtless such cases are rare in practice, but the illustration at least shows that we must be careful in assuming that our models are always well behaved.

The diagram can be used to study problems such as the effects of taxation on competitive pricing. A standard analysis seeks to determine what portion of a tax on manufactured goods will be paid by the producer and how much of it will be passed on to consumers in the form of higher prices. This is referred to as the problem of the *shifting* and *incidence* of taxation.

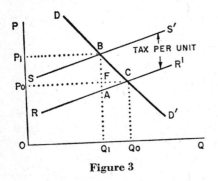

Figure 3

Figure 3 is another supply-demand diagram. The original supply curve is represented as RR'. Since, in the long run, this can be interpreted as an average cost curve, the addition of a fixed per-unit tax which raises businessmen's outpayments correspondingly, results in a uniform upward shift of the cost curve to SS'. We see at once that, while the tax per unit is represented by length AB, the resulting increase in price will be only FB. In other words, part of the tax burden (FB) will be shifted from the manufacturer to the consumer. But the incidence of the remainder, AF, will be on the producer.

By experimenting with the shapes of the diagram, the reader can verify the following results:

1. The smaller the slope of the demand curve, the greater will be the proportion of the tax paid by the supplier.
2. The smaller the slope of the supply curve, the greater will be the proportion of the tax which is shifted to the consumer.

These rules have a ready intuitive justification. For example, a steep demand means that buyers are willing to continue to purchase pretty much the same quantity almost no matter what the price. It is natural to expect that such anxious purchasers will end up paying the bulk of the tax.

4. Supply Curves; Some Comments

A supply curve is, of course, defined as a graph which shows what quantities of a commodity will be offered for sale at different prices—i.e., it summarizes the seller's quantity reaction to various prices. We have just seen that the long-run supply curve for the industry will coincide with its average cost curve.

The competitive firm, too, will have a supply curve, and it will also be related to costs, but in a quite different manner. In fact, the profit-maximizing *firm's* supply curve will coincide with (a portion of) its *marginal* cost curve. This proposition can readily be demonstrated with the aid of Figure 1a. As we have seen, our firm will find it profitable to produce up to a point where price (marginal revenue) equals marginal cost. Thus, at price OD, the firm's supply will be OQ_p, and, similarly, at price OU it will supply quantity OQ_s. Both of these price-quantity supplied combinations are represented by points (W and T) on the marginal cost curve, CMC. Since a similar observation holds for any other price at which the firm is willing to produce, our result follows—the firm's supply curve is the same as its marginal cost curve.[2]

The supply curve is, strictly speaking, a concept which is usually relevant only for the case of pure (or perfect) competition, and it will therefore not be encountered in later sections of this chapter. The reason for this lies in its definition—the supply curve is designed to answer questions of the form, "How much will firm A supply if it encounters a price which is fixed at P dollars?" But such a question is relevant just for the behavior of firms that actually deal with prices over whose determination they exercise no influence. Only in two situations may we expect firms to encounter such preset prices—if there is a central authority who sets prices by fiat, and in conditions of pure competition where the price is set by an impersonal market mechanism outside the control of any buyer or seller. In most other circumstances the firm will be able to set its own price, so the information given by the supply curve will be inapplicable to the operations of such a company.

[2] Strictly speaking, the supply curve includes only the rising segment of the firm's marginal cost curve. At price OD the firm will produce OQ_p and not OQ_r as has already been noted in footnote 1, above. Therefore, a point such as L, on the descending portion of the marginal cost curve, will form no part of the supply curve.

5. Pure Monopoly

In the case of pure monopoly the firm and the industry coincide by definition—the monopoly *is* the industry. The output of the monopolistic *firm* must therefore be compared with that of the *industry* under pure competition. This comparison can be made with the help of a diagram which combines the supply-demand analysis of the competitive industry with the marginal apparatus of the theory of the firm. This is done in Figure 4.

Here *DD'* and *SS'* are the competitive industry supply and demand curves. Suppose, now, that a monopolist takes over the competitive industry, and that in the process there occurs no change in the basic cost and demand conditions. The demand curve now becomes the monopolist's average revenue curve. Moreover, as we have seen, the long-run supply curve tends to approximate the average cost curve.

We can, therefore, construct the monopolist's marginal cost and marginal revenue curves, *SMC* and *DMR*, from this information by the methods of Chapter 3, Section 5. The monopolist's profit optimum output will, then, be OQ_M, which is clearly smaller than the competitive output OQ_C. So long as the slope of the supply curve is positive, or, if it is negative, so long as it is less steep than the demand curve, this will always be the case. For if the average cost curve cuts the average revenue curve from below, all outputs, such as OQ_L, above the competitive zero-profit point, OQ_C, will cause the firm to lose money, since average cost, Q_LC, will there exceed price, Q_LP. Only to the left of the competitive equilibrium point will there be any profits.

This is the standard well-publicized result that the monopolist tends to restrict his output. But this result must be treated with caution for two reasons.

1. It is likely that cost and demand conditions will change when a monopoly takes over a competitive industry. By centralizing purchasing and, perhaps, having one man replace 100 independent buyers, by effecting economies of large scale through the combining of plants, inventories, etc., the monopolist may be able to reduce his costs. On the other hand, the larger monopolistic firm may require a more cumbersome, more costly administrative machinery. In addition, monopolistic advertising may increase the demand for the monopolist's products. It follows that the simple comparison of monopolistic and competitive outputs of Figure 4 cannot be relied on.

2. Even if the competitive industry does produce the larger output, it is by no means obvious that this is always desirable from the point of view of consumers or anyone else. In a period of full employment an increase in output in one industry takes away resources from elsewhere in the

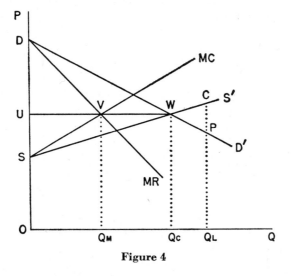

Figure 4

economy and forces a reduction in output and possibly a price rise there (the "guns vs. butter" problem). The basic point is that, under full employment, the determination of the outputs of the different industries is a matter of the *allocation* of resources. In popular discussions one tends to think that the larger the output of any industry, the better off is society, but it is easy to see that this can result in a misallocation of resources, just as, in the firm, a lopsided investment policy biased excessively toward one department may ease that department's operations but is hardly likely to be optimal from the point of view of the business as a whole.

6. Monopolistic Competition (Product Differentiation)[3]

The analysis of monopolistic competition is ordinarily confined to the individual firm and does not deal directly with the industry. In fact, it may be almost impossible to define an industry in such a situation. Differentiation of product means that no two firms put out the same item. Some products may, perhaps, be easily recognized as the same sort of item, but as one gets to less and less perfect substitute products one industry will tend to shade off into another. Hence, rather than well-defined industries, one tends to get something more like a continuum of products, although this assertion probably overstates the situation in practice.

Under monopolistic competition the demand curve for the product of

---

[3] This section is based on the work of E. H. Chamberlin. See *The Theory of Monopolistic Competition*, 7th ed., Harvard University Press, Cambridge, Mass., 1956, Chapters IV and V.

the firm may be expected to have a negative slope, even though the firm is as small as one operating under conditions of pure competition. For customers will have different degrees of loyalty to the firms from whom they make their purchases. A small reduction in one firm's price may only attract its competitors' most mercurial customers. But, as larger and larger price reductions are instituted, it may acquire more and more customers from its rivals by drawing on customers who are less anxious to switch.

The equilibrium of the firm involves the usual conditions—marginal cost equal to marginal revenue. Again, in the short run, the firms may or may not earn a profit. But under monopolistic competition one can also expect something like freedom of entry. Since firms are small, relatively little capital is required to set up business and turn out a product not quite the same as but still very like those already on the market.

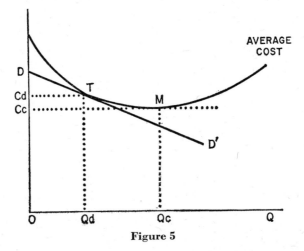

Figure 5

The result is that, as under pure competition, both profits and losses will tend to be eliminated in the long run. The average cost curve will be driven toward tangency with the demand curve, and we will end up with a situation like that depicted in Figure 5. The equilibrium point, T, will be the point of tangency between the average cost curve and the negatively sloping demand curve, DD'. For at any other output, unit costs will be larger than price and so such an output will involve a loss to the firm.[4]

---

[4] It follows that, since OQ_d is the maximum profit output, marginal cost must there equal marginal revenue. This also follows from the standard relationship

$$M = A + Q(dA/dQ)$$

where M and A represent marginal x and average x respectively (see footnote 3 of Chapter 3). This result shows that if two average curves (in this case average *cost* and *revenue*) are tangent, so that $A_1 = A_2$, $Q_1 = Q_2$, and $dA_1/dQ_1 = dA_2/dQ_2$, we must have $M_1 = M_2$.

The average cost curve is ordinarily taken to have the "U" shape indicated in the diagram on the argument that both very small and very large outputs are difficult and expensive to produce. Even economies of large scale apply only up to a point, beyond which administrative costs and diminishing returns, because of the presence of scarce (bottleneck) inputs, are generally expected to raise the unit costs of production.

If this is so, the point of tangency T between the U-shaped average cost curve and the negatively sloping demand curve must take place somewhere to the left of the minimum average cost point, M. This is in direct contrast with the equilibrium of the competitive firm whose long-run position is M (cf. Figure 1b, above). Hence, the output of the firm under monopolistic competition must be smaller, and its unit cost and price higher than it would be under pure competition.

In this case it can be argued that there is, from the point of view of the economy as a whole, something to be said for the superiority of the competitive arrangement. What may be called for is greater standardization of business firms. The diagram (Figure 5) shows that, by becoming larger, firms can reduce their unit costs from what they are at point T. That means that if a number of firms are merged, the total output may be kept the same (instead of 12 firms producing 500 units each we can, e.g., reduce the number of firms to 3, each producing 2000 units, and so keep the total output at 6000). But each of the firms will, as a result of the merger, have lower average costs. It follows by elementary arithmetic that if the same output is produced at lower unit costs there must be a net over-all saving to the community (if unit costs are reduced from $8 to $6, the total cost to the firms producing the 6000 total product, in our example, will be reduced from $48,000 to $36,000—a net gain to the community of $12,000 with no reduction in output!).

Hence, only if merger of these firms results in an important reduction in the variety of products available to the consumer, so that a real decrease in consumer choice opportunities occurs, is there any reason for society to "prefer" the product differentiation equilibrium point, T.

7. Monopsony

Under monopsony, a monopoly on the buyer's side, it is in the interest of the buyer to obtain his purchases (usually inputs) at as low a cost as possible, just as the monopolist seeks to obtain as large a return as possible. Thus the monopsonistic firm's output level will be chosen with an eye on the consequences for input prices of a change in its demand for inputs.

The optimizing buyer's demand curve is always a marginal curve. The business firm facing an input whose price is fixed will (Chapter 14, Section 5) purchase inputs up to the point where the input's marginal revenue product (the increase in revenue made possible by the purchase of an additional input unit) is equal to its price. The firm's input demand curve is, therefore, a curve of marginal revenue product, i.e., for every possible quantity of input purchase it indicates the value of its marginal revenue product. By exactly the same argument it can be shown that the optimizing consumer's demand curve must be a curve of marginal utility (with utility measured in money terms). That is, at any product quantity it shows the maximum money amount which the consumer would be willing to give up for an additional unit of the product.

From the point of view of the buyer, however, the *supply* curve of an input may be considered an average rather than a marginal curve. That is, it shows for every level of input purchase the price he will have to pay for each unit of this input—i.e., it gives the average cost to him of that input.

The profit-maximizing monopsonistic firm's equilibrium requires the usual marginal-cost-equals-marginal-revenue condition. This means that the monopsonist's input purchase must be at a level at which the marginal revenue product of the input is equal to its *marginal* cost to the firm. A similar argument would apply to monopsonistic purchasers of finished products (consumers).

Hence the monopsonistic equilibrium point will be the intersection of his demand curve with the curve *marginal* to the supply curve of the input (the average input cost curve). The reader may readily draw the diagram which represents the situation. It may be observed that if the input supply curve has a positive slope, the marginal input cost curve will lie above it (when an average curve is rising the marginal curve will always lie above it). Therefore, with a negatively sloping demand curve, the point of intersection of demand and marginal cost curves will lie to the left of the demand-supply curve intersection. In other words, the monopsonistic level of input purchases will tend to be smaller than those of a competitive industry or of a group of ordinary consumers.

8. Remarks on Discriminating Monopoly

The basic condition which must be met before price discrimination, that is, the sale of different units of a product at different prices, can be practiced successfully is that the market for the sel er's product be split off into separate sections and that it be difficult to transfer the seller's product from sector to sector. For example, the doctor can charge different prices to different patients because it is ordinarily impossible for a low-fee patient to resell his treatment to someone who pays more for the same services. An exporting firm can charge less abroad than the domestic price of his product because the costs of reimporting the product can be prohibitive or because of other obstacles to reimportation.

We may also note several other properties of the discriminating monopoly case:

1. If he sets his prices properly, the discriminating monopolist can always expect to earn at least as much as does an ordinary monopolist. For, in setting his prices independently in his different markets, he will always have the option of keeping the prices in several of his markets the same, if that is profitable. In other words, the discriminating monopolist can match every opportunity which is open to the ordinary monopolist and he has some others besides.

2. The basic rule of profit maximization in discriminating monopoly is that marginal revenue must be the same in all markets to which the firm sells. For if its marginal revenue is greater in market A than in B, it can increase its profits by decreasing the amount shipped to B and transferring it to A. Only when this transfer process raises the price in market B and lowers it in A to a point where marginal revenues in the two markets are equal will the firm have arrived at an optimal allocation of its goods between the two markets. The condition that marginal revenue must everywhere be the same thus determines the discriminator's shipments to all his markets, and his total output is determined by setting the marginal revenue equal to marginal cost.[5]

[5] The computation of prices and quantities involves the determination of the marginal revenue functions for each of the firm's n markets:

$$MR_1 = \phi_1(Q_1), \ldots, MR_n = \phi_n(Q_n)$$

where MR_1 and Q_1 are the firm's marginal revenue and shipments to market 1, etc. From these, the inverse functions (quantity demanded as a function of marginal revenue) must, in principle, be computed:

$$Q_1 = \phi_1^{-1}(MR_1), \ldots, Q_n = \phi_n^{-1}(MR_n).$$

The monopolist's total demand-marginal revenue relationship is then obtained by setting $MR_1 = \ldots = MR_n = MR$ (marginal revenue equal in all markets) and summing the demands in his various markets to yield

$$\sum_{i=1}^{n} Q_i \equiv Q = \sum_{i=1}^{n} \phi_i^{-1}(MR) \equiv \phi^{-1}(MR)$$

where Q is the firm's total output. This equation, together with the marginal cost equation $MC = \psi(Q)$ and the profit-maximization condition $MC = MR$, constitutes a set of simultaneous relationships which can be solved for the profit-maximizing values of Q, MR, and MC, and substitution of this MR value into each of the equations

$$Q_i = \phi_i^{-1}(MR)$$

gives us the optimal shipments to each of the monopolist's markets. (Footnote continued on next page).

9. Bilateral Monopoly

In this analysis it is convenient to extend the concept of the indifference curve and, in the present context, to be able to interpret it either as a curve of constant utility (as in the usual theory of the consumer) or as a curve of constant profitability so that any two points on such a curve are equally profitable. We deal here with the case of two people who are exchanging two commodities. If one of the items exchanged is money, one of the bilateral monopolists (the money payer) may be identified as the buyer and the other as the seller. Suppose that the buyer is an input purchaser and that the seller is an input supplier. We may draw an indifference map between money and X (the quantity of the input sold) for each of these persons. In Figure 6a we have such an indifference map for the input purchaser. Here it is assumed that the buyer starts off with $500 in money. In interpreting the indifference map it should be noted that we read *down* from this figure to determine the amount the buyer pays out.

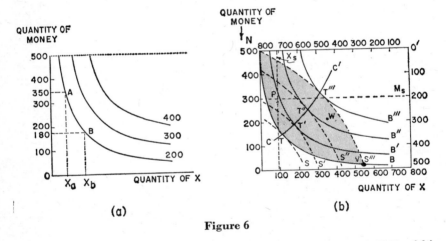

Figure 6

For example, at point A he ends up with X_a units of X and $350 of his original supply of money left. That means he must have spent the difference, $150, for the X_a units of A.

The optimum prices also follow from this calculation, for given the demand (average revenue) curve for the product in each market

$$Q_i = D_i(P_i)(i = 1, \ldots, n)$$

one may substitute in the optimal value of Q_i and solve for the value of P_i (the price) at which that quantity can be sold in market i. Of course these *average* revenue equations can be determined from the marginal revenue equations, $MR_i = \phi_i(Q_i)$.

Each such indifference curve is a locus of money-input purchase combinations which are equally profitable. All points on the lower curve (such as B) yield $200 in profit. Those on the next curve yield $300, etc.

A similar diagram can be drawn to represent the circumstances of the supplier, only in his case it will be the quantity of X which is measured from his maximum supply capacity level downward, and any one of his profit indifference curves must be the locus of all combinations of quantity supplied and revenue which yield him a fixed level of profit (after deducting the cost of production of that quantity of output from his total revenue at that point).

The two indifference maps can now be combined in an ingenious rectangular diagram[6] (Figure 6b). One of the indifference maps is turned upside down and the ends of the axes joined. Thus the buyer's total money supply determines the length of the vertical axis, and the fixed input production capacity gives the length of the horizontal axis. Now, any point in the diagram may be interpreted as a trade. That is, it shows simultaneously where both of the bilateral monopolists will end up after an exchange. For example, point P represents a trade in which the buyer ends up with 100 units of input and 300 units of money, while the seller ends up with the remainder—$200 (point M_s on the right-hand axis) and 700 units of X in the form of unused production capacity, point X_s on the top axis. (Note that the seller's holdings are read downward and to the left from the upper right-hand corner, O', which is the origin of his upside-down indifference curve.) Any point thus automatically indicates the ending position of *both* buyer and seller. Because of the fixed total of $500 in money, whatever does not remain in the hands of the buyer must go to the seller and the same applies to X (or, rather, capacity to supply X).

The solid indifference curves, B, are the buyer's indifference curves whereas the broken S curves are those of the seller.

Consider now the curve CC' which is the locus of all points of tangency (such as T) between the buyer's and seller's indifference curves. CC' is called the *contract curve*. It possesses two relevant features:

1. For every trade point off the contract curve, there exist trade points on the contract curve which are mutually advantageous to buyer and seller. For example, consider point V which is off the contract curve. Since it is not a point of tangency, the seller's and buyer's indifference curves S and B which go through that point must intersect. Hence there

---

[6] This device, as well as the concept of the contract curve, described below, was invented by Edgeworth. See F. Y. Edgeworth, *Mathematical Psychics*, Kegan Paul, London, 1881, pp. 17ff. For a derivation of the equation of the contract curve see Chapter 13, footnote 2, below.

will be a region between the two curves (shaded area) through which there passes higher profit indifference for both seller and buyer (e.g., indifference curve B' yields more profit to the buyer than does B, and S is more profitable to the seller than S'). We conclude that all points on the arc of the contract curve TT'' which lies in the shaded region will be preferred to point V by both buyer and seller.

2. Any move along the contract curve must be disadvantageous to *one* of the participants. Any move downward and to the left must be disadvantageous to the buyer (it gets him to a lower indifference curve), and any move in the opposite direction must adversely affect the seller, for an analogous reason.

It has therefore been argued that the actual trading point must end up somewhere along the contract curve, CC', for anywhere else it will be mutually advantageous to buyer and seller to renegotiate their deal, and only at a point on the contract curve will no such renegotiation be profitable to both.

The range of possible trading points can be narrowed down somewhat further. The point in the upper left-hand corner, N, represents the situation in which no exchange is made. The buyer holds on to his money and gets no X. Through this point there pass one of the buyer's and one of the seller's indifference curves (B and S'''). Neither buyer nor seller will be willing to accept any trade that leaves him on a lower profit indifference curve. For he can always refuse any such inferior proposition and stay at his "no deal" point, N. This means that all possible trading points must lie in the region between the indifference curves through N, the shaded region in the diagram. For that reason, the only possible points on the contract curve are those on arc TT'''.

Beyond this it is difficult to narrow down any further the possible locations of the final equilibrium point. Several suggestions have been offered—for example, the joint maximum point (the point which maximizes the sum of the profits of the buyer and seller together). However, it is difficult to see why one may expect that the bargainers should always be expected to end up at any one such point. For that reason, many economists have concluded that the bilateral monopoly problem is "indeterminate."

In fact, some have even suggested that the trade may well end up somewhere *off* the contract curve. If, for example, the trade happens to fall at point W, and the buyer feels that his bargaining position is so weak that a reopening of negotiation would move the trading point to somewhere along TT', he may prefer just to let sleeping dogs lie.

Similar indeterminacy problems will occur in the discussion of oligopoly which follows, and some degree of explanation will be offered in the course of the discussion.

10. Oligopolistic Interdependence

The oligopoly situation (including in this term the two-firm duopoly case) has one feature on which most of the economist's attention has been centered. This is the interdependence in the decision-making of the various firms, an interdependence which is recognized by all of them. In an industry which consists largely of a small number of sizable companies, if one of them opens a tremendous advertising campaign or designs a new model of his product which sweeps the market, he can be fairly sure that this will lead to countermoves on the part of his competitors. Every businessman in such a situation knows that at least some of his rivals' decisions depend on his own behavior, and he must take this fact into account in his own decision-making.

The reason for this interdependence in decision-making is, of course, that a major policy change on the part of one firm is likely to have obvious and immediate effects on the other companies which comprise the industry. As a result, the oligopolist has developed an armory of aggressive and defensive marketing weapons. For example, it is only under oligopoly that advertising comes fully into its own. Under pure competition no one has *any* motive to advertise because any producer can sell all of his product at the going price without incurring any advertising outlay. A monopolist will find some advertising to be profitable, perhaps when he is introducing a totally new commodity or where there exists a considerable body of potential consumers who have never tried this type of ware. But under oligopoly, advertising can become a life-and-death matter where a firm which fails to keep up with the advertising budget of its competitors may find its customers drifting off to rival products.

As a result, the oligopolistic businessman is sometimes rather surprised when the presence of competitive conditions in his industry is questioned. To him competition consists not in the quiescent stalemate of perfect competition where there is no battle because there is never anyone strong enough to disturb the peace. Rather, to him, true competition consists of the life of constant struggle, rival against rival, which one can only find under oligopoly (or, on a smaller scale, under conditions of monopolistic competition).

Oligopolistic interdependence has another consequence which is of more importance for the economic literature than for the operation of the economy. This feature of the situation has made the formulation of a systematic analysis of oligopoly very difficult. Under the circumstances a very wide variety of behavior patterns becomes possible. Rivals may decide to get together and cooperate in the pursuit of their objectives, at least so far as the law allows, or, at the other extreme, they may try to fight each other to the death. Even if they enter into an agreement[7] it may last or it may break down. And the agreements may follow a wide variety of patterns.

As a result, the literature of oligopoly theory is full of different models, many of which describe, at most, one particular arrangement—a price-leadership agreement or some particular method of using freight charges as a means for apportioning out market territories.

An even more serious analytical difficulty arises directly out of management's need to take account of its competitors' reaction patterns. When a businessman wonders about his competitors' likely response to some move which he is considering, he must recognize that his competitor, too, is likely to take this interdependence phenomenon into account. The firms' attempts to outguess one another is then likely to lead to an interplay of anticipated strategies and counterstrategies which is tangled beyond hope of direct analysis. For in this way management is only led to advance along an infinite sequence of compounded hypotheses: "If I make move A, he may consider making countermove B, but he may realize that I might then respond by making move C, in which case . . . ," and so on *ad infinitum.*

There are several ways out of this state of confusion, which is as unsatisfactory to the economic analyst as it is to the businessman who is saddled with its problems. Each of these approaches has something to be said for it.

1. *Ignoring interdependence.* The firm may simply ignore the entire matter, on the assumption that its competitor will also do so. There is some reason to believe that this is, in fact, what many firms do in their more routine day-to-day decision-making. They ignore the interdependence of the returns to the various firms in the industry because, as a practical matter, these complex effects of minor policy changes are not worth the effort required to take them into account. Since interdependence disappears from decision-making with such an approach, the analysis of this case is simply the standard analysis of the theory of the firm which was discussed in the preceding chapter. However, in the analysis of a really major decision—when an automobile manufacturer considers introducing a radical new design or a cigarette manufacturer is about to embark on a major advertising campaign—the decision-maker knows he cannot afford to dodge the issue in this way, and the complex problems of interdependence must re-enter the discussion.

2. *Predicting competitors' countermoves.* A second way of dealing with the problem is for a firm to attempt to anticipate the nature of competi-

---

[7] In any event, oligopolistic collusion will always be somewhat limited by legal restrictions and, in fact, by definition, for where all firms in an industry take all of their decisions jointly, they are in essence amalgamated into a monopoly.

tive reactions on the basis of guesswork or past experience. For example, the decision-maker may know that his competitors have usually matched his price changes within a few days or he may simply guess that they are likely to do so. In such a case, it is possible to take this definite reaction pattern into account and decide on a strategy which is optimal in terms of this assumption. The remainder of this chapter describes models which employ this second approach to the analysis of the interdependence problem. One difficulty which arises here, as we shall see, is that if two competitors both proceed on this sort of optimality calculation, each is likely to find that his prediction about the other was incorrect, *because the optimality calculation will lead him to act in a manner which was not predicted.*

3. *Preparing against optimal moves by competitors.* A third approach to the analysis of the interdependence problem in business decision-making is that of the theory of games. Here the businessman does not guess at his opponent's reaction pattern. Rather, he, in effect, calculates the optimal moves of the opposition—his rival's best possible strategies—and prepares his own defenses and countermeasures accordingly. Discussion of this third alternative has been postponed until Chapter 18.

11. Stability of Oligopoly Arrangements: Kinked Demand Curves[8]

Let us now examine several oligopoly models which have attracted considerable attention. First let us consider one which is *not* designed to deal with oligopolistic price and output determination. Rather, it seeks to explain why, once a price-quantity combination has been decided upon, it will not readily change.

The source of the problem is the fact that oligopolistic arrangements are notoriously undependable. For example, the history of price agreements contains case after case where "chiselers" seem to have found it advantageous to undercut the price which was agreed upon in order to grab off a larger share of the market. Yet, despite this phenomenon, prices in many oligopolistic industries appear to have exhibited a remarkable degree of stability, particularly in their resistance to change in the downward direction. The model which will now be described is one possible explanation of the "stickiness" of oligopoly prices.

Consider the effect on quantity demanded of a reduction in the price of

---

[8] The analysis of this section is based on the work of Sweezy, Hall, and Hitch. See Paul M. Sweezy, "Demand Under Conditions of Oligopoly," *Journal of Political Economy*, Vol. XLVII, August 1939, reprinted in American Economic Association, *Readings in Price Theory* (George J. Stigler and Kenneth E. Boulding, eds.); Irwin, Homewood, Ill., 1952, and R. L. Hall and C. J. Hitch, "Price Theory and Business Behavior," *Oxford Economic Papers*, No. 2, May 1939.

a commodity. This is, as usual, shown by the demand curve for the product. Suppose, first, that the reduction in the price which is charged by our firm is matched by other competing concerns. In that case the company may expect to increase its sales slightly, but since it is not likely to get any customers away from its rivals in these circumstances, no large addition to its sales is to be anticipated. Its demand curve (*DD'* in Figure 7) will be relatively inelastic.

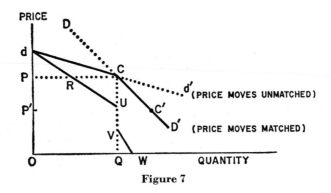

Figure 7

Now suppose, on the other hand, that our company is the only one to reduce its price. In that case a much larger increase in its demand is to be expected. Thus, where no one else follows its price moves, the firm is likely to have a relatively elastic demand curve like *dd'*.

Let point *C* represent the firm's current price-quantity combination. It has been argued that the large oligopolistic firm is likely to anticipate the following competitive reaction pattern to a price change:

1. *Price reductions:* If our company reduces its price, competitors will feel the drain on their customers quickly and so they will be forced to match this price cut. In other words, for downward price movements from point *C*, the relevant portion of the firm's demand curve will be segment *CD'* of the steeper demand curve *DD'*.

2. *Price increases:* If the company raises its price, it may expect that its happy competitors will welcome the new customers which they gain from the price-raising firm as a result, and they will have no motivation to match the price rise. Hence, for price rises the relevant part of the demand curve will be elastic segment *dC*.

In sum, given this view of competitive reaction patterns the company's demand curve will be the composite curve *dCD'*, characterized by a kink (a sharp corner) at the point *C* which represents the current price-output combination.

It is now easy to see that a company with such a competitive response pattern will be extremely reluctant to change its price. For a fall in its price will yield no large increase in sales, while a price increase will result in a substantial cut in business, and neither of these is a very attractive prospect.

The reader should also be able to show with the aid of the geometric technique of Chapter 3, Section 5, that the marginal revenue curve in this case is broken line $dUVW$. If the marginal cost curve happens to pass anywhere through the gap VU in the marginal revenue curve, the profit-maximizing firm will have no motivation to leave the current price, P. Even if there is, for example, a sharp rise in costs, so long as the marginal cost curve does not rise above point U it will lead to no price change.

This analysis has been questioned on empirical grounds.[9] Certainly it seems clear that in an inflationary period oligopoly firms do often follow one another's price *rises*, contrary to what is assumed by this model. However, the analysis does show how the oligopolistic firm's view of competitive reaction patterns can affect the changeability of whatever price it happens to be charging.

12. *Reaction Curves and Oligopolistic Pricing*

Let us now see how the businessman may go about setting his price if he has some definite ideas about his competitors' reactions to his decisions. For diagrammatic simplicity the discussion is confined to the two-firm (du-

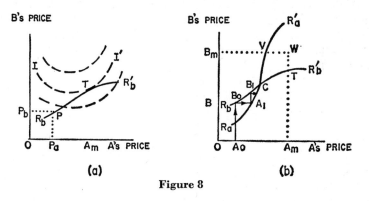

(a)   (b)

Figure 8

opoly) case. Figure 8a summarizes this anticipated reaction pattern. *Reaction curve R_bR_b'* contains the relevant information about the price reac-

[9] See George J. Stigler, "The Kinky Oligopoly Demand Curve and Rigid Prices," *Journal of Political Economy*, Vol. LV, October 1947, reprinted in American Economic Association, *Readings in Price Theory*.

tion of one firm, B, to the pricing decisions of another firm, A. For example, point P on this curve indicates that if firm A sets price OP_a for its product, and if firm B reacts in accord with the information given by its reaction curve, the price of B's product will become OP_b.

If B does stick to this reaction pattern, A's optimal price decision can be represented quite simply. The broken curves in Figure 8a represent the indifference curves of A's objective function, that is, they are his iso profit curves if A is a profit maximizer. Then the highest indifference curve which A can attain (the highest indifference curve compatible with B's reaction pattern) is II' which is tangent to B's reaction curve at point T. To get to this point, A must set his price at OA_m and, accordingly, this must be his optimum price.

So far so good. But, unfortunately for the analysis, two can play at optimization. Figure 8b contains, in addition to B's reaction curve, R_aR_a', which indicates the manner in which B expects A to react to his prices. B, in turn, may now pick an optimum point, say V, on A's reaction curve, R_aR_a', and thus he will set his price at OB_m. But if both A and B choose these "optimum" prices they will end up neither on point T nor on V. Rather, the resulting price combination will be represented by W, a point which lies on neither reaction curve.

The result will be that both players will be surprised at their earnings—they may either be pleasantly surprised (on higher indifference curves than they expected) or they may be disappointed. More important, they will both realize that the reaction curves have become falsehoods, for neither player is now reacting in accord with the dictates of his reaction curve. Once they realize this, they will know also that their optimality calculations have gone up in smoke. What was optimal for A so long as B stuck to his reaction curve need no longer be optimal once B strikes off on his own. Both firms must begin their calculations afresh, and we cannot say where they are likely to go from here.[10]

Thus we have not fully avoided the problems of interdependence in oligopoly price determination even if we have somehow found a reasonable

[10] An alternative oligopoly model investigates what will happen if both firms stay on their reaction curves. It is easy to show that if the curves have the correct relative slopes the price combination must tend toward C, the point of intersection of A's and B's reaction curves. For if A sets price OA_0, B will move to point B_0, the corresponding point on his reaction curve (price OB), but then A will raise his price accordingly (he will move to point A_1 on his reaction curve), etc. Prices will then move along the path $A_0B_0A_1B_1$. . . toward intersection equilibrium price combination C. This is a generalization of the grandaddy of all oligopoly models, that of Cournot. See A. A. Cournot, *Researches into the Mathematical Principles of the Theory of Wealth* (1838), English translation, Macmillan, New York, 1897. It is also possible to construct an Edgeworth contract curve from Figure 8b (Section 9 of this chapter). This is, again, the locus of points of tangency of the participants' indifference curves, and it has properties similar to those of the contract curve of bilateral monopoly.

method of constructing each oligopolist's reaction curve (and the number of models which have been proposed indicates that this matter is far from cut and dried).

This concludes our brief discussion of the theory of oligopoly and with it, our survey of the standard analysis of the various alternative market forms. A number of significant results have emerged from the analysis, but the need for a theory which is richer in empirical content seems quite apparent. Particularly, one is left with the feeling that the oligopoly analysis has involved a number of interesting observations and has provided us with a number of helpful analytical concepts, but some of its most critical questions remain unanswered.

REFERENCES

American Economic Association, *Readings in Price Theory* (George J. Stigler and Kenneth E. Boulding, eds.), Irwin, Homewood, Ill., 1952, Articles 18–22.

Baumol, William J., *Business Behavior, Value and Growth*, Macmillan, New York, 1959, Chapters 3–8.

Chamberlin, Edward H., *The Theory of Monopolistic Competition*, 7th edition, Harvard University Press, Cambridge, Mass., 1956.

Fellner, William, *Competition Among the Few*, Knopf, New York, 1949.

Haley, Bernard F., "Value and Distribution," in Howard S. Ellis, ed., *A Survey of Contemporary Economics*, Blakiston, Philadelphia, 1948.

Machlup, Fritz, *The Economics of Sellers' Competition*, Johns Hopkins, Baltimore, 1952.

Marshall, Alfred, *Principles of Economics*, 8th ed., Macmillan, London, 1922, Book V.

Modigliani, Franco, "New Developments on the Oligopoly Front," *Journal of Political Economy*, Vol. LXVI, June 1958.

Robinson, Joan, *The Economics of Imperfect Competition*, Macmillan, London, 1933.

CHAPTER TWELVE

General equilibrium and
the theory of money

1. Interdependence in the Economy: Substitutes and Complements

General equilibrium theory was developed to take account of a cardinal feature of the structure of our economy: the interdependence of its parts. A rise in the price of automobiles can reduce the demand for tires and increase the demand for bus transportation. A rise in wages may increase imports, reduce exports, and increase the use of labor-saving machinery. The set of examples can be expanded indefinitely.

Two types of interdependence relationship which have received considerable notice are substitutability and complementarity. *Substitute goods* are items which serve similar purposes, so that the buyer may choose from among the set of substitutes which serve his desires. Usually substitutes are imperfect so that the buyer will not be indifferent between them—they serve somewhat the same purpose, but do so imperfectly. Some examples of substitutes are raincoats and umbrellas, chicken and turkey, coal and fuel oil (which are also substitute inputs as well as substitute consumers' goods). *Complementary goods* are items which people (at least sometimes) wish to use jointly: cheese and wine, shirts and neckties, needles and thread. Note that labor and machinery may be either substitute or complementary inputs, depending on the context of the problem.

Substitute and complementary goods have been defined in terms of the effect of a change in the price of one of such a pair of goods on the demand for the other. If we omit the income effect, a reduction in the price of one of a pair of substitute items should decrease the demand for the other (a fall in the price of leather should reduce the demand for plastic furniture coverings) whereas the reverse holds for complementary goods (a reduction in the price of television sets may increase the demand for beer and aspirin).

It follows that many commodities whose relationship is only slight will be at least mild substitutes because they are competitors for the consumer's limited stock of purchasing power. A fall in the price of houses can reduce attendance at concerts because more houses may be bought and the new house owners may not be able to afford as many evenings out after meeting their monthly bank payments.

The upshot of the discussion is that a demand (or a supply) function for commodity x should not just include the price of x as its only price variable. In fact, to be on the safe side, it is customary in a general equilibrium demand frunction to include every price in the economy as a possibility, i.e., to say that the demand for any item is, at least potentially, dependent on the price of every other item in the economy.

2. Equations of General Equilibrium

Suppose an economy has 2053 different commodities, including bonds, stocks, and factories as well as ordinary consumer's goods. Let us treat money as another one of these goods—item 2054 in the list. In accord with the discussion of the last section, if hats are item no. 12, the demand for hats will be given by an expression

$$Q_{12} = D_{12}(P_1, P_2, \ldots, P_{2054}, A, M).$$

This states that the number of hats demanded depends on the price of every one of the 2054 commodities, $P_1, P_2, \ldots, P_{2054}$. In addition, demand will depend on the wealth of the economy (presumably the wealthier the economy, the greater the demands for commodities). The wealth of the economy is summed up by the variables A (an index of its holdings of physical assets—buildings, farm land, factories, etc.) and M, the stock of cash in existence. It will be noted that there is no explicit income variable included in this discussion since consumers' income is presumably given by the prices of the commodities which they sell for a living—e.g., the price of labor time (the wage rate)—and these prices already appear in the demand function.

There is a similar *supply* function for item no. 12 (hats) which may be expressed as

$$S_{12}(P_1, P_2, \ldots, P_{2054}, A, M).$$

The economy is said to be in a state of *general equilibrium* if the supply of every commodity is equal to the demand for it. That is, for the 2054 items in the economy, the following 2054 equations must all be satisfied:

$$S_1(P_1, P_2, \ldots, P_{2054}, A, M) = D_1(P_1, P_2, \ldots, P_{2054}, A, M)$$

$$S_2(P_1, P_2, \ldots, P_{2054}, A, M) = D_2(P_1, P_2, \ldots, P_{2054}, A, M)$$

$$\cdots\cdots\cdots\cdots\cdots\cdots\cdots\cdots\cdots\cdots\cdots$$

$$S_{2054}(P_1, P_2, \ldots, P_{2054}, A, M) = D_{2054}(P_1, P_2, \ldots, P_{2054}, A, M).$$

If we are given the values of A and M, we have as many unknown prices as equations and the system can therefore, presumably, be solved for the equilibrium values of the prices, $P_1, P_2, \ldots, P_{2054}$. Substitution of these values into the demand (or the supply) expressions will then indicate the quantities of the various commodities which will be exchanged. This, in essence, is the general equilibrium system and the method by which it determines the prices and quantities sold of the various commodities. It has been, and can be, expanded and complicated in various ways, by including other variables explicitly, e.g., *exogenous* variables (variables whose values are determined by noneconomic phenomena) such as temperature, and *endogenous* variables such as advertising expenditure, both of which clearly affect demand. We can also go beyond the supply relationships to take explicit account of the behavior of firms and the availability of natural resources. But until some recent developments which will be discussed in Chapter 16, the structure of general equilibrium analysis did not differ essentially from that just described.

3. The Redundant Equation: Walras' Law

There is one complication which arises even in this simple system. It requires discussion here because of the ideas to which it leads—and despite the fact that it turns out to be far less important than the earlier general equilibrium theorists believed. Of the 2054 prices which have been included as variables, the last, the price of money, is a rather peculiar animal. By definition, the price of any item, say a hat, is the number of dollars it takes to purchase a unit of that good. But the unit of money is a dollar so that the number of dollars it takes to purchase a unit of money is exactly one (1). It is, therefore, inconceivable that the price of money should be anything but unity. In other words, P_{2054}, rather than being a variable, must be the number "1". We have thereby lost one of our 2054 variables though we are still apparently left with 2054 equations. Now, as will be shown in Chapter 16, Section 1, having the same number of equations and unknowns does not guarantee that the system can be solved, nor is the absence of equality in the number of equations and unknowns necessarily fatal to the solvability of a simultaneous equation system. Nevertheless, earlier general equilibrium theorists set great store by this equality, so they considered it important to prove that one of the 2054 equations is redundant—that in reality we have only 2053 significant equations to match the 2053 unknowns.

For this purpose they discovered an important identity which has since come to be called *Walras' law*. Any person who demands a commodity is, by definition, prepared to supply, in exchange, an amount of money (or other commodities) of equal value. Similarly, anyone who supplies some amount of goods on the market demands in exchange its value equivalent in money or other commodities.

Every demand is thus matched by an equal supply (in dollar terms) of some other items and vice versa. It follows at once that the total money value of all items supplied must equal the total money value of all items demanded. In algebraic notation,

$$(1) \qquad \sum_{i=1}^{2054} P_i S_i \equiv \sum_{i=1}^{2054} P_i D_i$$

where the three-pronged *identity* sign, $\equiv$, means that (at least in an ordinary economy) this relationship must hold no matter what—whether there is equilibrium or disequilibrium, whether prices are high or low. This identity, which is little more than an accounting relationship (it is difficult to imagine an economy in which it does not hold) is Walras' law.

To show how Walras' law can be used to indicate that one of the general equilibrium equations is redundant, suppose that we find prices which satisfy all but one of the supply-demand equations, say every equation except the first. The sums of the money values of the supplies of all commodities (excluding the first) must equal the money values of their demands. Walras' law then tells us, by subtraction, that the supply and demand of the first item must then also necessarily be equal.[1] That is, if $P_1 S_1$ is unequal to $P_1 D_1$ but the values of all other supplies, $P_i S_i$, equal the corresponding demand values, the sums of all of these supplies together cannot possibly add up to the values of the demands as Walras' law requires. It follows that $P_1 S_1$ cannot possibly be unequal to $P_1 D_1$, i.e., if all other supplies and demands are equal, we must necessarily also have $S_1 = D_1$. Hence, if we find any prices which satisfy every supply-demand equation except the first, we need not bother testing them in the first equation, for we know, without trying them, that S_1 will equal D_1 at these

---

[1] *Proof:* Since $S_2 = D_2, S_3 = D_3, \ldots, S_{2054} = D_{2054}$, we have, multiplying by the corresponding prices, $P_2 S_2 = P_2 D_2$, $P_3 S_3 = P_3 D_3$, etc., and adding these equations together we obtain

$$\sum_{i=2}^{2054} P_i S_i = \sum_{i=2}^{2054} P_i D_i.$$

Subtracting this equation from the Walras' law identity we obtain our result,

$$P_1 S_1 = P_1 D_1 \quad \text{or} \quad S_1 = D_1.$$

prices. The first equation is then harmless and redundant—it adds no information which is not already given by the other equations, and causes no difficulties. We can drop the first equation and solve the others for the prices as if the omitted equation had never existed.

It is important to realize that the first supply-demand equation was picked for omission purely as a matter of expository convenience. Actually, *Walras' law permits us to drop any single equation of our choice.* Much confusion can be saved by realizing that no substantive issue is involved in the choice of the equation to be omitted, since whatever information it provides about any equilibrium prices and quantities will still be contained in the remaining equations.

4. Pitfalls in Determination of the Price Level [2]

Since the general equilibrium equations which have just been described presumably determine all prices in the economy in money terms, they also determine the level of prices—whether prices in general are high or low—inflated or deflated. If the matter is left here, no trouble need arise. However, for a long time the economic literature has contained fairly detailed and separate discussions of the theory of money and the price level. But what they wrote in these discussions often skated perilously close to contradictions with what had been said in the general equilibrium sections. It turns out that there are a number of well-concealed pitfalls in this area, in which some writers have, indeed, been caught.

In order for there to be a determinate price level, there must be one price level which is consistent with equilibrum, and all other price levels should produce disequilibrium and therefore be untenable. This is, for example, what is postulated by the quantity theory of money which states, in effect, that the higher the price level the more cash people will demand in order to be able to carry on their day-to-day business. Hence, given the supply of money, if the price level is very high, the demand for cash will exceed the supply. People will hold on to money rather than other assets (reduce their demands for goods) and the price level will be forced down towards its equilibrium value. Similarly, with a fixed money supply, if prices are below their equilibrium levels, the demand for money will be less than the supply; people will try to get rid of money by spending more, and prices will be forced to rise. This, then, is the classical mechanism of price-level determination. The central point merits repetition: In any theory of

---

[2] The next few sections are based on work of Lange and more particularly on that of Patinkin. See Oskar Lange, "Say's Law: A Restatement and Criticism," in *Studies in Mathematical Economics and Econometrics; In Memory of Henry Schultz*, ed. by Oskar Lange, Francis McIntyre, and Theodore O. Yntema, Chicago University Press, 1942, and Don Patinkin, *Money, Interest, and Prices*, Row, Peterson, Evanston, Ill., 1956.

price-level determination there must be one price level which produces equilibrium, and the others must result in disequilibrium, for otherwise there will be nothing to select out the price level so that any monetary theory must be impossible.

But here is where the conflict between price-level analysis and the rest of general equilibrium theory can arise. It is the essence of general equilibrium theory that what happens in one sector affects what goes on elsewhere. In particular, as we shall soon see again, Walras' law provides a strong link between the monetary sector and the rest of the economy. Assumptions about the structure of the nonmonetary aspects (the so-called "*real*" sector) of the economy can therefore affect the mechanism which determines the price level. But a number of more or less plausible-sounding assumptions have been made about the real sector which, without its being realized by those who made them, served effectively to destroy any mechanism for the determination of the price level. For *these assumptions make it impossible for any change in the price level to produce equilibrium or disequilibrium.* That is, under these assumptions, if there is equilibrium with price level A, there will also be equilibrium, other things being equal, with any other price level, B, whereas if one price level produces disequilibrium, any other price level will produce disequilibrium! There is, thus, no such thing as a unique equilibrium level of prices. Any attempt to graft a price-level theory onto this kind of system must produce a contradiction since such a theory, as we have seen, must state that some price level produces equilibrium, and the others disequilibrium.

The assumptions about the real sector of the economy which have such unexpected and distressing effects on the monetary analysis are the pitfalls of the general equilibrium analysis which were mentioned at the beginning of this section. Let us examine these assumptions one by one and see how they lead to trouble.

1. *The homogeneity postulate.* It has sometimes been argued that the demands for and supplies of commodities are affected only by relative prices, and not by their magnitudes in money terms. It makes no difference to hat and shoe purchases, in this view, whether hats are $1 and shoes $3, or hats $5 and shoes $15. In both cases the *relative* price—the hat-shoe price ratio, is three to one. The argument is that if, suddenly, the government were to double the face value of all coins and pieces of paper money— if all dollar bills were to have the legend "two dollars" stamped over their faces, nothing in the economy need be affected except its accounting records. Umbrellas would nominally cost twice as much, but the buyers' dollar incomes would be twice as high. Thus, the argument runs, if we increase all money prices but raise them strictly in proportion, no commodity's supply or demand will be affected.

This assumption has been called "the homogeneity postulate," the terminology being drawn from the mathematical expression for a relationship in which a *proportionate* change in all of the variables (the prices) has no effect on the dependent variables (quantities supplied and demanded). Demand and supply relationships in which a proportionate change in prices leaves things unchanged are said to be *homogeneous of degree zero in prices alone.*

This homogeneity assumption is inconsistent with the determination of any price level. It will be recalled that, by Walras' law, if there is supply and demand equilibrium in every market except one, then the remaining market must also be in equilibrium. Hence, in particular, if demand equals supply in every market in the real sector of the economy (demand equals supply for every commodity except money), then the supply of and demand for money must also necessarily be equal. In this case we must have an equilibrium price level. Suppose, now, that the price level changes, with all prices varying in exactly the same proportion. If the supply and demand relationships are homogeneous, then none of them will be affected by this change in price *level*—the demand for neckties will remain equal to the supply of neckties, the demand for pianos will remain equal to their supply, etc. This change in price level, with no change in relative prices, cannot disturb the equilibrium in any market of the real sector, so that, by Walras' law, the supply of and demand for *money* must also remain equal. Thus, it is impossible for any change in price level alone (leaving relative prices unaffected) to produce disequilibrium in the money market. In sum, we see that the homogeneity postulate, because it precludes the price level from affecting the real sector, also prevents it from affecting the money market. If we accept that assumption, it is impossible to have any monetary theory or any determinate price level—any price level will do as well as any other because they will all be equally consistent with equilibrium.

2. *Dichotomy of pricing in the real and monetary sectors.* A second and closely related assumption, which leads to similar difficulties, is the premise that it is possible to divide price determination into two completely independent parts—the determination of the absolute price level occurring entirely in the monetary sector of the economy and the determination of relative prices only in the real sectors of the economy. That is, relative prices are determined by the supply-demand equations for commodities, and then the price level is determined separately by the money supply-demand equation.

If this two-part, or dichotomized, price-determination premise implies that the price level has absolutely no effect on the real sector of the economy, it runs into the same trouble as the homogeneity postulate. If no change in price level can produce disequilibrium in any commodity market, by Walras' law, it cannot produce money-market disequilibrium either. Hence, this extreme form of the dichotomous price-determination assumption also produces a contradiction with any monetary theory. If the price level does not affect the commodity markets it cannot be determined in any market. However, we shall see later that there is another closely related, but entirely legitimate form of this dichotomy assumption.

3. *Say's identity.* A third and final assumption which can preclude the determination of a price level is one of the several (no longer fashionable) propositions which have at one time or another been labeled "Say's law." This version of the proposition attributed to Say is the one which is found in most modern references. It asserts that people offer things for sale only because they want other goods and services in exchange. If they accept money for the goods they sell, they do not do so because they want the money for its own sake but because they desire to take the money *at once* and buy other goods with it. In this way, every supply of a good brings with it a demand for an equivalent amount of *goods*. Whether prices are high or low, rising or falling, the supply of all goods taken together must equal the demand for all goods taken together. This version of Say's law is compatible with an overproduction of hula hoops or some other particular commodities, if, e.g., people's tastes have unexpectedly swung away from hula hoops. But the overproduction of these items must be matched by an undersupply of some other goods on which suppliers do want to spend their money. Thus, it is possible for producers to turn out the wrong goods but they can never turn out too many goods for the buying public. General overproduction of commodities is impossible.

This version of Say's law is a first cousin of Walras' law which states that supplies of goods and money together must equal demands for goods plus money. Say's law is the stronger assertion that people don't want money except to buy goods at once, so that the total supply of commodities alone (excluding money) is necessarily *identical* with the total demand for commodities alone. For this reason it has been proposed that this version of Say's proposition be called *Say's identity*.[3]

Since Say's identity requires that the goods markets, taken as a whole, must always be in equilibrium (total supply for all goods equals total de-

---

[3] In algebraic terms Say's identity may be written, using the notation of Walras' law identity (1) in Section 3, as

$$\sum_{i=1}^{2053} P_i S_i \equiv \sum_{i=1}^{2053} P_i D_i.$$

This differs from the Walras' law identity only in one respect. The numbers above the Σ's are 2054 in the Walras' law case but they are 2053 here. That is so because the supply of and demand for the 2054th commodity, money, do not enter into Say's identity.

mand) it follows by Walras' law that the remaining market, the money market, must also always be in equilibrium. It is impossible for any change in the price level (or any change in anything else, for that matter) ever to produce disequilibrium in the money market. As a result, Say's identity also precludes the determination of any price level by any relationship of monetary theory.

To summarize, we have now examined three assumptions which have at some time or another appeared in the economic literature—the homogeneity postulate, the dichotomization assumption, and the Say's identity assumption. We have seen that any one of these causes serious trouble for general equilibrium theory by making a monetary theory impossible. Only in a barter economy where money plays no role and there is no absolute price level can any of these assumptions be made without causing such difficulties.

5. *The Real Balance Effect*

In practice, a change in the price level can have very profound effects on demands for and supplies of commodities. Perhaps the most powerful influence of a price change is that which operates through the public's expectations. A rise in price level has, for example, been known to stampede buyers into purchasing goods in the fear that their prices will go up even further. Thus, a price change, by leading buyers or sellers to expect further price changes in the future, can induce them to speed up or to postpone purchases and sales of commodities.

Another influence of a change in price level is its effect on the purchasing power of a stock of cash. If a man has $1000 in cash, and prices fall by half, the value (purchasing power) of his stock of cash will have doubled. More generally, it can be seen that a rise in prices will lower the real value of cash holdings (it will reduce the real wealth of the owners of the money) whereas a fall in prices will raise the real value (purchasing power) of cash holdings. A proportionate fall in all prices may leave real *incomes* unaffected (if wages and commodity prices both fall 50 per cent, the purchasing power of workers' incomes are unaffected). But we see that the fall in prices must increase the real *wealth* of people who hold cash.

Let us now make the reasonable assumption that an increase in a person's wealth will lead him to increase his expenditures either on consumption or on investment goods, even if only by a small amount. Then the fall in price level must increase the public's demand for goods and services because, as we have just seen, it increases the real wealth of cash holders. Thus, changes in the price level must also affect demands for and supplies of goods.

The effect of price-level changes on demands and supplies which operates through the resulting change in the purchasing power of cash has been discussed in the literature under a variety of names. In different places it has been called the *Pigou effect*,[4] the *real balance effect* (the effect which operates via the purchasing power of cash balances), and the *wealth-saving relationship* (the effect of the change in real wealth on saving and expenditure).

The real balance effect amounts to a direct denial of the homogeneity postulate and the dichotomization assumption which were described in the previous section, for through this effect, a change in price level (a proportionate change in all prices) does cause variation in demands for and supplies of goods (unless, of course, cash stocks were also to change in the same proportion). In this way, absolute prices play a role in the real sector of the economy and not just in the money market. The real balance effect is also incompatible with Say's identity for it implies, e.g., that a sufficiently large rise in the price level can lead to such a reduction in the purchasing power of cash holders that the demand for goods will, taken as a whole, fall below the supply—there will be general overproduction—a phenomenon which, Say's identity asserts, is impossible.

The real balance effect is an essential piece of the machinery which works to produce equilibrium in the money market. Suppose, for example, that for some reason prices fall below their equilibrium level. This will increase the real wealth of cash holders, lead them to spend more money, and that in turn will drive prices back up toward equilibrium. Thus, the real balance effect is a part of the equilibrating mechanism of the money market. It is a force behind the working of the quantity theory or whatever analysis we wish to use to explain the determination of the equilibrium price level.

6. Comparative Statics: General Equilibrium Analysis

Suppose, however, we were to decide to ignore problems of disequilibrium and confine our attention only to general *equilibrium* problems. For example, if there is an influx of money into the economy, we may ask not about its impact effects, but rather, what it will have done to the economic situation after the economy has had a chance to adjust to the new money supply—after it has reached its new equilibrium. This approach is called the method of *comparative statics*. If an exogenous change occurs, we do not, as in dynamics, trace out the course of the resulting developments as time passes. Rather, we compare the initial equilibrium position only with the new equilibrium which might eventually result from this change. We compare only two static equilibrium situations.

[4] After A. C. Pigou, to whom the idea was attributed.

In such a comparative statics analysis, it turns out that the real balance effect may lose much of its importance so that in such cases a modified sort of homogeneity postulate and dichotomization assumption may become legitimate.

For suppose there is a doubling of the supply of money. Suppose, moreover, that after the smoke has had a chance to clear away, all prices will have doubled, and the demand for money will also have doubled. In this situation there is no change in relative prices, and the supply and demand for money are once again equal (at twice their original level). The purchasing power of stocks of money will have been reduced back to its original level (there are twice as many dollars but each dollar is worth only half as much as it was).

With all relative prices unchanged, and with the purchasing power of money stocks back where it began, there is no reason for any change in the demand for or the supply of any commodity. In sum, whereas a change in price level may have affected these supplies and demands, once prices have doubled any change in the real value of cash balances may well have disappeared, and the consequent effects on commodity demands and supplies will then also have disappeared. Hence, if we began from a position of equilibrium, a doubling of all prices as a result of a doubling of the money supply may well restore equilibrium again.

The change in money supply will thus have affected the absolute price level, but it will not have had any effect on the real sector of the economy. Equilibrium relative prices and commodity supplies and demands will all be back at their old levels.

We see that these assertions come very close to the homogeneity postulate (price-level changes do not affect demands for and supplies of goods) and the dichotomization assumption (events in the money market determine only the price level and have no effect on the real sector of the economy, which can be analyzed separately). However, these two assumptions are legitimate only in their modified form in which they refer just to equilibrium prices and equilibrium supply and demand levels. Only in such a comparative statics context are these premises acceptable. It is important to recognize that the classical and neoclassical economists often used equilibrium concepts and comparative statics techniques without specifying explicitly that they were doing so. When homogeneity and dichotomization assumptions are encountered in their writings, it is necessary to recognize, therefore, that they may well have been meant in an innocuous comparative statics sense so that no error need have been committed at that point in their discussion.

This section has argued that only where questions of dynamics and disequilibrium are considered do the homogeneity and dichotomization assumptions *necessarily* run into trouble. However, the reader should realize that even *equilibrium* supplies and demands *may* be affected by price-level changes. If in the course of a price rise there is, for example, a redistribution of real wealth, as will often be the case, demands will shift in accord with the tastes of those whose purchasing power has been increased. All that the preceding argument has shown is that it is *possible* for equilibrium demands to be unaffected by a price rise so that there is no logical impossibility in the homogeneity postulate when applied to equilibrium supplies and demands. It has *not* been maintained, even in a comparative statics analysis, that this postulate must always, of necessity, be valid.

7. *Optimal Cash Balances*

Before leaving our discussion of the theory of money, let us inquire a little more closely into the structure of the demand for money.

Keynes, in his *General Theory*, divides the demand for liquid funds into three categories: that which is desired for transactions purposes (the cash needed to meet foreseen payments like a firm's payments which are required by contract); that for precautionary purposes (cash needed to meet payments whose magnitude is not known in advance); and that to be used for purposes of speculation. Keynes implies that the demand for cash for transactions and precautionary purposes will be rather strongly responsive to changes in expenditure levels, but that these demands will be relatively interest inelastic.[5]

It is, of course, possible to accept this as an assumption or as an impression garnered from observation, but usually, on such a question, the theorist prefers to probe somewhat more deeply. Why should people and firms keep more cash when their expenditures rise? And if there is a reason for their balances to be increased in these circumstances, what determines the amount by which their money holdings should rise? Finally, we may well ask whether interest rates should not also influence *significantly* the magnitudes of these cash holdings. These are all questions of good management. Cash is kept not for its own sake but because it helps the consumer and the businessman to carry on his activities. The questions to be asked, then, are whether there is some way in which an optimum cash balance can be computed and, if so, how this optimum cash balance figure will be affected by changes in incomes and interest rates. These are obviously important questions for business management, as well as for economic theory.[6]

[5] See J. M. Keynes, *The General Theory of Employment, Interest and Money*, Harcourt, Brace, New York, 1936, pp. 196–97.

[6] Much of the analysis which follows is based on my article, "The Transactions Demand for Cash: An Inventory Theoretic Approach," *Quarterly Journal of Economics*, Vol. LXVI, November 1952. See also James Tobin, "The Interest Elasticity of Transactions Demand for Cash," *Review of Economics and Statistics*, Vol. XXXVIII, August 1956.

A firm's cash balance can usefully be interpreted as an inventory—an inventory of money which its holder stands ready to exchange against purchases of labor, raw materials, etc. It is really no different in principle from a shoe manufacturer's inventory of footwear which he stands ready to trade for the distributor's cash. The reason for comparing cash on hand with a commodity inventory is that we already possess a body of techniques for determining optimum inventory levels.[7] These techniques can be used to balance off the advantages of a sizeable cash balance against its costs.

It is, of course, convenient to keep a sizeable cash balance on hand because that can make it so much easier to meet required disbursements, particularly because it is not always possible to foresee in advance the precise magnitudes of required expenditures. But it is expensive to tie up large amounts of capital in the form of cash balances. For that money could otherwise be used profitably elsewhere in the firm, or it could be used to pay off debt and reduce the firm's interest burden, or the money could be invested profitably in securities. When tight money limits the funds which are in practice available to the businessman, he must recognize that every dollar he keeps in the form of cash on hand means one dollar less available for the purchase of labor, raw materials, etc.

To see precisely how the optimum cash inventory computation is handled, let us go directly to the calculation of the optimum level of that portion of a company's cash inventory which is used to meet payments whose magnitude is known in advance. Suppose the company receives $80 thousand in cash on the first day of each month which it will pay out in regular daily installments over the next month. Rather than keep all of this cash idle, some of it can be invested in securities, say at a return of 5 per cent. But each time some cash is invested cr withdrawn there is a fixed brokerage charge, say $25. The company may then consider the three alternatives shown in Table 1 for a 4-week month.

Notice that as the frequency of withdrawals increases, the average investment goes up from 0 to $20,000 to $30,000; thus, the annual interest earnings at 5 per cent rise from 0 to $1000 to $1500. But in method A there are no brokerage charges. In method B there is one investment and one withdrawal per month, or 24 broker transactions per year which result (at $25 per transaction) in a total brokerage fee of $600. Method C requires four investment and withdrawal transactions per month, or 48 per year, which will cost about $1200. Thus we have the results shown in Table 2.

Clearly, method B is the more profitable way for the firm to manage its cash.

More generally, it is possible to show how the optimum balance (in-

[7] See the illustrative inventory analysis of Chapter 1 and the list of references at the end of that chapter.

TABLE 1

	Week				Average Investment Holding
	1	2	3	4	
POSSIBILITY A: NO INVESTMENT (ZERO BROKER TRANSACTIONS PER MONTH)					
Investment purchases	0	0	0	0	
Investment holdings	0	0	0	0	0
Withdrawals	0	0	0	0	
Payments	$20,000	$20,000	$20,000	$20,000	
POSSIBILITY B: TWO BROKER TRANSACTIONS PER MONTH					
Investment purchases	$40,000	0	0	0	
Investment holdings	$40,000	$40,000	0	0	$20,000
Withdrawals	$40,000*	0	$40,000	0	
Payments	$20,000	$20,000	$20,000	$20,000	
POSSIBILITY C: FOUR BROKER TRANSACTIONS PER MONTH					
Investment purchases	$60,000	0	0	0	
Investment holdings	$60,000	$40,000	$20,000	0	$30,000
Withdrawals	$20,000*	$20,000	$20,000	$20,000	
Payments	$20,000	$20,000	$20,000	$20,000	

* This amount is in fact never invested or withdrawn—it represents the amount witheld from the initial investment.

ventory) of cash not held in short-term investments will increase when the volume of transactions or the brokerage fee increases, and decrease when the interest rate increases. The inventory analysis of Chapter 1 indicates that these will not be proportionate variations. For example, the optimal cash balance will increase only as the square root of the volume of trans-actions—i.e., there will be economies of large scale in the firm's optimum cash balance.

TABLE 2

	Average Investment	Annual Interest Earning	Broker Trans-actions Per Year	Annaul Broker Cost	Net Gain (Interest Minus Broker's Cost)
Method A	0	0	0	0	0
Method B	$20,000	$1000	24	$ 600	$400
Method C	$30,000	$1500	48	$1200	$300

The reasons for this result can be suggested without the aid of mathe-matics. Most important, it must be noted that a given volume of payments can be met with different cash withdrawal levels. We observed that the $80,000 could be paid by keeping the entire $80,000 on hand, or by invest-ing it and withdrawing $40,000 twice a month, etc. In other words, even when the firm's total payments are fixed, the average cash balance used to meet these payments can be varied. We can see why this amount will vary directly with the value of the brokerage fee and inversely with the interest rate. Clearly, if the brokerage fee goes up it will pay to cut down the number of withdrawals, i.e., the optimal cash balance will rise. Similarly, if the level of the interest rate goes up, it will pay to make withdrawals as small and as late as possible, i.e., the optimal balance of idle, noninterest-earning cash will fall. In sum, if firms are efficient profit maximizers, Keynes was probably wrong in playing down the influence of the interest rate on the transactions demand for cash.

In addition, we now have a firmer foundation for his view that the demand for cash should increase with the volume of transactions. But why should they not increase proportionately (as Keynes suggests)? That is—why should the most economical cash holding increase relatively less than the volume of expenditures which this cash is used to finance? The answer is to be found in the nature of the cost of investment transactions. The minimum broker's fee is what makes it unprofitable to take cash out of investments in frequent small driblets, although doing so will keep cash invested until the last possible moment. But the larger the amounts involved, the smaller, relatively speaking, will be the brokerage costs. On a $1000 bond purchase, minimum brokerage fees can be prohibitive. On a million-dollar transaction they are negligible. Hence, the larger the total amounts involved, the less significant will be the brokerage costs, and the more frequent will be optimal withdrawals. For this reason optimal withdrawals and cash balances will rise when the volume of transactions per firm increases, but will rise less than in proportion with the volume of transactions payments.

For expository simplicity, this discussion has assumed that any reduction in cash holdings is used to purchase short-term securities. In practice, tight money means that frequently funds can more profitably be invested inside the firm. This does not alter the nature of the analysis in any fundamental way. The same methods can be employed to take this fact into account in determining the way in which the firm can use cash most effectively and most economically.

It is also interesting to note, without any attempt at explanation, that on not entirely implausible assumptions, somewhat similar results can be derived for the precautionary demand for cash, though the method of analysis is considerably different from that which has just been described.

Some final remarks are appropriate to tie in the discussion of this section with the rest of the chapter. We have seen throughout the general equilibrium discussion how large a role was played by the demand for cash balances. Now, with the aid of inventory analysis we have been able to make some deductions about the nature of that demand.

In particular, we can now say something about the relationship between changes in the price level and the demand for cash balances. Suppose prices rise by 37 per cent; will people end up demanding 37 per cent more money as is so often assumed in the general equilibrium discussions? Our inventory model tells us that (if the pattern of the cash holders' purchases does not change)[8] they will—that optimum cash balances will increase in precisely the same proportion as the price level. If price level goes up by this percentage, the money value of the buyer's transactions will clearly also rise by 37 per cent, and this might lead us to suspect that the demand for cash will rise by only a smaller proportion. But a uniform rise in prices means that brokerage fees will also rise by 37 per cent so that larger cash balances will become desirable in order to avoid investments and withdrawals and the brokerage costs which they incur. The two effects together—that of the increased money value of transactions and that of the increased brokerage fee—can easily be shown to lead to a rise in the optimal demand for cash in precise proportion with a change in the price level.[9]

REFERENCES

Becker, Gary S., and Baumol, William J., "The Classical Monetary Theory: The Outcome of the Discussion," *Economica*, Vol. XIX, November 1952.

Cassel, Gustav, *The Theory of Social Economy*, T. Fisher Unwin, London, 1923, Chapter IV.

Hicks, J. R., *Value and Capital*, 2nd edition, Oxford University Press, New York, 1946, Chapters IV and XX.

Lange, Oskar, *Price Flexibility and Employment*, Cowles Commission Monograph No. 8, Principia Press, Bloomington, Indiana, 1944.

Patinkin, Don, *Money Interest and Prices*, Row, Peterson, Evanston, Ill., 1956.

Walras, Léon, *Elements of Pure Economics* (trans. and ed. by William Jaffé), Irwin, Homewood, Ill., 1954.

[8] This implies either that full equilibrium has been achieved or that the real balance effect can, for present purposes, be ignored.

[9] To prove this the reader need merely glance at the final expression for the optimal inventory in Section 6 of Chapter 1. This result states that

$$D = \sqrt{\frac{2a^*Q^*}{k^*}}.$$

In terms of the current discussion we can interpret D (or, rather, $D/2$) as the optimal average cash inventory, Q^* as the volume of transactions (payments to be met), k^* as the interest cost of carrying cash (the interest rate), and a^* as the brokerage fee (reorder cost). Then, if brokerage fee and the volume of transactions are each increased by a factor of W (each rises to W times its former level), the expression under the square root sign then rises by W^2 so that the optimal cash balance also goes up to exactly $\sqrt{W^2} = W$ times its initial level.

CHAPTER THIRTEEN

General equilibrium and welfare economics

Welfare economics is the branch of economic theory which has investigated the nature of the policy recommendations that the economist is entitled to make. Its literature has mostly discussed two types of subject: (1) the fundamental but quasi-philosophical problems involved in distinguishing a "legitimate" from an "illegitimate" recommendation and (2) the construction of a theoretical framework which can be applied to some actual policy problems. We shall be concerned primarily with the latter, leaving the first, more methodological problem until the end of the chapter.

1. Resource Allocation and General Equilibrium

Welfare economics has concerned itself mostly with policy issues which arise out of the allocation of resources—with the distribution of inputs among the various commodities and the distribution of commodities among the various consumers.

This is a general equilibrium problem because, if resources are moved into one industry, they must presumably be taken out of another, and the interrelationships of the two industries constitute the heart of the matter. The problem of determining the optimum outputs of the various commodities produced in the economy arises only because the quantities of all resources are limited. In such circumstances, it is no answer to say that more of any commodity is a good thing. If we produce more guns, there will be less farm labor available to produce butter. It may be highly undesirable to increase the output of product a because the required concomitant decrease in product b is (on some criterion) more valuable. The optimal allocation of resources between the two items is a matter of the relative urgency of the demands for them and their relative costs of production. No product's optimal output level can therefore be determined in isolation but only in a comparison with other commodities with which it competes for society's limited resources. This is the basis for the conclusion that, at least in principle, resource allocation is necessarily a matter for general equilibrium analysis.

2. *Marginal Rules for Optimal Resource Allocation*

One way to attack the problem is to set up a number of conditions which must be satisfied by an optimal allocation of resources. There are a number of questions to be answered: How much of each commodity should be produced (the allocation of resources proper)? How much of any input should be used in the production of any output (the technological production decisions)? How should the commodities be divided up among the various consumers (distribution of final goods)? The marginal analysis permits the formulation of rules about these and the other more specific decisions involved in the allocation of resources.[1] We shall see that these rules can be exceedingly helpful, but in the nature of the case they are highly incomplete.

There are two major difficulties which are encountered by such rules:

(1) *Distribution of income and wealth.* There is nothing in economic analysis which permits us to say that individual A should optimally receive 1.73 as much income as B. The value judgments involved in recommending a distribution of income must somehow be grafted onto the economic information, and they cannot be produced magically by any manipulation of the marginal analysis. But, in practice, almost any economic decision is virtually certain to affect someone's real income. A tariff reduction can increase the real income of most people at the expense of those who are employed in the protected industry. A decision to produce more beans and fewer potatoes can increase the real income of bean lovers at the expense of potato connoisseurs, etc.

Economists have several alternative approaches, none of them fully satisfactory, to the problem of income distribution: (a) Some have virtually ignored the entire matter; (b) others have, as a working hypothesis

---

[1] For more details see A. P. Lerner, *The Economics of Control*, Macmillan, New York, 1946, and M. W. Reder, *Studies in The Theory of Welfare Economics*, Columbia University Press, New York, 1947, Chapter II.

(sometimes implicitly), accepted the *status quo* distribution; (c) still others have argued that we can only recommend policies which hurt no one—not even a little bit; (d) some have argued that we must measure and compare the (neoclassical cardinal) utilities of everyone involved and recommend a policy if and only if there is an over-all net gain in utility; (e) some have argued that we must accept the arbitrary judgment of some authority or group of authorities (Congress or the public as a whole as indicated by a referendum) as to an optimum distribution of income; (f) still others have argued that, other things being equal, the less the inequality of income the better. In any event, we shall see that the marginal optimality rules are either silent or prejudiced on the question of income distribution and are, therefore, necessarily incomplete or unsatisfactory even on questions where distribution is not the primary issue.

2. *Difficulty in obtaining data.* A second problem arising out of the marginal rules is that they call for data which do not always have a satisfactory counterpart in statistical and accounting information. Aside from the fact that the records usually contain average rather than marginal values (see Chapter 3, Section 7, above), there is another important difficulty. The cost to society of producing some item may contain elements which can never be expected to show up in books of the producing firm. If the production of some item causes soil erosion or pollution of water or leads to the growth of slums, these are matters which the economist must take into account in deciding whether, and in what quantity, the item should be produced. Similarly, the production of the item may provide social benefits such as improved technology, advantages for national defense, and other advantages which are not reflected in the revenues of the firm. Hence the cost and revenue figures which are required for an optimum allocation computation may not be the data which one finds bearing similar names in statistical tables. Differences between social and private costs and benefits and their consequences for optimal policy will be discussed again presently.

Let us now state some of the most important marginal rules of welfare economics, those relating to the allocation of resources among the various commodities, to the production arrangements, and to the division of goods among consumers.

3. Optimal Distribution of Products Among Consumers

Given the amounts of the various goods which have been produced, how can these commodities best be divided up among the members of the consuming public? It would seem that this problem runs us right into insuperable problems involved in deciding who deserves what. But we can avoid this issue and yet arrive at

[handwritten: $MRS_1 = MRS_2$]

RULE 1. *Optimum allocation of goods among consumers:* For any two products, x and y, and any two consumers, 1 and 2, consumer 1's marginal rate of substitution of x for y must be the same as that of consumer 2, that is, to both consumers the ratio of the marginal utilities of the two products must be the same.[2]

To show that this must be so, we note that if the condition were violated so that an additional unit of x were not worth the same number of units of y to both consumers (unequal marginal rates of substitution), they could both benefit by a simple exchange. Suppose that to consumer 1 an

---

[2] *Proof:* Let us see how far we can increase the utility, $U_1 = f_1(x_1, y_1)$, of the first consumer without reducing the utility, $U_2 = f_2(x_2, y_2)$, of the other, using any arbitrary utility index consistent with the preferences of the two consumers. Here x_1 is the amount of x in the hands of the first consumer, y_2 is the amount of y which the second consumer possesses, etc. Our task, then, is to

$$\text{maximize} \quad U_1 = f_1(x_1, y_1)$$

subject to $f_2(x_2, y_2) = U_2^*$ (a constant), i.e., the second consumer must not be hurt, and

$$\left. \begin{array}{l} x_1 + x_2 = X^* \\ y_1 + y_2 = Y^* \end{array} \right\} \quad \text{i.e., the total available amounts of } x \text{ and } y \text{ are fixed.}$$

To find this maximum we form the Lagrangian expression (Chapter 4, Section 8)

$$U_{1\lambda} = f_1(x_1, y_1) + \lambda_a[f_2(x_2, y_2) - U_2^*] + \lambda_b(x_1 + x_2 - X^*) + \lambda_c(y_1 + y_2 - Y^*).$$

Differentiating partially in turn with respect to x_1, x_2, y_1, and y_2 and setting each of the results equal to zero we obtain

$$\frac{\partial U_{1\lambda}}{\partial x_1} = \frac{\partial f_1}{\partial x_1} + \lambda_b = 0, \qquad \frac{\partial U_{1\lambda}}{\partial x_2} = \lambda_a \frac{\partial f_2}{\partial x_2} + \lambda_b = 0$$

$$\frac{\partial U_{1\lambda}}{\partial y_1} = \frac{\partial f_1}{\partial y_1} + \lambda_c = 0, \qquad \frac{\partial U_{1\lambda}}{\partial y_2} = \lambda_a \frac{\partial f_2}{\partial y_2} + \lambda_c = 0.$$

Now a moment's thought should indicate that we have $\partial f_1/\partial x_1 = MU_{x1}$ (the marginal utility of x to individual 1, etc.), and solving the preceding equations for these marginal utilities we obtain

$$MU_{x1} = -\lambda_b; \quad MU_{y1} = -\lambda_c; \quad MU_{x2} = -\lambda_b/\lambda_a; \quad MU_{y2} = -\lambda_c/\lambda_a.$$

Thus by straightforward division

$$\frac{MU_{x1}}{MU_{y1}} = \frac{MU_{x2}}{MU_{y2}} = \frac{\lambda_b}{\lambda_c}$$

which is Rule 1.

The other theorems of the next few sections can be derived similarly. Note the basic trick: where two items which we want as large as possible (U_1 and U_2) cannot be compared directly and added together into an objective function (the "you can't add apples and bananas" problem), we maximize one of them (U_1) while preventing the other from falling (U_2 = a constant).

Note that Rule 1 provides us with the equation of the contract curve (see Chapter 11, Section 9) since it determines what is the best that can be done for one consumer without harming the other.

additional unit of x has the same utility as 1.7 additional units of y, whereas to consumer 2 the marginal unit of x is worth 1.9 additional units of y. If they trade, 1 giving a unit of good x to 2 and receiving, say, 1.8 units of y in exchange, each consumer must consider himself 0.1 units ahead. Each consumer receives a higher utility in exchange for a lower—a clear gain for both parties. This same sort of mutually profitable trade can, for the same reasons, always be arranged if the conditions of Rule 1 are violated so that the distribution of commodities cannot be optimal because some opportunities to improve the situation remain unused.

This proposition thus tells us something about how commodities should be distributed among individuals *without saying anything about how income should be distributed among them!* It does this by telling the consumers that they should end up somewhere on the contract curve (Chapter 11, Section 9) but dodging the important problem of their optimal location on the contract curve. The rule avoids talking about distribution by committing itself to little more than the apparently trivial assertion that if you have a bottle of whiskey (which you dislike) and I have a fifth of gin (which I detest), why—let's swap! However, the result should not be scorned. Many a sage has missed this apparently simple point and argued that whatever one of the traders gains he must have taken away from the other, so that there can be no net advantage from trade. Moreover, out of such apparently trivial statements are formed the axiom systems on which powerful theories are built and important insights gained. We shall see presently how the weak result of this section can be used as a basis for some conclusions about the design of a rationing system.

4. Optimal Use of Resources in Producing Given Outputs

We come now to a second marginal social optimality rule:

RULE 2a. *Optimal allocation of an input:* If an input i can be used in producing both commodities x and y, then the marginal social product of i in the manufacture of x must equal the marginal social product of i in the manufacture of y.

For if these numbers were unequal (say, if the marginal social product of i were greater when i is used in making x) then the situation could not possibly be optimal because the transfer of some i from the manufacture of y to that of x must involve a net gain to society. The value of the y lost in the transfer must be less than the value of the x gained. Note that this proposition talks about the marginal *social* benefit, not about the marginal revenue product of i, which is the nearest concept relevant to the calculations of the private firm. This is an example of the second of the welfare economics marginal-rule problems which was just discussed in Section 2.

The difficulty can be ducked to some extent by using the following closely related rule. Let MP_{ix} represent the marginal *physical* product of input i when used to produce output x, i.e., $MP_{ix} = \Delta x/\Delta i$, the increase in output of x when one additional unit of i is used in its manufacture, all other things being equal. Then

Rule 2b. *Optimal allocation of several inputs:* An optimal use of any two inputs i and j, in the production of outputs x and y, requires that

$$(MP_{ix}/MP_{jx}) = (MP_{iy}/MP_{jy})$$

i.e., it requires that the ratio of the marginal physical products of i and j in the production of x be the same as the corresponding ratio for commodity y.

This is so because if equality does not hold, say if the first fraction is larger, i will be relatively more efficient in producing x than is j (i will have a *comparative* advantage in x production) and it will pay to shift some of input i into x production and out of y production, and to shift some of j the other way, from x to y. The argument is slightly more complex but precisely analogous with that involved in the preceding marginal rules. Suppose (as an illustration), we have the figures

$$MP_{ix} = 20, \quad MP_{jx} = 8, \quad MP_{iy} = 4, \quad MP_{jy} = 2$$

so that, as the reader can verify, the left-hand fraction is the larger of the two. Now move one unit of i out of y production and into the manufacture of x so that the output of y decreases by 4 units. Next, move enough of input j in the other direction *to keep the output of y on the same level as it was originally;* i.e., move 2 units of j into y production (where each unit produces two units of y) so that the output of y goes up by $2 \times 2 = 4$ units, back to its old level. The result is a net increase in the output of x (with the output of y remaining unchanged) for x's output has first been raised by

$$\Delta i MP_{ix} \text{ units} = 1 \times 20 = 20 \text{ units}$$

and then been decreased by $\Delta j MP_{jx} = 2 \times 8 = 16$ units, leaving a net gain of 4 units. The reader can try other illustrative figures and see that they always yield similar results.[3] Moreover, we can instead keep the output of

---

[3] A more general proof is the following. Let Δi be the increase in i used in producing x (or the reverse of the decrease in i used in producing y). Then we have $(\Delta i MP_{iy}/\Delta j MP_{jy}) = 1$ (the output of y is kept unchanged by the substitution of input j for input i) and by hypothesis,

$$MP_{ix}/MP_{jx} > MP_{iy}/MP_{jy}.$$

(footnote continued on next page)

commodity x unchanged and increase that of y or obtain smaller increases in both outputs.

The upshot is, that if this last marginal equation is violated, a switching around of inputs can give us something for nothing—it can increase one or both outputs without any increase in input use! Hence, because there are such unused opportunities, the inputs cannot possibly be optimally employed when this last equation is violated. Where the marginal analysis is applicable, production is therefore said to be *inefficient* when this equation does not hold, and *efficient* if the equation is satisfied. We will come across this concept again in Chapter 16.

Note finally, before leaving this discussion, that the last equation is a purely technological requirement—it refers to the most efficient ways of producing whatever we are going to produce and therefore avoids all problems about the distribution of income which arise in deciding *what* should be produced. The social-costs-and-products problem can, however, arise even here if the use of an input, i, to increase some output, x, makes it easier to manufacture another output, y. This might happen, for example, if the increased use of i in x production led to the training of more mechanics in the use of this piece of equipment and if that skill were also useful in industry y. In this case there is a secondary benefit in the use of i—the training of a labor force which is needed in other industries. The relevant social marginal product of i statistic should take into account both the direct (industry x) and secondary (industry y) benefits from this use of i.

5. *Marginal Rule for Optimal Output Levels*

We come now to what is perhaps the most important and most controversial of the marginal rules of welfare economics. This is the rule which tells us how much coffee and how much salami should be produced with society's scarce resources. The formal rule is very simple and, as far as it goes, absolutely valid.

RULE 3a. *Optimum output of a commodity:* Given the level of employment of society's scarce resources on the output of any commodity, x, it should be such that the marginal social utility of x is equal to its marginal social cost.

This is so because if the rule is violated, some change in output can benefit society; e.g., if the marginal social cost of x exceeds its marginal social benefit, society will gain by reducing the output of x.

Multiply both numerators by Δi and the denominators of both fractions by Δj to obtain

$$\Delta i MP_{ix}/\Delta j MP_{jx} > \Delta i MP_{iy}/\Delta j MP_{jy} = 1$$

which at once gives the required result,

$$\Delta i MP_{ix} > \Delta j MP_{jx}.$$

This rule, although valid, conceals the allocative aspect of the problem. That is, it is not apparent from the form of the rule that at least part of the social cost of increased gun production is the decrease in butter output which results from the increased use of resources for military preparation.

The allocation of a limited quantity of resources among alternative outputs is more clearly dealt with by the following optimality rule which is closely related to the one we have just discussed:

RULE 3b. *Optimal relative outputs:* If resources are to be allocated optimally between any two outputs x and y, then the ratio of the marginal social utility of x (MSU_x) to the marginal social cost of x (MSC_x) must equal the corresponding ratio for commodity y; i.e., we must have

$$\frac{MSU_x}{MSC_x} = \frac{MSU_y}{MSC_y}.$$

(Here marginal cost of x may be interpreted to mean the quantity of resources needed to produce an additional unit of x, etc.)

The reasoning is so close to that behind the previous marginal rules that it need not be repeated. The reader should be able to show that if output levels are such that the equation is violated, total social utility can be increased by an increase in one output together with such a decrease in the other that there is no net change in total social costs (the use of society's resources). So once again, if this equation is violated, society has missed an opportunity to get something (utility) for nothing, and therefore output levels cannot be optimal.

The crucial and unsettled question is: What do we mean by social utility and how do we measure it? If Ellen likes marmalade and Daniel likes jam, how do we know what happens to social utility when we produce more jam and less marmalade? To this problem also we will return, but even then no fully satisfactory solution will be offered.

6. An Optimal Price System

Let us temporarily ignore the distinction between *social* and *private* costs and benefits. Suppose we institute a price system which has the following characteristics:

1. All inputs and outputs have fixed prices which are the same for every buyer and seller and which no buyer or seller can change.

2. All quantities supplied are demanded and hence sold, i.e., these are the equilibrium prices of the general equilibrium system.[4]

[4] Here we have to ignore free goods which are a drug on the market. Not all the water near a large lake will find buyers, and desert land in the middle of the Sahara is likely to go begging for customers. This skips over the problem of deciding which goods

3. Any firm can enter (or leave) the production of any commodity at these prices if it finds it profitable to do so.

It is possible to show that under these circumstances, if every consumer maximizes his utility and every firm maximizes its profits *all of the preceding marginal optimality requirements will automatically be satisfied*. This is a fundamental theorem of welfare economics. Before we get to some applications of this result let us show, rule by rule, that it is valid.

Proof that Rule 1 must hold under such a price system: We know (Chapter 8, Section 5) that if prices are fixed, each consumer will, if he behaves optimally, buy any two commodities x and y in such amounts that for him the marginal rate of substitution of x for y is equal to the ratio of the prices of the two items. Since these prices are the same for all consumers by characteristic (1) of our price system, the marginal rates of substitution of x for y must be the same for all consumers, as Rule 1 requires.

Rule 2a: As is shown in Chapter 14, if its output and input prices are fixed, it will pay a firm to hire any input, i, up to the point where its price is equal to the value of its marginal product (for if, for example, the value of the marginal product of i exceeds its price, it clearly pays to hire more of i). Hence, any firm (or a division of a firm) which buys a unit of i whose cost is D dollars to each and every firm must obtain a marginal product worth D dollars in return. Thus, the marginal product of any input i must have the same value (D dollars) in all uses as Rule 2a requires (remember, we are temporarily measuring social values by the corresponding private values).

Rule 2b: This follows at once from the preceding result by simple division. For, symbolically, that result states that for *any* input i and any two outputs x and y, $MP_{ix} = MP_{iy}$. Hence for any other input, j, we must also have $MP_{jx} = MP_{jy}$, so that by straightforward division it follows that Rule 2b must also hold, i.e., that

$$MP_{ix}/MP_{jx} = MP_{iy}/MP_{jy}.$$

Rule 3 is somewhat more difficult to derive and the argument will only be sketched in. (As in the previous paragraph, Rule 3b follows from 3a by division so that no more will be said about 3b.) In outline, the argument consists in showing that every industry will expand its output to a point where its marginal cost is equal to the price of the product. Moreover, all consumers will expand their purchases to a point where the marginal utility of the commodity is to them equal to its price. Marginal cost and marginal

will be free, for that cannot be known in advance. Whether or not some item will be unwanted depends on how much money customers have left over from their other purchases. See Chapter 16, Section 5.

utility will therefore both be equal to the same price and, therefore, equal to each other as Rule 3a requires.

Let us go over this argument in somewhat greater detail. First let us see why every commodity's output will be expanded to a point where its marginal cost is equal to its price—that is, society will have no way of producing an additional unit of the good at a cost lower than its price.

What are the alternative ways of expanding this output? That can be done either by increased production by existing firms or by the creation of new firms. But we know that every profit-maximizing firm will expand its output until its marginal cost rises to the level of the price (if price is fixed). Moreover, by provision (3) of the price rules under discussion, any new firm which can produce the good at a lower cost will have been motivated to enter the industry and expand its operation to a point at which its marginal cost equals the fixed price of the output. Hence, there will remain no unused opportunity to expand output at a marginal cost lower than price—any further unit expansion in output anywhere in the industry which produces it must involve an addition in cost at least equal to price.

On the consumer side, the argument is simpler and far less satisfactory. We know that every consumer is motivated to buy a commodity up to a point at which its marginal utility (in money terms) is reduced to its price. Since, by provision (2) of the price arrangement under consideration, the entire output is sold, we see that a unit decrease in the output of the item must deprive some consumer of a unit of the commodity, which involves a loss in marginal utility equal to the price of the item.

This completes the argument involved in showing that marginal Rule 3a for the optimal allocation of resources must hold under the price system which has been proposed. Since the marginal utility and the marginal cost of any good will both be equal to the price of the item, they will be equal to one another, as Rule 3a requires.

However, we must still examine a fundamental weakness involved on the consumer side of the argument in which a bit of chicanery has been employed. The problem here is that we have measured marginal utility in money terms. But $5 worth of utility is not the same thing to all men—it may mean the next few days' meals to a poor family and a bit of small change to a member of "the international set." A statement that the marginal utility is the same for all consumers because it is measured by the same amount of money for everyone conceals a very strong and very questionable value judgment, which says that when any person, P, receives a unit of a commodity this adds to the utility of society as a whole an amount which is measured by the amount of money that P is willing and able to pay for it. In effect, this procedure tells us to determine the allocation of resources on the basis of an election in which some voters get to vote many times—where each dollar the consumer has to spend entitles him to another vote so that the wealthy can exercise an influence proportioned to the magnitude of their wealth. We decide that an optimal allocation of resources requires us to produce more marmalade for Ellen rather than more jam for Daniel if Ellen can afford to pay for it and Daniel cannot. Thus, in this interpretation of Rule 3a we have not avoided committing ourselves on the question of a good distribution of wealth—rather we have, by default, decided to accept the *status quo*.

7. Pure Competition and Monopoly

Using the theorem that the price system of the preceding section guarantees the satisfaction of the marginal optimality rules, we can at once deduce several of the best-known results of welfare economics.

First, there is the result that perfect or pure competition will tend to yield an optimal allocation of resources. For under pure competitive equilibrium prices are fixed as far as any individual consumer or businessman is concerned; supplies and demands are all equal, and, in the long run, all firms which can produce any product profitably will enter that industry. Thus all three requirements of the price system of the preceding section will be met by a pure-competition equilibrium which must therefore satisfy all of the marginal requirements for an optimal allocation of resources. Hence, there is a presumption that under pure competition the allocation of resources will be optimal.[5] This result and the material of the two previous sections constitute the elaborate superstructure which has been superimposed on the old common-sense notion that competition is a good thing because it prevents monopolistic exploitation of consumers and labor. However, one may well wonder whether the common-sense notion is still not more persuasive than its highly subtle and ingenious rationalization.

The nature of the theoretical argument is brought out intuitively by contrasting the world of pure competition with one in which there are a few monopolistic industries. Since, under monopoly, the price of the product falls as output expands, a monopoly will produce an output which is smaller than that of an otherwise identical competitive industry (unless

---

[5] Actually this is no more than a presumption and there remain a number of flies in the competitive ointment. We know that any optimal allocation to which marginal analysis is applicable must satisfy these marginal rules, but the converse is not necessarily true—an allocation may satisfy these rules yet not be optimal. There are two specifically important sources of possible difficulty: the second-order optimum conditions (see Chapter 4, Section 5) may not be satisfied, and social and private costs and benefits are unlikely to be equal throughout the economy. The second of these problems is discussed in Section 9 of this chapter. For an explicit and extremely lucid discussion of the relevance of the second-order conditions, see J. de V. Graaff, *Theoretical Welfare Economics.* Cambridge University Press, 1957, esp. pp. 22–26 and 66–70.

there are very extreme economies of large-scale production) as was shown in Section 5 of Chapter 11. This means that, given the total level of their employment, less resources will be used in the manufacture of monopolistically produced outputs and more of these resources will go into the remaining industries than would have been the case in an economy where pure competition was universal. Too little will be produced by the monopolies and too much by the competitive industries. Resources will be overallocated to competitively produced commodities, and monopolistic output restricted—to the social detriment.

However, the reader should observe that the argument breaks down in a world of monopolies where there are no industries operating under a regime of competition. Given the level of employment of resources, a misallocation can arise only if the demand for inputs of one set of industries (the monopolists) is low *in comparison with* that of the remaining industries. If each of a number of runners slows down, none of them need come in ahead of the others, and if each industry is weak in its bidding for resources, no lopsided allocation of these resources need result. We see, then, that some competition may conceivably be worse than none!

8. Centralized Planning Without Central Direction

The theorem about the optimality results which can be achieved with the aid of the pricing system of Section 6 has had yet another application—to the economics of socialism and central planning. A number of theorists have argued that government planning does not have to involve elaborate controls and instructions, such as factory-by-factory production targets.[6] The central authority need only compute a set of prices which satisfies the three conditions described in Section 6 and order factory managers to maximize their profits (profit maximization, too, could be made more or less automatic by basing managerial wages on the profits shown by the plants which they run). The result would then be automatic—a self-policing system for the achievement of an optimal allocation of resources. One would achieve the alleged economic benefits of central direction without the costly administrative burden and unpleasant bureaucratic interference which goes with detailed central supervision.

The "socialism by price guidance" proposal has come to be known by one of its characteristics, *marginal cost pricing*. Every firm would be forced to sell as much as it produced and to sell this output at a price equal to its marginal cost. This is the essence of the pricing arrangement.

The idea is attractive but it encounters a number of important difficulties. Perhaps the most important is that the equilibrium which results

[6] See, e.g., Lerner, *The Economics of Control,* and Oskar Lange and Fred M. Taylor, *On the Economic Theory of Socialism,* University of Minnesota Press, Minneapolis, 1938.

will maximize private rather than social net benefits. If, for example, it is important for the nation, on some criterion, to sacrifice some current consumer welfare for military preparedness or long-run economic growth, the price system of Section 6 does not take these social goals into account. Other problems of differences in social costs and returns will be discussed presently. The upshot is that the proposed pricing system may fail to accomplish one of the main purposes of central planning—the achievement of social goals which are not reflected in private returns.

Another somewhat more technical problem which plagues such a scheme for decentralized control arises if the firm's average costs decrease when the scale of its production increases (increasing returns).[7] If average costs are falling, by the standard rules of the average-marginal relationships (Chapter 3, Section 3), marginal cost must be less than average cost. Therefore, if the firm sells at a unit price equal to *marginal* cost, price must be less than average cost, i.e., unit costs will exceed unit returns so that the firm must lose money on each and every unit it sells! There is nothing the management of such a firm can do to make any profits, no matter how efficient its operations, if it sticks to a marginal cost price. Thus (even though it may sometimes be socially desirable to operate some industries which are unable to produce a profit) marginal cost pricing must, at the very least, lead to serious administrative difficulties in decreasing cost firms.

9. *External Economies and Diseconomies of Production and Consumption*

Much of the preceding discussion requires re-evaluation when we take into account divergences between private and social costs and returns. The basic idea behind the argument that the competitive price system is optimal is roughly that the businessman (like other members of the economy) can make money only by producing and marketing useful products and services. Hence he benefits only by benefiting the community and, conversely, by promoting his own interests he necessarily promotes those of the rest of the community as well. Unfortunately, there are many cases where this crucial premise breaks down—when members of the economy do things which benefit others in such a way that they can receive no payment in return, or where their actions are detrimental to others and involve no commensurate cost to themselves. In such cases of divergence between social and private returns, self-interest and social interest do not coincide. This statement must be interpreted carefully—it is not meant to contrast the welfare of individuals with some sort of abstract "social good." Rather, it says

---

[7] This problem is closely related to the difficulties which arise when the second-order maximum conditions are not satisfied. See footnote 5, above.

that when each person independently pursues his own interests he may end up less well off than he would under an optimal arrangement. Where social and private returns do not coincide, it is possible that all members of society will lose out if each of them does his best to promote his own aims.

Let us see, now, how such divergence between private and social returns are likely to arise and how they can lead to a misallocation of resources. Specifically, let us examine how they affect the theorems of the preceding sections. For this purpose it is convenient to deal, in turn, with four types of divergence between private and social returns: external economies of production, external diseconomies of production, external economies, and diseconomies of consumption.

1. *External economies of production:* This category of divergence between private and social returns has received a great deal of attention in the literature. The concept was first formulated explicitly by the English economist, Alfred Marshall, at the end of the last century.

The reader is doubtless thoroughly familiar with the idea of economies of large-scale production—the case where a firm can produce each unit of output more cheaply when it increases its scale of operations. Such a situation is referred to as a case of *internal* economies—the benefits of the firm's expansion are reaped internally, within the company. By contrast, the *external economies* case is one where an increase in the firm's production produces benefits at least part (and often a substantial part) of which devolve on others. *or others help you*

This may arise in at least two ways: (a) By expanding its operations the firm may perform a direct service to others. The standard example is the training of a labor force. If one glass-blowing firm on the island of Murano expands its operations, it may have to train more glass blowers who are potentially available for employment by its competitors, and those competitors will incur no training costs if they recruit any of those skilled workers.

(b) A second sort of external economy arises when an expansion in the operation of one company makes it cheaper to supply services to all the firms in this industry. A rise in the production of Ford automobiles will result in an increase in steel production. If there are internal economies in steel manufacturing (ordinary economies of large-scale production), steel prices may subsequently fall, and so Ford's competitors also will obtain their raw materials more cheaply as a result of the increased output of Ford cars. In sum, economies which are external to the firm may arise when the expansion of one firm makes it cheaper for all firms in the industry to obtain their inputs.

Both of these types of external economies of large-scale production clearly involve divergence between private and social returns. The firm's expansion makes it cheaper for other companies to operate, but under the prevailing price system there is no remuneration to the expanding firm for these benefits which it has conferred on others.

2. *External diseconomies of production:* An expansion of the scale of a company's operations can also have analogous disadvantageous effects. These are called *external diseconomies* of large-scale production, or simply, external diseconomies of scale. The literature abounds with illustrations of this phenomenon. If one company's increased output leads it to keep more trucks in operation, it will crowd the roads and, in particular, make it more expensive and time-consuming for other companies to ship goods by truck. Increased fishing by one group depletes the supply of fish and makes it harder for others to obtain their catch. Increased use of water or more drilling of oil wells can make it harder for others to get these resources. Increased farming of land which erodes the soil very often makes it more difficult for neighbors to produce and maintain the fertility of their territories. There is no need to add still further to these illustrations.[8]

3. *External economies and diseconomies of consumption:* An increase in consumption can also cause analogous advantages or disadvantages to others—advantages or disadvantages which are not reflected in the returns of the person who produces them. As in the production case, these external economies and diseconomies arise from subtle interdependences in the welfare of different economic units—interdependences which cannot readily be reflected in the pricing arrangement. *A* affects *B*'s welfare not just by delivering some goods to him and receiving money in return.

For example, where the Smiths try to keep up with the Joneses, if Jones buys a new cream-colored Cadillac convertible, he makes life harder for Smith. Smith must now consume more than he did before in order to accomplish no more than just maintain his old level of satisfaction. Here is an external diseconomy of consumption. On the other hand, if I purchase more education for my children I make them better citizens (or, at least, so educators would have us believe). This confers an advantage on others—it makes it possible for others to achieve a given level of satisfaction with a smaller expenditure of their own resources. In sum, any increase in consumption which makes the consumer a more efficient or inefficient producer,

[8] These are all examples of what are called *technological* external diseconomies—increased output by one enterprise requires the use of larger physical inputs by other firms to produce any given result. A different type of external diseconomy which has no such significance for welfare economics is called a *pecuniary* diseconomy. This occurs when one firm, by increasing its output, causes a rise in the price of its inputs. That makes it more expensive *in money terms* for other companies who use similar inputs. But it does not increase the social cost of their production because this production requires no larger input quantities or expenditure of time and effort than before. Increased use of leather by a shoe manufacturer may raise leather prices and hence the money costs of other shoe firms, but it need not make it any harder for them to make shoes.

or any increase in consumption which affects the consumption patterns and desires of other buyers, will produce external economies or diseconomies. If many women purchase more short skirts, they will make those with low hemlines feel increasingly dowdy and less able to resist the pressure to buy short skirts themselves; the fact that a book enters the bestseller lists may help promote its sales, etc.—in each case, any consumer's purchase has had an indirect but very real effect on his fellows.

Here, then, are some of the most significant classes of cases in which social and private returns diverge.[9] Some of the illustrations may not seem to represent cases of great social significance. But one must not conclude that external economies and diseconomies play no major role in the economy. Taken together, they assume very great significance. The fact that a large industrial firm finds it incomparably easier and more profitable to operate in an industrial community than in an underdeveloped area is in large part a result of external economies. The presence of other firms makes it far easier to run a plant—they bring with them a skilled labor force, financial institutions, organizations which can efficiently supply technical services and raw materials, and so on. Indeed, the scarcity of operating firms and the external economies which they provide has often been cited as a major problem of the backward areas—without such an initial group of firms and the external economies of their operations, it is very difficult to get enterprises started. Industry is needed to encourage further industrialization.

On the consumer side, the forces of external economies and diseconomies are also very powerful. The tastes and the demands of consumers are very heavily conditioned by the societies in which they live. Foods, clothing, housing, and many other tastes differ from country to country and from region to region, at least partly because the consumption pattern of one consumer is highly dependent on those of other members of society. In sum, the interdependence of consumer demands—the external economies and diseconomies of consumption—is by no means negligible.

It remains for us to see how these external economies and diseconomies affect the allocation of resources. The connection is easily described. If a firm or an individual makes a contribution to social welfare for which he receives no payment, he is likely to engage in this activity to a smaller extent than the interests of society require. If the production of some

[9] Many other examples can easily be cited. Air and water pollution which result from increased industrial output are classic examples of external diseconomies of production. The Piazza San Marco in Venice is the site of a case of an externally conferred benefit which, by overextension, incurs an external social cost. The cafes hire bands to serenade their customers. But, being outdoors, they cannot avoid providing music to the patrons of adjoining bistros. Unfortunately, however, with four or five of these going at once it becomes impossible to hear the music anywhere.

commodity confers external economies, private enterprise is likely to produce a less than optimum amount of this item. Company A, in deciding whether to expand its output, will not usually be led to do so by the fact that this will make things cheaper for companies B and C.

Similarly, where there are external diseconomies of production or consumption, private enterprise is likely to overallocate resources—to produce an overoptimal amount, because part of the cost of the operation is external to the firm—it is borne by others. Notoriously rare is the firm which refrains from expanding its operations because it will increase the pollution of the atmosphere or because it leads to soil erosion or the depletion of a natural resource which it does not own (such as fish in the sea).

To summarize, external economies and diseconomies can lead to a misallocation of resources even in the world of perfect competition. Too much will be produced by industries in which external diseconomies prevail, while there will be a less than optimal output of commodities whose production involves external economies. In principle, it is even possible that, where there are external diseconomies, the presence of monopolies can lead to outputs smaller, and therefore more nearly optimal, than those which would result from competition.[10]

10. Some Standard Theorems of Welfare Economics

By way of illustration of the results obtained with the aid of welfare theory, let us now summarize briefly three standard theorems of welfare economics. Each of them can be criticized in a number of respects but each result, if taken with a grain of salt, yields some useful policy insights.

THEOREM I: In a world of pure competition a tariff must result in a misallocation of resources and in a reduction in net social welfare when all affected nations are considered together.

[10] Moreover, if an industry is taken over by a monopoly, external economies or diseconomies may sometimes disappear in the process. If the expansion of one firm saves money for another firm in the same industry, this external economy becomes internal when the two firms combine into one—all the benefits accrue to the same management. This also illustrates the danger of decentralized decision-making in a single company—the manager of one division will not always pay adequate attention to the effects of his decisions on other divisions in the company (the effects of his decisions which are external to his division). As a result, a set of decisions which are optimal for the branches of the company, taken by themselves, may be far from optimal for the company as a whole. Cf. Charles Hitch and Roland McKean, "Suboptimization in Operations Problems," in Joseph F. McCloskey and Florence N. Trefethen, *Operations Research for Management*, Johns Hopkins Press, Baltimore, 1954. See also Charles Hitch, "Economics and Military Operations Research," *Review of Economics and Statistics*, Vol. XL, August 1958.

This result is almost a direct consequence of the results of Section 7. If the allocation of resources which results from competitive prices is optimal, any reallocation of resources, which results from the imposition of a tariff, and the consequent modification of prices, must be presumed to reduce welfare. This result does not say that the tariff-levying country cannot gain in the process, but any gains to this country must be more than offset by the losses of the inhabitants of other nations.

Before we go on to the next theorem, the reader should be reminded that points rationing is a method of distributing limited supplies by providing each consumer with some fixed number of ration "points," say 250 point tokens, and requiring that he give up 5 points for every pound of beef he buys, one point with every pound of sugar, etc. In this way the consumer still retains a fair amount of discretion in the choice of his purchases even though his total consumption is restricted. By making its "point price" (the number of points given up with a purchase) sufficiently high, consumption of any item can clearly be cut down as far as is appropriate.

We can now formulate

THEOREM II: Wherever it is necessary to restrict the use of a number of commodities, it is better to do so by means of a system of point rationing, in which each consumer is assigned an equal number of points to be used by him as he prefers, rather than the more usual method of assigning an equal amount of each good to each consumer.

Proof: If each consumer is, for example, assigned 1 pound of beef and 1 pound of lamb per week, in an ordinary rationing procedure, the result is necessarily disadvantageous both to consumers who prefer beef and to those who prefer lamb. If, on the other hand, each consumer is given ten points and told that he must give up five points with every pound of meat he purchases, beef lovers will get their two pounds of beef and lamb eaters their two pounds of lamb.

Indeed, if points are really so effective in limiting consumption that money income is no longer a real limit on consumption, the ration points, rather than the money prices, will become the relevant prices in the purchases of these rationed commodities. Then each rationed consumer will purchase commodities in such proportions that the marginal rate of substitution of any one commodity for another will be equal to the ratio of their fixed point prices. Hence, under points rationing, these marginal rates of substitution must be the same for all consumers as marginal optimality Rule 1 (Section 3, above) requires, whereas the rule will almost certainly be violated under a more rigid rationing system.

Points rationing may only be undesirable for one of two reasons: (a) If some consumers are considered irresponsible—say, if they will spend points on gin rather than orange juice for their children (or vice versa, depending on the point of view)—it may then be preferable to issue a fixed orange juice (gin) ration which cannot be traded for anything else. (b) If money prices are permitted to rise so much that the poor cannot afford to use up all of their ration points, fixed rations may be desired for morale purposes, to keep the wealthy from getting too large a share of the available produce in times of scarcity.

This theorem on rationing illustrates how the relatively innocuous marginal optimality Rule 1, which requires equality of marginal rates of substitution for all consumers, can help lead to significant policy conclusions.

THEOREM III: If the government decides to obtain some *fixed amount* of money by means of taxation, it is better to do so by income taxation rather than by excise (sales) taxation.

This theorem has been derived by many different arguments and has led to many counterarguments. Only one of the more subtle derivations (which avoids the questionable "consumers' surplus" concepts involved in the earlier discussions) will be outlined here. The central idea of the argument is that a taxpayer who has K dollars taken from him by means of an income tax can, *if he wishes*, always afford to purchase the combination of goods which is the most preferred of the combinations available to him if he had *exactly the same amount* taken from him by a sales tax on *some single commodity*, and started off with the same income, as will now be shown by example. It follows at once that if the man pays the income tax he must be *at least* as well off as he would be after the sales-tax payment. For the income-tax payer has available the best of the options which would be open to him as a sales-tax payer (as well as some options which would then not be available).

Consider a consumer who has an income of $100 and buys 3 units of commodity x at $10 each (Table 1). If, say, a tax of $1 on each unit of x

TABLE 1

	Income	Income after Tax	Price of x	Units of x Bought	Income Left to Spend on Items Other than x
Before tax	100		10	3	70
Excise tax	100		11	U	$100 - 11U$
Income tax (possible)	100	$100 - U$	10	U	$100 - U - 10U$
Income tax (actual)	100	$100 - U$	10	?	?

sold leads the buyer to reduce his purchase of x down to U units (his *preferred* purchase of x at this new price), a $1 excise tax on x will clearly yield the government U dollars in sales-tax money from this person (line two of the table).[11] Since the consumer now spends $11 (including $1 tax) on each of U units of x, he will be left with $100 - 11U$ dollars to spend on his other purchases.

Suppose, on the other hand, that the government were simply to collect an equal amount, U dollars, out of the income of the consumer instead of setting up a sales tax. The consumer could, if he wished (line 3 of the table), still buy U units of x (now at $10 each) and be left with 100 minus the U dollars tax minus his $10U$ dollars outlay on x, again leaving him $100 - 11U$ dollars in total to spend on other commodities. Thus, this hypothetical allocation of his money after payment of an income tax would, if he chose it, leave him exactly as well off as the sales tax, because in either case he ends up with exactly U units of x and $100 - 11U$ dollars to spend on other items. But, in fact, the income-tax paying consumer may not wish to do exactly what he would have done in the presence of a sales tax. He will, very likely, spend the $100 - U$ he has left after income taxes in some way other than buying U units of x (line 4 of the table). If so, he presumably adopts this alternative because he prefers the situation in line 4 to that in line 3. But since line 3 is identical with line 2, the *best* of the alternatives available to him under a sales tax on commodity x, *he must prefer his state after payment of income tax* (line 4) *to his situation after payment of the sales tax.* Any other numbers or algebraic symbols can be substituted in the table and the reader can see they lead to the same results—the income tax generally hurts the consumer less than does the excise tax.

In intuitive terms, what is the logic of this result? It is simply that an excise tax distorts prices from their optimum levels and forces the consumer to reallocate his expenditures among commodities in a less desirable manner. An income tax reduces the consumer's over-all purchasing power but does not directly change relative prices, and so does not force him to redirect his expenditures.

The validity of the argument has been questioned on a number of grounds. First of all, an income tax also motivates the individual to change his pattern of behavior. But it distorts his income-earning plans rather than his consumption pattern. It can lead him to work either harder or less hard than he would have if no tax had been imposed on his earnings. This does not show up in Table 1, which assumes that the consumer's total income before taxes is fixed at $100. It is true, of course, that an excise tax *also* reduces the consumer's real income so that we may still argue that the sales tax distorts consumer behavior in two ways whereas an income

---

[11] More generally, if with a sales tax the person would buy X units of x at a price of P dollars and the government wishes to collect K dollars, it must levy a tax K/X dollars on each unit of x sold, so the consumer ends up with $100 - PX - K$ dollars.

tax does so in only one. But the net effect is now a matter of judgment rather than a subject for rigorous analysis.

In practice, excise taxes can be advantageous in a number of ways. For example, they may be the more effective counterinflationary measure because they discourage spending directly and because, being regressive, they fall most heavily on the section of the public with the largest propensity to spend. Other pros and cons can easily be listed. However, there is no point in doing so because our object here is not to recommend tax policy, but to give some illustrative theorems of welfare economics and to indicate both their suggestiveness and their limitations.

11. Criteria for Welfare Judgments

As mentioned earlier, a decade ago there was much discussion of the circumstances under which the economist is entitled to make any welfare pronouncements—when he can say that policy A will, in some sense, increase the welfare of the community as a whole. This problem lies at the foundations of welfare economics, for unless the economist knows how to distinguish between a policy change which is an improvement and one which makes things worse, he is in no position to make any recommendations at all.

It is my opinion, however, that the protracted discussion of this issue was neither very necessary nor very illuminating. I believe that there is a wide variety of policy recommendations which economists have long made and can continue to make with clear consciences. On many issues the desires of the community are rather obvious. For example, during the Great Depression it required little justification for the profession to adopt the reduction of unemployment as a prime objective. Similarly, in an impoverished country, an increase in per capita income can surely be assigned a high priority. Even where the situation is not so clear-cut, the economist has enough to say on policy matters by sticking to questions of the means appropriate for the achievement of given ends. For example, in a country in which the government is seeking to build up gold and dollar reserves, the economist is clearly the person who must consider whether a devaluation will make things better or worse in this respect.

In any event, I believe that the discussion of welfare criteria was relatively sterile and was largely foredoomed to failure. Any attempt to construct a rigorous and universally applicable criterion for distinguishing what policy change is an economic improvement must founder on the problem of interpersonal comparisons. Where a policy change affects some persons favorably and others adversely, as is usually the case, there is no *a priori* way of weighing the net result. Of course, we can and must make interpersonal comparisons—we judge, reasonably, that flood victims must occupy the government's attention and receive emergency assistance at the cost of other taxpayers. We decide that the building of a road will serve the general welfare even if it is inconvenient for a few homeowners who are located in its path, and so on. However, these judgments must be rough and ready and can only be handled case by case. No abstract and general formula can be invented which handles all such problems satisfactorily.

It is nevertheless worth examining several of the general criteria which were proposed for this purpose—criteria designed to test whether or not a proposed policy change is an improvement.

1. *The Pareto criterion.* The first criterion, originally formulated by the Italian Vilfredo Pareto about half a century ago, is perfectly straightforward and perfectly unobjectionable as far as it goes. It states simply that

> Any change which harms no one and which makes some people better off (in their own estimation) must be considered to be an improvement.

This statement is certainly persuasive, and it is less empty than may at first appear. Some rather striking analytical results can be obtained with its help. For example, the argument of Section 10, that points rationing is ordinarily better than fixed-ration quantities, relies on no more than the Pareto criterion. Points rationing may permit *every* consumer to benefit by adjusting his purchases in accord with his own tastes and desires and no one need be harmed by it. For a similar reason, Rule 1 of Section 3 can be considered to be founded upon the Pareto criterion.

Unfortunately, there are many policy proposals which cannot be judged with the aid of this criterion. The Pareto criterion does not apply to any proposal which will benefit some and harm others. In other words, the Pareto criterion works by sidestepping the crucial issue of interpersonal comparison, that is, by dealing only with cases where no one is harmed so that the problem does not arise.

To compare it with the other criteria, it is convenient to translate the Pareto criterion into graphic terms. For simplicity, let us deal with a community in which there are only two persons, X and Y. In Figure 1a, let us represent the utility of individual X along the horizontal axis and that of Y along the vertical axis.[12]

The Pareto criterion then states that if we start off from a situation

[12] For this purpose it does not matter how we measure this utility (cf. Sections 5–6 of Chapter 8 and Chapter 17). The utility scales of the two individuals need not be comparable. All that is required for our purposes is that a movement toward the right in the graph, say from point A to B, always corresponds to some (unspecified) increase in X's welfare and that an upward movement represents an improvement in Y's well-being.

which is represented by a point like A, then a policy change is an improvement if it results in a move to any point like B, C, or D which lies to the right of A, or above A, or above and to the right of A. For at B, X is better off than at A with Y as well off as before, whereas the move to C benefits X without harming Y, and the move to D benefits both persons.

Pareto

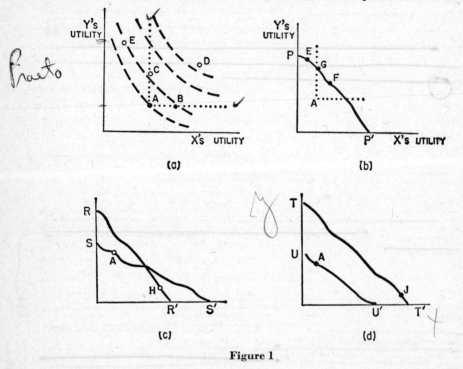

Figure 1

However, a move from A to E cannot be evaluated on the basis of the Pareto criterion, for this change increases Y's welfare but it does so at X's expense.

2. *The Kaldor criterion.* In order to permit the economist to pass judgment on a move such as that from A to E, Kaldor proposed the following criterion:[13] Suppose we ask individual Y how much he would pay (the maximum amount) rather than forego the move from A to E, and call this amount K_y. Similarly ask X how much he is willing to pay to prevent this change (call the amount K_x dollars). Then if K_y exceeds K_x Kaldor argued that Y could compensate X for his loss in welfare and yet keep some part of the gain for himself. In other words, the change is a net gain, on balance, according to Kaldor, because, at least in money terms, the gain to Y out-

---

[13] A very similar criterion was formulated by Hicks, and, later, Little drew on these to put forward a more guarded criterion of his own.

weighs the loss to X. Note that Kaldor does not require that X actually be compensated so that no one would end up with a loss. Such a change *with compensation* would be an improvement even under the Pareto criterion. Kaldor merely requires that the gainer be able, *potentially*, to make this compensation out of his gains. The Kaldor criterion then states that

> A change is an improvement if those who gain evaluate their gains at a higher figure than the value which the losers set upon their losses.

To translate this into graphic terms we must introduce a device called the utility possibility curve (PP' in Figure 1b). Suppose we start off at point F and consider what happens if X gives up some of his wealth and presents it to Y. This might result in the move to point G where X is worse off and Y better off than at F. Still another such redistribution of wealth might move us to E and so on. Thus, PP' is the locus of all combinations of X's and Y's utility levels which can be achieved by a redistribution of wealth between individuals X and Y and where this redistribution is accompanied by no other change.

Consider now the change from point A to E, which, we have seen, cannot be evaluated by means of the Pareto criterion because it involves a gain for Y but a loss for X. PP' is the utility possibility curve through point E. But there are points such as F and G which can be attained from E by a redistribution of wealth, and which lie above and/or to the right of A. On the Kaldor criterion, then, the move from A to E is in this case an improvement because it is possible to redistribute wealth at E in such a way that no one loses as a result of the change. At G and certainly at F, X has been compensated for his loss. We conclude that, on the Kaldor criterion, any move from a point A to a point E is an improvement if and only if A lies underneath the utility possibility curve through point E.

3. *The Scitovsky double criterion.* Scitovsky soon pointed out that the Kaldor criterion suffers from a serious weakness. It is possible, on this criterion, that a move from A to H (Figure 1c) will be considered an improvement, but that, at the same time, the return move from H back to A will be an improvement as well! This is shown in Figure 1c where A lies below the utility possibility curve RR', through H, but at the same time, H lies below SS', the utility possibility curve through A! It will be observed that this odd situation occurs as a result of the intersection of the two utility possibility curves in Figure 1c.

To avoid this embarrassing possibility, Scitovsky proposed a stricter test involving two parts:

(a) Use the Kaldor criterion to see if the move from the initial point to the new point is an improvement.

(b) Use the Kaldor criterion to make sure that the return

move from the new point back to the initial point is not an improvement. On this criterion, *if and only if the move passes* both *parts of the double test* is the move an improvement, according to Scitovsky.

In my view, both the Kaldor and the Scitovsky tests operate on the basis of an implicit and unacceptable value judgment. By using a criterion involving potential money compensation, they set up a concealed interpersonal comparison on a money basis. If Y's gain is worth $200 to him whereas X evaluates his loss at $70, we are not entitled to jump to the conclusion that there is a net gain in the move from A to E in Figure 1a. If X is a poor man or a miser, $70 may mean a great deal to him, whereas if Y is a rich man or a profligate, the $200 may represent a trifle hardly worth his notice. Thus, unless X is actually compensated for his loss (in which case the Kaldor criterion is unnecessary—and the Pareto criterion can do the job) the change from A to E may represent a major loss to X and a trivial gain to Y even if it passes the Kaldor criterion with flying colors.

The Kaldor and Scitovsky criteria have thus ducked the basic problem—the interpersonal comparison required to evaluate a policy change which harms X but aids Y. They duck it by saying, implicitly, that the economist's recommendation should be based on X's and Y's relative willingness and ability to pay for what they want. They accept the *status quo* distribution as a measure of the relative strength of feeling of the two individuals.

It is no answer to this criticism to say that these criteria are just designed to measure whether production, and hence potential welfare, are increased by a policy change—that these criteria disentangle the evaluation of a production change from that of the distribution change by which it is accompanied. Consider a change in production which increases gin output but reduces the output of whiskey. If X likes highballs but Y prefers martinis, the question whether this is an increase in *production* is inextricably tied in with the question of the distribution of these beverages between X and Y.

Even if the utility possibility curves never intersect (Figure 1d) the same problem can arise. At point J, X is better off but Y is worse off than at A. Thus, even though the Kaldor and the Scitovsky criteria both tell us that J is better than A because J's utility possibility curve lies above A (but not vice versa), it is not at all clear that we are entitled to this conclusion.

4. *The Bergson criterion.* A final criterion to be described here is due to Bergson. He suggests, reasonably, that the only way out of the problem is the formulation of a set of explicit value judgments which enable the analyst to evaluate the situation. These judgments as to what consti-

tutes justice and virtue in distribution may be those of the economist himself, or those set up by the legislature, by some other governmental authority, or by some other unspecified person or group.

In effect, this amounts to the construction of an indifference map ranking different combinations of the utility which may accrue to the various members of society (the broken lines in Figure 1a). Such an indifference map is called the *social welfare function*, and it does permit the analyst to judge definitively whether or not a proposed policy change is an improvement. Thus, in Figure 1a, E must be considered better than A (the change from A to E is an improvement) because E lies on a higher indifference curve of that social welfare function.

Essentially, the Bergson criterion must be judged right, if not very helpful. To decide whether E is better than A, we must certainly employ some value judgments, and unless these judgments are explicit they must be treated with suspicion. Implicit value judgments only too often are at variance even with the intentions of those who make them, as would seem to be the case with the Kaldor and Scitovsky criteria.

But the Bergson criterion, though it provides us with a highly useful frame of reference, unfortunately does not come equipped with a kit and a set of instructions for collecting the welfare judgments which it requires. Thus, it still leaves us with the difficult part of the job unsolved. At any rate, it is not advisable to approach the problem as one noted economist is supposed to have done—by confronting the chief executive of a large underdeveloped country and saying to him, "Please describe your social welfare function to me."

12. A Theorem on Democratic Group Decisions

Several economists have recently devoted considerable attention to the relationship between individual and group decisions. That is, given information about the desires of the various persons who make up the group, the problem is that of setting up reasonable procedures for the reconciliation of those desires into a group decision. It will be noted that this problem has a family resemblance to that of the preceding section.

The discussion of this subject stems largely from the work of Kenneth J. Arrow.[14] His procedure is to list some plausible acceptability criteria for social decisions and to examine their implications. He originally proposed the following four minimal conditions which social choices must meet in order to reflect individuals' preferences: (1) social choices must

---

[14] See, particularly, his *Social Choice and Individual Values*, Cowles Commission Monograph No. 12, New York, Wiley, 1951. See also Duncan Black and R. A. Newing, *Committee Decisions with Complementary Valuation*, London, Hodge, 1951, and the references to Black's work in Arrow, *op. cit.*

be consistent (transitive) in the sense that if A will be decided in preference to B, and B in preference to C, then C will not be decided in preference to A; (2) the group decisions must not be dictated by anyone outside the community or by any one individual in the community; (3) social choices must not change in the opposite direction from the choices of the members of that society; that is, an alternative which would otherwise have been chosen by society must never be rejected just because some individuals come to regard A more favorably; and (4) a social decision as between two alternatives must not change so long as no individual in the community changes the order in which he ranks these alternatives in accord with his preferences. In other words, the social preference as between two alternatives, A and B, must depend *only* on people's opinions of *just these two alternatives*, A and B (and not on any other alternative which does not happen to be immediately relevant).

At first glance, these requirements for social choice may seem a rather appropriate set of conditions for democratic decision-making. However, Arrow has shown that the matter is not so simple. He has demonstrated that it is impossible to choose among all possible sets of alternatives without violating at least one of his four criteria. In other words, it would appear that social choice must be in a sense inconsistent or undemocratic! This negative result is the central theorem of Arrow's book.

Let us illustrate how such difficulties can arise. The obvious and most standard procedure for reaching group decisions is the ballot. But it has long been known that the voting procedure runs afoul of Arrow's first requirement. That is, majority rule can lead to a pattern of social choices which is not transitive even though *every* voter has transitive preferences. This can be illustrated by an example. Three individuals, Smith, Jones, and Mznch, are to vote among three alternatives, A, B, and C, by writing a "3" next to the alternative they like most, a "2" beside the one they rank next highest, etc. Suppose, then, we get the following record of this balloting:

	A	B	C
Smith	3	2	1
Jones	1	3	2
Mznch	2	1	3

A glance at the table shows that both Smith and Mznch prefer A to B, that Smith and Jones both prefer B to C, and that Jones and Mznch prefer C to A. Hence, the majority prefers A to B and B to C but it also prefers C to A! We see then that majority voting can easily lead to intransitive social choice patterns.

Later examination of the problem has suggested, however, that Arrow's requirements are more strict than they seem at first view and that inconsistent or "undemocratic" social choice-making are not really the only alternatives.[15] The difficulty pointed out by Arrow's research can be ascribed, in part, to the fact that the fourth condition, above, is considerably more restrictive than first appears and is not merely the postulate of popular sovereignty that it seems. First, it implies that in deciding as between two alternatives the public's preferences as among still other alternatives be treated as irrelevant.[16] Suppose, for example, that half the public prefers the erection of a bridge to the digging of a tunnel under a river at comparable cost, while the other half ranks the projects the other way. The fourth condition requires that the government's decision be uninfluenced by the fact that the tunnel advocates feel this to be the most important of the public works projects currently under discussion, while those who want the bridge really think that almost any other project is of greater significance.

[15] See Clifford Hildreth, "Alternative Conditions for Social Orderings," *Econometrica*, Vol. XXI, January 1953; and Leo A. Goodman and Harry Markowitz, "Social Welfare Functions Based on Individual Rankings," *American Journal of Sociology*, Vol. LVIII. November 1952. For a more technical criticism of Arrow's argument, see Julian H, Blau, "The Existence of Social Welfare Functions," *Econometrica*, Vol. 25, April 1957.

[16] As an example of the intent of this assumption of "independence of irrelevant alternatives" consider the balloting described in the following two tables which violate the premise:

	A	B	C	D			A	C	D
Smith	4	3	2	1		Smith	3	2	1
Jones	4	3	2	1		Jones	3	2	1
Mznch	2	1	4	3		Mznch	1	3	2
Total point vote	10	7	8	5		Total point vote	7	7	4

In the left-hand table A wins by 10 points to 8 points for C. But if only irrelevant alternative B is dropped from consideration (the right-hand table) A and C become tied. In effect, the assumption states that the decision of a third party to put up a candidate who stands no chance of winning himself should not affect the outcome of the election as between the Democratic and Republican candidates.

However, it may be questioned whether it is really socially desirable to exclude such "irrelevant alternatives" from consideration. A weaker third party, such as the Liberal Party in Great Britain, derives much of whatever power it posesses from the possibility that its decision to run candidates may affect the outcome of an election. Elimination of this sort of influence may materially weaken the protection which the political system affords to the "irrelevant" minority groups. One may suspect that the popularity among mathematical economists of the axiom of "independence of irrelevant alternatives" stems as much from its spectacular consequences as from its attractiveness as a political tenet.

In addition, Arrow's fourth condition requires that only *rankings* be considered. This means that no weight be given to the intensity of desires. For example, if 50 per cent of the public demands the tunnel with considerable emotion because it feels that the bridge will deface the beauty of the area, while the other half of the public has a slight preference for the bridge because of its slightly lower cost, the difference in intensity of these preferences must, on this fourth condition, be disregarded.

Of course, we do not know how to measure intensity of feeling. Still there are cases where there would be consensus on this and where, in fact, a choice in accord with the Arrow condition would be unacceptable in principle to most of us. For example, in deciding whether to allocate labor to the production of some drug needed to treat a rare but dangerous disease or to the manufacture of Scrabble sets, we may recognize that, compassion aside, more people will want the Scrabble sets than the medicine. Yet on the crudest sort of interpersonal comparison of benefits, we may decide that the public as a whole will gain more from the production of the medicine because its potential users feel much more strongly about their preference than do the others.

However we may feel about the outcome of this discussion, it must be agreed that Arrow has again called our attention to the presence of pitfalls and treacherous problems in the analysis of group decision-making. Moreover, although the reader is given no hint of their flavor here, Arrow has made a very important contribution in his choice of mathematical tools. For he has shown that the subject matter lends itself well to the methods of symbolic logic, and by means of this demonstration he has made what may well prove to be a significant addition to the economist's stock of useful analytic equipment.

13. Concluding Remarks

In this chapter we have seen that welfare economics has run the gamut from specific (though abstractly derived) policy conclusions on particular issues like rationing, to broad, rather philosophical investigations into the proper foundations for the entire area of investigation. More recently, welfare economics seems to have gone off into a relatively new direction. It has been used in operations-research type of analysis of specific problems of government [17] and as training material for operations researchers who can learn from the special concepts of welfare economics to avoid some frequently encountered analytic booby traps. For example, the idea of external economies and diseconomies has taught us to beware of policies which yield optimal results for each of the various divisions of a firm taken

[17] See, e.g., Roland McKean, *Efficiency in Government Through Systems Analysis*, Wiley, New York, 1958.

by themselves, because by not taking into account the effects of its decisions on the rest of the company, policy-making, division by division, may yield results which are far from optimal for the company as a whole. We see, then, that the emphasis in welfare economics has swung from its rather abstract subject matter in the forties toward the other extreme—to very applied work and concrete problems of day-to-day economic decision-making.

REFERENCES

Arrow, Kenneth J., *Social Choice and Individual Values*, Cowles Commission Monograph No. 12, Wiley, New York, 1951.

Baumol, William J., *Welfare Economics and the Theory of the State*, Longmans, London, 1952.

Graaff, J. de V., *Theoretical Welfare Economics*, Cambridge University Press, New York, 1957.

Hicks, J. R., "The Foundations of Welfare Economics," *Economic Journal*, Vol. XLIX, December 1939.

Kahn, Robert F., "Some Notes on Ideal Output," *Economic Journal*, Vol. XLV, March 1935.

Kaldor, Nicholas, "A Note on Tariffs and the Terms of Trade," *Economica*, Vol. VII, November 1940.

Lange, Oskar, and Taylor, Fred M., *On the Economic Theory of Socialism*, University of Minnesota Press, Minneapolis, 1938.

Lerner, Abba P., *The Economics of Control*, Macmillan, New York, 1946.

Little, I. M. D., *A Critique of Welfare Economics*, Oxford University Press, New York, 1950, 2nd edition, 1957.

Pareto, Vilfredo, *Manuel d'Économie Politique*, 2nd edition, Girard, Paris, 1927, pp. 617–18.

Pigou, A. C., *The Economics of Welfare*, 4th edition, Macmillan, London, 1932.

Reder, Melvin, *Studies in the Theory of Welfare Economics*, Columbia University Press, New York, 1947.

Samuelson, Paul A., *Foundations of Economic Analysis*, Harvard University Press, Cambridge, Mass., 1947, Chapter VIII.

Scitovsky, Tibor, "A Note on Welfare Propositions in Economics," *Review of Economic Studies*, Vol. 9, November 1941.

CHAPTER FOURTEEN

Theory of distribution

The theory of distribution deals with the determination of the levels of payment to the various factors of production—the prices of the economy's inputs. Since general equilibrium analysis seeks to account for the determination of every price in the economy, it includes the pricing of inputs within its scope; that is, the analysis of distribution is a portion of the general equilibrium theory. Although this remark is necessary for an understanding of distribution theory where interdependence with other economic phenomena is always at the heart of the matter, it is, by itself, not very satisfying. General equilibrium analysis is, almost of necessity, so abstract that it gives us very little of the institutional flavor and special characteristics which constitute the flesh of the theory of distribution.

In this chapter there is no attempt at a systematic discussion of the traditional land, labor, and capital. So simple a breakdown has long been out of fashion, since each of these categories includes within it so huge a variety of heterogeneous elements. It is often not helpful to treat coal, cloth, and a drill press as one homogeneous element—capital. Nevertheless, the categories still retain considerable convenience as shorthand analytic devices and they will be used where they prove handy.

The discussion which follows considers separately the elements which determine the supplies of and the demands for the economy's inputs. Let us begin with the supply side.

1. Inputs in Fixed Supply

In standard analysis it is customary to treat some inputs as being absolutely fixed in supply. The economy is endowed with some set of natural resources and there is nothing which can be done to change the amounts of land, mineral deposits, and other such items. The supplies of these objects are therefore taken to be of zero elasticity—no rise in price can increase the available quantities.

In a geological sense this is perfectly correct, but from the economic point of view it is almost certainly false. What is important for our purpose is not the total territory of a country, but the amount which is in use; not the amount of oil under the ground, but the rate at which it flows into the pipe lines. But a sufficient rise in price can always be counted upon to increase the rate of flow of these items into the economy. More will be done to find new oil locations and more speculative drilling will be undertaken. Mines which had been abandoned as uneconomic will be reopened, and less wasteful methods of mining will be developed and adopted. Poor land will be irrigated and fertilized. Only in the very short run, before there is time to do much about the level of production, will supplies of any inputs be fixed. And even then, it will be possible to do something. More of an input whose price has risen will be taken out of inventory and put into production; raw materials which become more expensive will be used more carefully to reduce waste—more thought will be given to cloth cutting patterns, and gold dust recovery procedures will be tightened up by the goldsmiths; finally, other inputs, which are more abundant, will be used in larger amounts to help the firm economize on the employment of these scarce items—if there is a shortage of equipment it can be worked on a three-shift basis thus increasing the labor/capital ratio; if there is a shortage of one metal, another will be employed more frequently in its place.

In sum, as Professor Viner has pointed out, input supply functions are virtually never zero elastic from the economic point of view except, possibly, in the very short run.

2. Backward-Rising Input Supply Curves

What, then, is the nature of input supply functions? No general pronouncements on this subject are possible, but a number of observations about particular types of input can be fruitful.

Most inputs are supplied by business firms. That is obviously the case with coal, iron, oil, lumber, and many other items. Given their demand, the analysis of the supplies of these items is therefore identical with that of the determination of any output level in the theory of the firm. The discussion of Chapters 9–11 applies here without change.

However, a number of important inputs are supplied by individual persons rather than by business firms. The worker who supplies labor time, the saver who supplies funds for investment, and even the small farmer may be considered to fall into this category. Each of these groups supplies items which they can also use for themselves. The worker can use in leisure pursuits the portion of his time which he does not sell, the investor can conserve the money which he does not lend out, and the farmer can use for himself at least some of the products which he does not sell. We say that each of these sellers has a *reservation demand* for his product—he wants to reserve some for himself.

The amounts of such inputs which will be supplied then depend both on the quantities which are produced and the amounts which the sellers choose to demand for themselves. The theory of demand of Chapter 8 therefore becomes highly relevant for the analysis of these input supplies.

What will happen to the supply of such an item when its price rises? Usually we expect that a rise in price will increase the supply of a good, but we shall see now that in the reservation-demand situation this will not always be true—a rise in price may well cause a reduction in supply.

To see how this works out, let us consider the supply of labor time desired by one worker. He has 24 hours to divide between work and leisure. His desired labor supply, then, is simply what is left over from the 24 hours after his reservation demand for leisure time. Suppose there is a rise in the hourly wage rate—the price of his labor time. This means that the price per unit (per hour) of leisure time has risen. The effect on his supply of labor time can then be determined residually by determining the effect of this price rise on his demand for leisure.

As in the ordinary theory of demand, we can divide the effect of the price rise on his demand for leisure into the substitution effect (the effect of the *relative* rise in the cost of leisure compared to that of his other purchases) and the income effect (the effect of the change in his real purchasing power which results from this rise in price). As in the ordinary theory of the consumer, the substitution effect of a rise in the price of leisure will make him want to purchase less. Other consumer goods will have become relatively cheaper, hence there will be more attractive ways to spend his money. Thus the substitution effect of a rise in wages will, indeed, tend to raise the labor supply since it will work to reduce the amount of time which he wishes to keep for himself.

But the income effect will work out quite differently from the way it does with an ordinary consumer product. First, the income effect is now virtually certain to be much stronger. The consumer usually spends only a small proportion of his income on any one product, so that a rise in its price alone will have very little effect on his real income. But a worker's income is largely or even entirely dependent on the sale of his labor time. Hence, a rise in hourly wages (the price of leisure) will have a substantial effect on his income and therefore, in turn, on his purchases. The income effect of a rise in the price of leisure will, therefore, be far more important than that of a rise in the price of shoes.

A second difference between the reservation-demand and the ordinary consumer-demand cases is that the income effect in the two situations will ordinarily be of opposite direction. A rise in the price of shoes reduces the consumer's real purchasing power and therefore tends to reduce the demand for shoes—it works in the same direction as the substitution effect. But a rise in the price of his labor time makes the worker richer and permits him to afford more of the good things in life—leisure among them. Thus the income effect of a rise in the price of leisure is likely to be an increased demand for leisure. The (very likely substantial) income effect works in the reverse direction from the substitution effect. The net result may well be that a rise in the price of leisure increases its reservation demand; that is, a rise in wages may reduce the supply of labor. In this way we may well have a negatively sloping (so-called *backward rising*) supply curve of labor.

Of course, the individual worker does not usually have the option of reducing his working hours. If a factory is geared to a 40-hour week it cannot very well suit the different preferences of individual employees by hiring some people for 47 hours and others for 28 hours. But a negatively sloping supply curve of labor has nevertheless played a persistent role in the history of labor—via union demands for shorter hours which accompanied rising hourly wages. The shorter work week has occurred with the consent—indeed, as a result of the demands—of an increasingly prosperous labor force.

For similar reasons, the possibility of negatively sloping supply curves arises also in the case of savings. It has often been assumed that a rise in interest rates—the price of savings which are loaned out—will lead people to save more. But a rise in interest rates also increases the income of the lender, and he may consequently prefer to increase the proportion of his income which he spends on himself. As in the case of wages, and for exactly the same reasons, the income effect of a rise in interest rates is likely to be substantial and in the opposite direction from the substitution effect—it will tend to make for reduced savings. The net result of the income and substitution effects is in this case in considerable doubt. Some have concluded that, for the community as a whole, the supply of savings which are available for lending is on balance relatively interest inelastic—a change in interest rate will make little difference to supply because the income and substitution effects will tend to cancel out. In individual cases, however, this will not always be so. Cassel and Keynes have described one extreme case in which the savings supply curve is likely to have a pronounced negative slope.[1] Suppose a man is saving money and lending it out at interest with the objective of having enough to buy a boat when

[1] See J. M. Keynes, *The General Theory of Employment, Interest and Money*, Harcourt, Brace, New York, 1936, pp. 94 and 182.

he retires in five years. If the price of the boat does not change, the higher the rate of interest the less he will have to put away in order to achieve his objective. A rise in interest rate will therefore clearly decrease his motivation for saving because it increases his income from his lendings.

3. *Labor Supply Institutions; Keynes' Hypothesis*

The labor market is characterized by institutional peculiarities. Labor legislation, unionization, and traditional practices such as systems of seniority have made this market a world unto itself. In a theoretical volume like this it is impossible to do much more than hint at the wealth of such material which has been collected by labor economists. This subject will, therefore, be dropped with little more than a warning about the importance of the omission. However, several special hypotheses relating to the nature of the labor supply should be mentioned. The first of these is associated with Keynes,[2] and states essentially that, because of unionization, the labor supply curve is almost perfectly horizontal up to the point of full employment (however this may be defined) and that then it will become almost vertical. In more concrete terms this assertion means that despite unemployment, wages will never fall below their usual levels because the unions will hold out against any wage reductions. But once the labor force is fully employed, no increase in wages can enlarge the labor supply because there is no more labor to be had, and so the labor supply will become perfectly inelastic at that level.

Doubtless this hypothesis contains an important element of truth. Historically, wages have often risen while there were small amounts of unemployment. During the 1958 recession much publicity was given to the disturbing fact that continuing inflation and unemployment occurred side by side. This goes even further than the Keynesian assertion which states simply that wages will not fall when there is unemployment.

However, in some ways this hypothesis must be considered an exaggeration. Certainly a sufficient rise in unemployment can and has weakened unions and forced reductions in wages. At the other end of the supply curve—the region which involves a high level of employment—it should be noted again that the quantity of labor, like any other input, is never absolutely fixed in supply. A sufficient rise in wages can bring (and has brought) more women into the labor force, it can bring workers out of retirement, and it may induce more people to work overtime—and all of these clearly increase the total labor supply. Thus, the fixed level of full employment at which the supply curve rises vertically is, at best, a useful approximation.

---

[2] *Ibid.*, pp. 7–14.

A comment on the relation between the Keynesian and the backward-rising supply curve of labor is called for. Though they may appear contradictory there is really no necessary conflict between them. They have been used for the analysis of totally different types of problem. The backward-rising supply curve has been used to account for long-term changes in working hours while the Keynesian labor supply curve has been employed in discussions of the shorter-run problems of depression and unemployment.

4. Unions as Monopolies: Alternative Union Goals

It is a standard observation that unionization has made the analysis of wage determination a matter for the theory of monopoly rather than that of competition. Indeed, the wage-bargaining process is, in some discussions, taken to be a case of pure bilateral monopoly, with negotiation and the decision-making entirely in the hands of a set of union representatives on the one side, and a monolithic industry (management) group on the other. The theory of bilateral monopoly with its superimposed sets of indifference curves (as described in Chapter 11, Section 9) has therefore sometimes been applied with little or no modification to the analysis of wage negotiation.

In any event, if labor is treated as a monopoly or a quasi-monopoly, the supply curve of labor becomes an inapplicable construct. For it will be recalled that under monopoly there is no overriding industry price which the firm is forced to accept, and to which it adjusts its supply. It is therefore inappropriate for the analyst to look for the firm's supply response to various alternative given prices (the supply curve). Rather, the monopolist can set whatever price best suits his objectives by marketing an appropriate supply, and that is the only price which is applicable—there is no relevant range of supply prices to be recorded in a supply curve.

But what is this supply-price, labor-supply combination which best serves the unions' interests? Even the objectives of a firm are not self-evident, as we have seen (Chapter 10). Some firms may be interested in maximizing their profits, others their market share; still others may pursue hybrid objectives, and all of these are usually only vaguely and only implicitly defined.

The plausible objectives of trade unions are perhaps even more diverse than those of business firms. Just to suggest the nature of some of the possibilities and to indicate some of their implications, let us consider the following three alternatives:

1. that the union wishes to keep all of its members employed;
2. that the union wishes to maximize the total income of its members;
3. that the union wishes to maximize hourly wages and keep at least a steady core group of its members employed.

Figure 1a shows some of the implications of these three objectives and demonstrates that they are likely to be incompatible. Here DD' represents the industry demand curve for labor.[3] If the total membership of the union is OE_1, the union which seeks to get jobs for all of its members will have to settle for wage OW_1 per worker because any higher wage will cut the demand for labor to below OE_1. On the other hand, the union

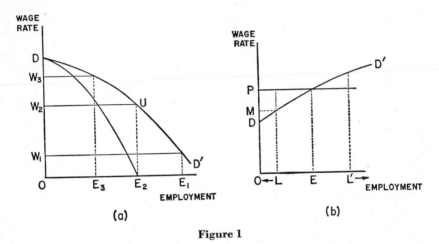

Figure 1

which wishes to maximize the total wage earnings of its members should demand wage OW_2 which corresponds to the point of unit elasticity, U, on the demand curve (for it will be remembered that where elasticity is greater than unity, a fall in labor price will increase total industry expenditure on labor, whereas where elasticity is less than unity, a rise in price will have the opposite effect). The total-wage-income-maximizing level of employment, OE_2, can also be identified by the condition that at OE_2 the marginal revenue curve, DE_2 (corresponding to the demand = average revenue curve DD'), must cut the horizontal axis, i.e., the additional wage payment resulting from an increase in employment must be zero.

Finally, if the union's core membership is OE_3, the corresponding maximum wage per worker is OW_3. Thus, depending on which objective it adopts, the union will find different policies appropriate and there will be no one decision which effectively pursues all three objectives simultaneously.

The second and third illustrative objectives require some further comment. A union which maximizes the total wage receipts of its members (objective 2) must be prepared to accept the unemployment of what may

---

[3] The use of a demand curve implies that the industry is not a monopsonist—a single unified buyer of labor for whom there is no relevant input demand curve—for the same reason that the monopolist has no supply curve in the ordinary sense.

be a substantial number of its members (E_2E_1). Nevertheless, such a policy can make good economic sense. If the total wage "take" of the employed workers is somehow redivided among all of the union members (either by an unemployment assessment on the employed members or by long "vacations" which keep all members employed part-time), the income per worker (including those who are unemployed) will be higher than it would be if all union members were fully employed. For if the union membership is fixed at OE_1, then an increase in the *total* wage receipts, which are divided among this fixed number of men, must clearly raise the average wage level.

The last of the three policies just considered, the maximization of wages for "core" union members, may be appropriate if the industry is prepared to hire a number of temporary workers who are offered membership in the union but who are not really accepted as "belonging" by the permanent members, so that their welfare is not a paramount union goal.

There is no need to expand this list of possible union objectives. It is clear that the matter is more complex than the discussion has indicated and involves considerations like the desire of the union leadership to stay in office, and the militancy of the membership. Enough has been said to indicate that no one *a priori* labor supply relationship is likely to be universally applicable.[4]

This completes our discussion of the supply of labor. Though they will not be discussed here, it must be emphasized that institutional considerations are also highly relevant for the analysis of the pricing of other inputs, e.g., the rent of land and the interest on savings.

5. *Demand for Inputs: Marginal Productivity*

Having discussed input supply, let us turn now to the demand side of the analysis. Here we find the part of distribution theory which has attracted the major share of the theorists' attention. It should be noted first that the demand for an input is a *derived demand*, that is, such an item is wanted not for itself alone. The extent to which an input will be demanded depends on its ability to assist in production and on the market value of the commodities in whose production it is employed.

The basic proposition of the standard analysis of the demand for inputs is very simple. Define the *marginal revenue (value) product* of an input to be the increase in total revenue which the firm obtains by acquiring one additional unit of this input. Then, *if the price of an input is fixed*, it will pay the firm to buy (or hire) just so many units of that input that its marginal value product is equated to its price. For if the marginal value product exceeds the price of the factor, the firm can, by definition, increase its

---

[4] For a highly suggestive theoretical analysis of alternative union policy possibilities, see John Dunlop, *Wage Determination Under Trade Unions*, Macmillan, New York, 1944.

profits by acquiring more units of the input since additional units bring in more to the firm than they cost. The reverse will be true if the price of the factor exceeds its marginal revenue product. The reader will recognize this as the usual argument behind any of the marginal conditions of equilibrium in any economic problem.

Normally, increased use of an input may be considered to have two types of effect on the firm's total revenue. One of these will usually be favorable to the firm and the other unfavorable: the additional input will increase the physical output of the firm and so tend to add to its receipts, but on the other hand, this increase in output will tend to depress the price of the product. The net result, the difference between these two effects on revenue, is the marginal revenue product. Specifically, it is equal to the price of the product multiplied by the additional output produced by one more unit of input, minus any reduction in the price of the product *multiplied by the number of units of output sold by the firm*.[5] This result makes good intuitive sense. If, for example, a firm has been producing 100,000 units of some product which sells at $5 per unit, and an additional machine can produce an additional 32,000 units of output which, when dumped on the market, reduce the price to $4, the net effect is the following: It has added to the firm's revenues 32,000 units at $4 each $(P \cdot \Delta Q/\Delta L)$, but this is offset by the $1 reduction in earnings on each of the remaining 100,000 units sold $(Q \cdot \Delta P/\Delta L)$.

In the special case of pure competition where the price of the firm's product is fixed by the market and is unaffected by any (necessarily insignificant) increase in the output of any one firm, no reduction in price will result from the acquisition of more units of an input $(\Delta P/\Delta L = 0)$ so that the marginal revenue product of the input will then simply be equal to $P \cdot \Delta Q/\Delta L$, its marginal physical product, $\Delta Q/\Delta L$, multiplied by the price of the commodity produced. We refer to this quantity as the *value of the* factor's *marginal product*, and obtain the theorem (a special case of the preceding result) that under pure competition a firm will find it profitable to hire so many units of an input that its price equals the value of its marginal physical product.

It follows from these two theorems that a firm's demand curve for any input whose price is fixed will coincide with that factor's *marginal revenue productivity* curve, the curve which shows the marginal revenue product of the input corresponding to every possible level of employment of that in-

---

[5] *Proof:* Let L be the quantity of an input and let P and Q be the price and quantity produced of the item in whose manufacture the input is used. Then the firm's total revenue is PQ, and the input's marginal product is

$$\partial PQ/\partial L = P\partial Q/\partial L + Q\partial P/\partial L$$

where $\partial P/\partial L$ is normally negative. This result is obtained by the standard rule for the differentiation of the product of two functions.

put by the firm (within the relevant range). To show that this is so, let us go back to labor demand curve DD' in Figure 1a. If the wage level is fixed at OW_1, a profit-maximizing firm will, by the preceding theorems, hire so many workers (OE_1) that the wage (OW_1) equals the marginal revenue product of a worker. Hence, with employment level OE_1, the marginal revenue product of labor must be OW_1. Similarly at employment level OE_2, the marginal revenue product of labor must be OW_2, etc. DD' therefore is clearly a marginal revenue productivity curve.

The negative slope of this demand curve is traditionally explained on the basis of the "law" of diminishing *marginal* returns. This law asserts that if the quantities of all other inputs used by a firm remain constant, and our input is subjected to successive increases in quantity, eventually this input will begin (and continue) to yield diminishing (marginal) output returns. (Cf. Chapter 9, Section 4, above.)

This, then, is a law of diminishing marginal *physical* product. In addition, an increase in output is very likely to result in a reduced market price for the product so that marginal *revenue* product is likely to fall even more sharply than does marginal physical product. That is, if a 9000th worker contributes 100 bushels of output (at $2 each) while a 10,000th worker adds only 80 bushels more and at a price of $1.75 per bushel, it is clear that marginal *revenue* product will certainly have fallen. Thus, we may well expect in most cases that as more of an input is employed, its marginal revenue product will fall, i.e., the demand curve for that factor will have a negative slope.

The law of diminishing returns is also helpful in another way. The equilibrium demand for an input is a useful analytic device only if firms are in fact motivated to hire this quantity. Otherwise there will be no reason to expect that the equilibrium quantity will even roughly represent what the firm actually does. As will now be shown, the law of diminishing returns acts like a magnet which pulls the profit-maximizing firm's input purchases toward their equilibrium levels. If the firm hires an amount of some input which is smaller than the equilibrium quantity, then diminishing returns will motivate management to *increase* its holdings of this input, thus changing its purchase level toward the equilibrium amount; and if the firm hires more than the equilibrium amount, diminishing returns will make it profitable for the firm to reduce its holdings of this item.

To see why this is so, suppose the firm hires a number of units (OE_3 in Figure 1a) of some input at which the factor's marginal revenue product, OW_3, exceeds price, say, OW_2. We know the firm will then be motivated to increase its use of that input, i.e., to move to the right toward equilibrium employment, E_2. But if marginal returns are diminishing, such an increase in the use of that factor will reduce its marginal revenue product toward the level of its price. That is, this move toward the right from employment level OE_3 must bring the firm closer to the equilibrium point U, where the marginal revenue product curve is at level of the price, OW_2. We may contrast this with the situation depicted in Figure 1b, where marginal returns are increasing. Here if we start off, e.g., at employment level OL at which the price of the input OP exceeds its marginal revenue product, OM, the firm will be motivated to reduce its use of the input (see arrow), i.e., to move toward the left in the diagram, and hence, away from the equilibrium employment level, OE.[6] The reader should show that the firm will also find it profitable to move further away from the equilibrium point when its initial position is, like OL', to the right of the "equilibrium point" as the arrow indicates. We see, then, that it is the negative slope of DD' (diminishing returns) that makes it profitable for the firm to adjust its input quantity toward the equilibrium point where price equals marginal revenue product.

6. Demand for Heterogeneous Inputs: Differential Rents

So far, we have dealt with homogeneous inputs, all of whose units are identical in productive capacity. This implicit assumption is required to permit us to talk about hiring additional workers without specifying which workers we are talking about. If the labor power of different workers were not the same, the advisability of hiring another worker would clearly depend on which worker was available for the job, a consideration which we have so far left completely out of account.

There is again a simple marginal equilibrium condition which tells the firm in what proportions to hire inputs which differ in their qualitative characteristics. Let us consider two different inputs, a and b, which may be taken to differ either only slightly (e.g., a may consist of unskilled workers and b of semi-skilled workers), or which may be totally unrelated (e.g., a may be bags of fertilizer and b may be shovels). Let P_a, P_b, MRP_a, and MRP_b be the respective prices and marginal revenue products of the two inputs. Then, the profit-maximizing firm *and also the revenue-maximizing firm* will hire these inputs in such proportions that the following condition holds:

---

[6] Actually, one may well question whether input level OE in Figure 1b should be considered an equilibrium amount. Clearly OE is a point of *minimum*, not maximum profit (a move in either direction from OE increases the firm's profits) so that there is absolutely no reason for the firm ever to wish to be at point E. The difficulty is that (Chapter 4, Section 5) at point E the first-order maximum conditions are satisfied but the second-order conditions are not. This indicates that the second-order profit-maximization condition for the determination of the hiring level of some input is that there be diminishing marginal returns to that input.

$$\frac{MRP_a}{P_a} = \frac{MRP_b}{P_b}.$$

The logic of this condition is obvious. If the condition does not hold, say if the left-hand fraction is the larger of the two, then an additional dollar's worth of input a will add more to revenue and to profit than does a dollar spent on b. It will then pay the firm to reallocate its budget between a and b, spending more on a and less on b, so that a budget in which the above equation does not hold cannot possibly represent an equilibrium allocation.

We can probe deeper into the matter and find out something more about the relative prices of inputs whose productivity differs. Consider two workers, c and d, both employed at similar jobs by different firms, and suppose that c is more productive than d, specifically, that the return on c's output per month is $1000 and that the corresponding figure for d is $950. In the long run, competition among the firms will tend to make the monthly wages of c and d differ precisely by the difference in their *total* value output, $50. For, suppose that c's wage is only $20 higher than d's. It will then pay d's employer to offer to hire c (instead of d) at a wage increase of, say, $10 per month, thereby increasing his (the employer's) receipts by $50 and his wage payments by only $20 + $10 = $30, which is clearly profitable. But when d's employer makes this bid to c, it will pay c's original firm to try to keep him rather than being stuck with the less efficient worker, d. This firm will therefore be forced to bid c's wage up even higher, and so on, until c is receiving exactly $50 more than d—so that it will be equally remunerative to a firm to hire either of these inputs; c's wages will not be bid any higher than this, since if his monthly wage were, say, $75 more than d's when his output is only $50 larger, d's labor time will clearly be the better buy, and either c's wage will tend to fall or that of d will be bid up. In practice, of course, wage differences are never that closely matched to differences in product vity.

There are various obstacles which prevent firms from bidding against one another for their inputs and prevent inputs from moving from firm to firm, to where earnings are highest. Firms do not have complete information on the productivity of the inputs currently hired by other companies, there are *transfer costs* involved in moving an input from one firm to another, including the possible loss of seniority and pension rights for workers who move to a new firm, as well as transportation costs and family dislocation costs if a move requires a worker to change his home. Nevertheless, despite these reservations, there is considerable validity in the theorem that the prices of inputs will tend to reflect the differences in their total productivity. The rent on a more fertile piece of land will be considerably higher than that on a barren area. Land desirably located in the center of a large city rents for much more than land in a sparsely inhabited area. Skilled labor receives higher wages than unskilled labor. A new, efficient factory will sell for more than one which is obsolete.

This bonus to a more efficient unit of an input is sometimes called its *differential rent*. The terminology harks back to the classical rent theory from which the analysis is derived. The classical rent discussion argued that at any point in time only better parcels of land will be in use and those which are not in use are the less productive areas which, even if they were available free, would yield no profit. Some lands, the *marginal lands*, are just on the borderline, yielding neither profit nor loss and their price must be zero since no one is motivated to pay anything for such a parcel. Any other piece of land will rent at the difference between its value yield and that of a piece of marginal land which is equal to it in area. Thus, all employed pieces of land will be hired out at their differential rent level and all parcels of land will yield the same net profit to those who use them after deduction of rental costs.

If there is an increased demand for land, it will pay to increase the extensiveness of use of those parcels which are currently employed (by more careful cultivation, more irrigation, more fertilizer, etc.) but it will also pay to bring some formerly submarginal lands into cultivation. This means that the lands which were formerly marginal must now be more productive than the territory which is now on the borderline of profitability, and the rental price of the formerly marginal land must therefore rise from zero to this difference in productivity. The rents on all other lands must then also rise accordingly. This, in summary, is the classical rent analysis which was first described here in more generalized form to account for the differences in the prices of any heterogeneous inputs.

7. Summary: Outline of a Theory of Distribution

We have now gathered together the elements of a theory of distribution. Both the supply and the demand sides of the problem have been discussed. The supply relationships for those inputs which are produced by ordinary business enterprises have exactly the same structure as the supplies of ordinary consumers' goods. Other supply curves may be backward-rising because of the income effect of a rise in the price of an input. Still other special supply relationships were also outlined. On the demand side it was shown that the profitability of the hiring or purchase of an input depends on its marginal physical productivity and on the price of its product. Equilibrium wages, rents, and other input prices are then determined by the condition that their markets be cleared—that all input supplies and demands be equal. If, for example, a union succeeds in fixing wages at some preferred level at a bargaining session, firms will then hire that number of workers whose marginal physical product is equal to the wage per worker. A slight complication arises if an increase in demand for labor by the firm raises wages (wages are not fixed and unaffected by the behavior of the firm as was assumed throughout the preceding discussion). In that case we must apply the usual marginal profit-maximization rule: marginal *cost* equals marginal revenue. The firm should see that the marginal revenue product of labor is equal *not* to the wage per laborer but to the *marginal wage cost*, the increase in wage payments which results when the firm hires another worker—the wage of the additional worker plus any addition to the wage of the rest of the labor force which results from his being hired.

This result is still deeply embedded within the general equilibrium theory. Clearly, the demand for any input depends also on the price of co-operating and substitute inputs. A rise in the price of cloth can put tailors out of work, while a rise in the price of machinery can increase the demand for labor to do the jobs which would otherwise be mechanized. This result follows from the theorem that in equilibrium the ratio of its price to the marginal revenue product of any input, x, must equal the corresponding ratio for any other input, y. We have also seen that demand for inputs depends, in turn, on the prices and demands for the products which they turn out. We are back at the simultaneous relationships of general equilibrium analysis.

This is not an entirely satisfactory state of affairs, because although a number of useful results have already been described, it is not always easy to obtain theorems with substantial empirical content out of a complex and highly abstract set of general equilibrium relationships, few of which are specified in any detail. Perhaps the most noteworthy exception is the classical theory of rent which played an important role in the classical views on public policy and in their dynamic model, neither of which will be described here. The rest of this chapter will discuss several attempts to obtain other interesting theorems from the theory of distribution.

8. A Macroeconomic Model of Distribution

One way of obtaining more fruitful results from the analysis of general equilibrium models has been the use of *aggregative* or *macroeconomic* models. Such models lump together large numbers of moderately diverse economic variables and relationships and treat the resulting aggregates as homogeneous economic elements. In this way, manageable models involving small numbers of variables and relationships are obtained. Some violence is always done to the facts in the process of aggregation. For example, the statement that the economy is in equilibrium when the total effective demand for commodities equals the total supply is misleading in that this condition can conceal serious difficulties of oversupply in some industries and shortages in others. One must therefore seek fruitfulness rather than rigor in a macroeconomic model. A completely formalistic macro model is likely to be the worst of both worlds because it is apt to offer neither empirical insights nor an accurate analytic mechanism.

The use of macroeconomic models in the theory of distribution is most readily illustrated by the Keynesian interest analysis. The liquidity preference theory is clearly such a construct and its policy implications have been widely discussed. However, because it can be described more briefly and because it is less well known, it will be more useful, for our purposes, to describe another macroeconomic model whose primary aim is to analyze the share of wages in the total national product.[7]

In outline, the model is based on two propositions: that the share of wages is dependent on the level of national income and that the effective demand for national income (output) is, in turn, dependent on the share of wages. These two relationships together determine (simultaneously) the level of national income and the proportion of wages to other forms of income.

Suppose that the annual wage rate, W, is somehow set by union-industry bargaining so that at every level of annual national output, Y (dollars), managements can decide what is the optimal number of workers to hire, and the level of employment is therefore a function of national income, $f(Y)$. This level of employment, $f(Y)$, multiplied by the wage rate, W, is the total payment of wages, $W \cdot f(Y)$. The rest of output, $Y - W \cdot f(Y)$, is then the income which accrues to other classes of income earners.

Assume now that workers spend a larger proportion of their incomes than do other economic groups, say that workers spend the proportion k of their incomes (their average and marginal propensity to spend is k) whereas the corresponding figure for the rest of society is k^*, where, by assumption, $k > k^*$. Total expenditure (effective demand) will, therefore, be equal to worker expenditure, $kWf(Y)$, plus nonworker expenditure, $k^*[Y - Wf(Y)]$. Equilibrium is given by the condition that total production, Y, be equal to the demand for it, i.e., that

$$(1) \qquad Y = kWf(Y) + k^*[Y - Wf(Y)]$$

where W, k, and k^* are assumed to be known constants. This is a single equation, with one unknown, Y, which can be solved for the equilibrium level of national income, Y_e. The corresponding equilibrium share of wages can then be computed from the expression $Wf(Y_e)$.

---

[7] The discussion is a variant of the model originally constructed by Kaldor. See Nicholas Kaldor, "Alternative Theories of Distribution," *Review of Economic Studies*, Vol. XXIII, No. 2, 1955–56.

The analysis suggests an interesting policy conclusion. Suppose equilibrium national income is below the full employment level, and that the employment function, $f(Y)$, is independent of the level of wages. Then a rise in wage level will transfer income from a group of low spenders to a group of high spenders so that total effective demand and hence employment and the level of national income must all rise![8] The moral is, apparently, that during a period of depression a wage rise is likely to be a good thing and may produce at least part of the income necessary to pay it. Boulding has called such a construct a "widow's cruse" model, after the legend of the widow who found that emptying her pitcher only filled it up again. Here the payment of more wages out of national income helps to produce the wherewithal to pay them by increasing demand and therefore improving business prospects.

Of course, such a model cannot be accepted at face value. A rise in wages may, for example, lead to mechanization in an effort by employers to replace workers, so that the demand for labor at every level of income, $f(Y)$, may fall when wages rise, and the result may be that a rise in wages reduces the share of wages out of national income. The effect of a rise in wages on business expectations is also difficult to predict and it, too, may conceivably affect employment adversely. Nevertheless, despite this and other reservations, this macroeconomic model does at least yield results which are suggestive and applicable to policy problems, something which is rarely obtained from a complex and abstract general equilibrium model.[9]

[8] *Proof:* A rise in wage level by amount ΔW will raise workers' expenditure to $k(W + \Delta W)f(Y)$, and nonworkers' expenditure will change to $k^*[Y - (W + \Delta W)f(Y)]$ so that total demand will have changed from

$$kWf(Y) + k^*[Y - Wf(Y)]$$

to $\qquad\qquad k(W + \Delta W)f(Y) + k^*[Y - (W + \Delta W)f(Y)].$

By subtraction, we see that demand will have changed by $(k - k^*)\Delta Wf(Y)$, that is, effective demand must have risen, since $k > k^*$.

[9] The model as presented in the text is incomplete. It does not tell us what determines the level of wages, W, which we took to be set to begin with. The model can be *closed* (completed) by assuming, for example, that the level of wages depends on the level of employment—the greater the demand for labor, the higher the wage level. This gives us a wage function

(2) $\qquad\qquad\qquad\qquad W = g(E)$

where E is the level of employment, i.e.,

(3) $\qquad\qquad\qquad\qquad E = f(Y)$

so that these two equations together with the income equilibrium (supply = demand) equation (1) can be solved for the unknown equilibrium values of the three variables, Y, E, and W.

In this form the structure of this model closely parallels that of the entire chapter. Equation (1) describes the demand for goods from which the demand for labor is derived via equation (3) whereas Equation (2) is a supply equation for labor which can, e.g., be interpreted as the Keynesian supply function described in Section 3, above.

9. The Constancy of Labor's Share

There is a fair amount of empirical evidence that the share of wages in the national income of the United States has remained relatively constant for as long a period as is covered by our records.[10] There have been a number of attempts at explanation of this apparently remarkable fact. The usual explanation of the relatively fixed proportion between wage payments and total national income is based on the hypothesis that the production function is linear and homogeneous, i.e., that it yields constant returns to a proportionate increase in the use of all inputs (see Chapter 9, Section 5), and that, moreover, it takes the special form

$$Y = kL^a C^{(1-a)}$$

where k and a are positive constants (and $a < 1$). Here Y represents national output (income), L is the quantity of labor input, and C is the quantity of capital employed. This is called a *Cobb-Douglas production function*, after the authors of this empirical hypothesis.[11]

It is easy to show that this formula is that of a linear homogeneous production function.[12]

Moreover, if labor is paid a wage equal to its marginal product, it is easy to show with the aid of some simple differential calculus that this production function will yield a share of wages relative to total output which is fixed and independent of the values of the variables Y, L, and C as the empirical evidence seems to indicate. In fact, the ratio between total wage income and total output, Y, must in these circumstances be exactly equal to a, the exponent of L in the Cobb-Douglas production

---

[10] For the most sophisticated and most recent discussion, see Melvin W. Reder, "Alternative Theories of Labor's Share," *The Allocation of Economic Resources: Essays in Honor of Bernard Francis Haley*, by Moses Abramovitz and others, Stanford University Press, Stanford, Calif., 1959. But see Robert M. Solow, "A Skeptical Note on the Constancy of Relative Shares," *American Economic Review*, Vol. XLVIII, September 1958.

[11] See Paul H. Douglas, *The Theory of Wages*, Macmillan, New York, 1934, Chapters V–IX, esp. p. 133, and Reder, "Alternative Theories of Labor's Share." The widow's cruse theories described in section 8 have been used in an alternative explanation of the constancy of labor's share.

[12] For if we increase L to vL and C to vC (where v is any constant), then output is increased to

$$k(vL)^a(vC)^{(1-a)} = v^a v^{(1-a)} kL^a C^{1-a} = vkL^a C^{1-a} = vY$$

i.e., output will have risen from Y to vY—it will have increased in the same proportion as did the labor and capital inputs, so that there are, indeed, constant returns to scale. For the derivation of the rule that $v^a v^{(1-a)} = v$, see Chapter 2, Section 4, above.

function.[13] A similar result must clearly apply to the income of capital.

It is to be observed that there is no *a priori* reason for accepting the validity of the Cobb-Douglas production function. It is merely an empirical hypothesis which has been proposed to explain an empirical observation. But that is good scientific procedure which always builds and tentatively accepts theoretical constructs only because their implications accord with (explain) observed phenomena. It is to be added that, at least so far, the statistical evidence does not appear to contradict the Cobb-Douglas hypothesis.[14]

10. The Adding-Up Controversy

This chapter ends with a discussion which may be of interest primarily as a curiosum in the history of economic doctrines. When the marginal productivity theory first achieved popularity just before the turn of the century, some economists attempted to use it as a basis for moralizing. It was even suggested that since the analysis showed that every input was paid the value of its marginal product, the distribution of income under free competitive capitalism must be morally right and just.[15] It is easy to show loopholes in this curious argument, which, for example, implies that there is justice in the landlord's collection of rent because he happens to own land and that land contributes to the production of food! To paraphrase one modern writer, this view represents an attempt to impute virtue to partial derivatives (the marginal products). The marginal productivity theory is an empirical hypothesis, and from it no legitimate evaluative conclusions can be drawn without the careful and explicit addition of a set of value judgments which can serve as the criteria of good and evil.

But this is only by way of introduction to the subject matter of this section. In the course of the distributive-justice discussion there arose another question. Suppose every productive input is paid the value of its marginal product. Does this mean that the entire product will always thereby be handed out to those who worked on it, or may something be left over to fall into the clutches of an exploiter? Indeed, is there always enough on deposit in the production bank to pay out all of these marginal

---

[13] *Proof:* The marginal product of labor, $\partial Y/\partial L$, is found by differentiation of the production function to be $akL^{(a-1)}C^{(1-a)}$. Since this is the wage per worker, total wage payments must equal this amount multiplied by the number of workers, L, i.e., the wage bill must be

$$LakL^{(a-1)}C^{(1-a)} = akL^aC^{(1-a)} = aY.$$

[14] See Robert M. Solow, "Technical Change and the Aggregate Production Function," *Review of Economics and Statistics*, Vol. XXXIX, August 1957, and Reder, "Alternative Theories of Labor's Share."

[15] See J. B. Clark, *The Distribution of Wealth*, Macmillan, New York, 1899, esp. Chapter I.

product claims? It became important to the discussants to show that the sum of the marginal products *added up* exactly to the total output—that there was neither surplus nor deficit left at the end.

Here the linear homogeneous production function again came to the rescue. There is a standard mathematical result, called *Euler's theorem*, which tells us that if a production function involves constant returns to scale, the sum of the marginal products will actually add up to the total product.[16]

The injection of the homogeneous linear production function into the discussion by Wicksteed[17] opened a long controversy over the plausibility of the hypothesis that the production function will take this form in practice. Closely related alternative solutions were also proposed but there is little point in going into them here. The primary purpose of the discussion

---

[16] The proof depends on another differentiation theorem, the total differentiation proposition which states that if we have the function $z = f(x, y)$ and that if, in turn, x and y are both functions of some variable t, i.e., $x = F(t)$ and $y = G(t)$, then

$$\frac{dz}{dt} = \frac{\partial f}{\partial x} \cdot \frac{dx}{dt} + \frac{\partial f}{\partial y} \cdot \frac{dy}{dt}.$$

This preliminary result is easy to prove by the methods of Chapter 4, Section 2, but the proof would take us too far afield. However, the result is intuitively plausible and states that the effect of a change in t on z is composed of two parts: the part which is transmitted via the effect of t on x and the part which is transmitted through y. Thus, the latter is represented by the expression $(\partial f/\partial y)(dy/dt)$. For (dy/dt) is the change in y produced by the increment in t and $(\partial f/\partial y)$ is the resulting change in z produced by each unit of this change in y.

Now, to derive Euler's theorem, we note that for a linear homogeneous production function $P = g(L, C)$ we have, for any k

$$kP = g(kL, kC).$$

Taking the total derivative of kP with respect to k (i.e., setting $kP = z$, $kL = x$, $kC = y$, and $k = t$ in our formula for dz/dt) we obtain

$$\frac{dkP}{dk} = \frac{\partial g}{\partial kL} \cdot \frac{dkL}{dk} + \frac{\partial g}{\partial kC} \cdot \frac{dkC}{dk}$$

or

$$P = \frac{\partial g}{\partial kL} L + \frac{\partial g}{\partial kC} C.$$

Since this result holds for *any* value of k it must also be valid for $k = 1$ so that

$$P = \frac{\partial g}{\partial L} L + \frac{\partial g}{\partial C} C.$$

This is Euler's theorem for the linear homogeneous production function $P = g(L, C)$. The proof holds for any number of inputs. Since $\partial g/\partial L$ is the marginal product of labor and $\partial g/\partial C$ is the marginal product of capital, the equation states that the marginal product of labor multiplied by the number of laborers (each of whom is paid this amount) plus the corresponding total payment to capital exactly equals the total product, P.

[17] See Philip Wicksteed, *The Coordination of the Laws of Distribution*, Macmillan, London, 1894.

has really been to indicate another property of linear homogeneous production functions—Euler's theorem—which has also been highly useful in many theoretical discussions, and to indicate once again that the distribution of income is closely tied in with the form of the production function.

As for the controversy itself, as Samuelson pointed out[18] the discussion really seems to have missed the main point. Whether there are any profits of exploitation left over for the capitalist to haul in is really a matter of market conditions. For example, as we have seen, in the long run under perfect competition prices of outputs and inputs will settle toward levels at which there is nothing left over for payment to the entrepreneur in excess of his managerial wages and interest on his capital, but under monopoly there will normally be profits in excess of this amount. The older discussion abstracted entirely from the product and input markets in which the distribution of income is determined and where competitive pressures, if anything, will rob the exploiter of the fruits of his exploitation.

REFERENCES

American Economic Association, *Readings in the Theory of Income Distribution*, Blakiston, Philadelphia, 1946.

Douglas, Paul H., *The Theory of Wages*, Macmillan, New York, 1934.

Dunlop, John, *Wage Determination Under Trade Unions*, Macmillan, New York, 1944.

Haley, Bernard F., "Value and Distribution," in Howard S. Ellis, ed., *A Survey of Contemporary Economics*, Blakiston, Philadelphia, 1948.

Hicks, J. R., *The Theory of Wages*, Macmillan, New York, 1932.

Kaldor, Nicholas, "Alternative Theories of Distribution," *Review of Economic Studies*, Vol. XXIII, No. 2, 1955–56.

Reder, Melvin W., "Alternative Theories of Labor's Share," *The Allocation of Economic Resources: Essays in Honor of Bernard Francis Haley*, by Moses Abramovitz and others, Stanford University Press, Stanford, Calif., 1959.

[18] *Foundations of Economic Analysis*, Harvard University Press, Cambridge, Mass., 1948, pp. 83–87.

PART III

Recent Developments
in Mathematical Economics

CHAPTER FIFTEEN

Input-output analysis

1. The Economic Problem and the Assumptions

Input-output analysis, for which we are indebted to Professor Leontief, is the name given to the attempt to take account of *general equilibrium* phenomena in the *empirical* analysis of *production*. The three italicized elements in this statement are crucial and merit further discussion. Reversing their order, we observe, first, that the analysis deals almost exclusively with production. Demand theory plays no role in the hard core of input-output analysis.[1] The problem is essentially technological. The investigation seeks to determine what can be produced, and the quantity of each intermediate product which must be used up in the production process, given the quantities of available resources and the state of technology.

The second distinctive feature of input-output analysis is its devotion to empirical investigation. This is primarily what distinguishes it from the work of Walras and later general equilibrium theorists. A consequence of this no doubt long-overdue concern with the facts is that compromises have been forced on the investigator. Input-output employs a model which is more severely simplified and also more narrow in the sense that it seeks to encompass fewer phenomena than does the usual general equilibrium

[1] This is strictly true only of the *open model* which is described here. In this model the final demand sector is, in effect, taken to be outside the production economy and final products are "exported" to the consumer inhabitants of this "foreign" demand sector. There is, however, a *closed model* in which labor is treated as a produced commodity and consumption as the raw materials used up in the production of labor. Here at least some rudimentary demand analysis must enter to show how the levels of consumption demands are related to the levels of labor outputs supplied.

theory. Its narrowness lies in its exclusive emphasis of the production side of the economy. Its oversimplifications I shall discuss presently.

The third distinctive feature is its emphasis of general equilibrium[2] phenomena. Input-output seeks to take account of the interdependence of the production plans and activities of the many industries which constitute an economy. This interdependence arises out of the fact that each industry employs the outputs of other industries as its raw materials. Its output, in turn, is often used by other producers as a productive factor, sometimes by those very industries from which it obtained its ingredients. Steel is used to make railroad cars and railroad cars are, in turn, used to transport steel and the coal and pig iron which are used in its manufacture. Other examples should come to mind at once.

The basic problem, then, is to see what can be left over for final consumption (consumer, military, etc.) and how much of each output will be used up in the course of the productive activities which must be undertaken to obtain these net outputs. It should be clear that a successful attack upon these problems can result in an abundance of applications. It can be used in predicting future production requirements if usable demand estimates can somehow be obtained. Particularly, it can be used for economic planning including problems of economic development in "backward areas" and problems of military mobilization. A more modest purpose which it has already successfully begun to serve is the provision of a very illuminating detailed structure for national income accounting.

As was stated earlier, the intransigence of the empirical materials and the computational problems have forced on input-output analysis a number of simplifying assumptions even more extreme than those usually employed in our theoretical models. Particularly noteworthy are two assumptions, each of which has to some extent been relaxed in practice. One assumption, which will not be discussed, states that no two commodities are produced jointly. Each industry produces only one homogeneous output. But this restriction can be somewhat relaxed by interpreting this good as a composite commodity which is made up of several items produced in fixed proportions. Such a compound good can, for example, consist in packages of chewing gum and fertilizer in which there are always ten sticks of gum and one pound of fertilizer.

Perhaps more serious is a second assumption which states that in any productive process all inputs are employed in rigidly fixed proportions and that the use of these inputs expands in proportion with the level of output.

---

[2] The term "equilibrium" is misleading here. The outputs found by this method need not satisfy market equilibrium conditions. The analysis qualifies for the title "general equilibrium" in that it takes account of the interdependence of the various sectors of the economy. Perhaps we can say, more properly, that the model is characterized by the "general" without the equilibrium.

This is a special case of an assumption of constant returns to scale (see Chapter 9, Section 5). But the fixed-proportions assumption is far more restrictive. Constant returns to scale is perfectly consistent with the substitution of one factor for another. A linear homogeneous production function (constant returns to scale) permits both labor-intensive and capital-intensive processes. The firm whose production function exhibits constant returns can, if it wishes, have one hundred workers for every $1000 invested in machinery, or it may use machines which require only ten workers per $1000 machine investment. A linear homogeneous production function requires only that if the firm decides to triple the scale of either of these types of operation, the result will be a tripling of output. Not so the Leontief fixed-proportions premise, which requires that a manufacturing process which is labor-intensive offer no option of a capital-intensive alternative.[3] If 53 men per $1000 of investment are required at any level of operation, it is assumed that the same ratio will be required no matter how much the size of the firm expands or contracts. Whether this assumption is relatively innocuous or does considerable violence to the input-output results is still under dispute. But as has been argued in Chapter 14, the premise is certainly never absolutely true, even in those cases where chemistry and engineering dictate fixed proportions between some ingredient and output.

2. The Mathematics

Basically, the input-output analysis consists in nothing more complicated than the solution of a set of N simultaneous linear equations in N variables. To illustrate this, let us consider a three-industry economy which produces coal, steel, and the service of railroad transportation. Each of these is measured in dollar terms. Each of these industries employs the products of the others in its manufacture, say in proportions shown by the following table:

User of Output

		Steel	Coal	R.R.
	Steel	0.2	0.2	0.1
Producer	Coal	0.4	0.1	0.3
of	R.R.	0.2	0.5	0.1
Input	Labor	0.2	0.2	0.5
	Total	1	1	1

For example, the first column of the table states that every dollar's worth

[3] But cf. the Samuelson substitution theorem described in section 4 of this chapter.

of steel uses in its manufacture 20¢ in steel, 40¢ in coal, 20¢ in railroad transportation, and 20¢ in labor.

Suppose, now, that somehow there have been set consumer output targets of \$100 million in steel, \$20 million in coal, and \$40 million in railroad transportation. How much of each of these goods will have to be manufactured for both consumer and industrial use to meet the final output goals? Let S, C, and R represent the dollar value of this total output of steel, coal, and railroad transportation, respectively. Let us first examine the demands on the steel industry: In addition to the 100 demanded by final consumers, there will be the demand for its product for internal use which (the table tells us) amounts to 2/10 of the total steel output or $0.2S$. Similarly, the railroad industry will require 1/10 of a dollar of steel for every dollar of its service, so that the total railroading demand for steel will be $0.1R$, etc. Thus we have the equation

(total steel output) equals (amount used in steel mfg.)
$$S \qquad = \qquad 0.2S$$

plus (use in coal mfg.) plus (R.R. use) plus
$$+ \qquad 0.2C \qquad + \qquad 0.1R \qquad +$$

(amount left over for consumption)
$$100$$

or
$$S = 0.2S + 0.2C + 0.1R + 100.$$

Similarly, we have the following two equations giving the amounts of coal and rail transportation available for final consumption:

$$C = 0.4S + 0.1C + 0.3R + 20$$

and
$$R = 0.2S + 0.5C + 0.1R + 40.$$

These are three simultaneous linear equations in the three unknowns, S, C, and R. If we solve the equations for the values of these variables we find what we started out to seek—the total outputs of the three commodities needed to meet the stated consumer targets. Only one more step is required. We note from the input-output table that \$0.2 of labor time are consumed in the manufacture of \$1 of steel, so that $0.2S$ dollars of labor will be needed to produce the required S dollars of steel production. Continuing in this way we see that $0.2S + 0.2C + 0.5R$ dollars worth of labor will be needed to produce the outputs of the three commodities required by our program. Taking the price of labor to be fixed, we see that this involves a specific requirement of labor man-hours. If this computed number does not exceed the available supply, all is well—the targets are feasible. Otherwise more modest targets must be substituted. That is the core of the theory of input-output.

We can see now why it is so convenient to work with fixed coefficients of production. With variable input proportions, single numbers will not suffice in the input-output table. Instead we would have to deduce, from the available statistics and engineering information, functional relationships between the level of output of each industry and the quantity of each input which would be required to produce it. The enormous statistical problems should be obvious enough. It is equally clear that the relevant equations would be complicated enormously. Even with the huge economy effected by the fixed-coefficients premise, the statistical and computational difficulties are tremendous. We can see that the three first rows of our table contain nine figures, the three inputs required by each of the three industries. Similarly, a four-industry model would require more than 16 figures, and so on. The number of required pieces of statistical information increases as the square of the number of industries considered, although in practice the work is reduced by the fact that many of the entries in the input-output table are zeros because some industry, A, does not use as an input any of the products of some other industry, B. It can also be shown that the number of computational steps involved in solving the equations increases as the cube of the number of industries. Thus, the labor involved in an input-output analysis rapidly becomes astronomical as the breakdown of industrial classifications becomes finer. A table has been constructed for a model involving some 450 industries, but most computation has involved considerably fewer industries. Certainly even 450 industries is too coarse a breakdown for most detailed planning purposes in an economy where the number of items produced can be considered to go well into the millions.

3. A Dynamized Input-Output Model

The Leontief model has appeared in a number of modified forms. One which is of considerable analytical interest is a dynamic model in which specific account is taken of the interrelationship of current and past outputs, and, in particular, of the building up of stocks of capital goods (factories, goods in process, machinery, etc.).[4] For purposes of this discussion we may consider that a current output can be used for any or all of the following three purposes: for current consumption; as an input in the production of some other output; and, finally, as an addition to the economy's stock of capital. The first two uses of an output have already made their appearance in the static input model. It is the last possibility,

---

[4] See Wassily W. Leontief and others, *Studies in the Structure of the American Economy*, Oxford University Press, New York, 1953, Chapter 3. For a critical discussion see Robert Dorfman, Paul A. Samuelson, and Robert M. Solow, *Linear Programming and Economic Analysis*, McGraw-Hill, New York, 1955, Chapters 11 and 12.

capital investment, which is the novel feature that characterizes the dynamic model.

If the output in question is a building material or a piece of machinery it is clear how it can be used to add to the stock of equipment, factories, and other productive facilities. But other outputs can also help to facilitate economic activities—production and marketing in the future. Inventories of raw materials and goods in process are obviously indispensable for smooth production, and effective marketing clearly requires stocks of finished goods. Hence the accumulation of outputs which are not used up when they are turned out can be essential for future production. This observation constitutes a tie-in between present and past (or between present and future), which is the crucial characteristic of any dynamic model.

The mathematical relationships which make up the dynamic system are a fairly straightforward extension of the ordinary input-output equations. The dynamic conditions are of two kinds:

1. Current output of each commodity must suffice to cover consumption demands plus interindustry demands plus demands for addition to inventory. Thus, the first equation of the preceding section would now read

$$S \geq 0.2S + 0.2C + 0.1R + 100 + (K_{st+1} - K_{st}).$$

Here K_{st} is the current (period t) accumulated capital stock of steel and K_{st+1} is therefore next year's steel stock. Assuming away wear and depreciation, the difference, $K_{st+1} - K_{st}$, is, therefore, the amount which is added to steel capital stocks out of current production. The reason for the use of inequality rather than an equation will be discussed presently.

2. The second type of relationship which constitutes the dynamic Leontief system requires that the capital stock be as large as is necessary to produce the planned output levels for the current period. For example, if each unit of steel output requires 4.2 units of steel capital goods (in the form of equipment, etc.), and if each unit of coal production requires 2.7 units of steel capital, and each unit of railroad transportation output requires 3.6 units of steel equipment, we need a capital stock sufficiently large for all three purposes, i.e., we must have

$$K_{st} \geq 4.2S + 2.7C + 3.6R.$$

These are the basic requirements of the dynamic input-output system. Together they can help us to plan not only for present production, but for future output as well. The model takes explicit account of what must be put aside today in order to be able to achieve our plans for tomorrow.

The presence of the inequality signs in the preceding relationships takes account of the possibility of overproduction and excess capacity. If, for example, in the last relationship we end up with K_{st} *greater than* the sum of the terms on the right-hand side, it must mean that the economy's steel equipment is not being fully used—there is excess capacity in this type of equipment. The reason such excess capacity can arise is that capital equipment is inherited from the past, and it can easily turn out that its composition does not fit in precisely with current output needs. It may involve too much steel and too little coal for our current production pattern. In an extreme case, excess steel capacity can become unavoidable because we simply do not have enough coal on hand to run the machines. But, in any event, we have the choice of producing various different combinations of final outputs *and investment goods.* Consider one such set of commodities, A, whose manufacture uses a great deal of steel and very little coal, whereas another, B, involves the opposite sort of input requirement. If it is decided to produce collection A, the economy may well end up with an excessive coal inventory, whereas if collection B is produced, there may be excess steel-equipment capacity. Even given the set of consumers' goods which the economy wishes to turn out, different production patterns will arise depending on the quantities of the various goods which it is decided to put into capital investment. It follows that the dynamic input-output system cannot just be solved to give us a unique set of output requirements for any set of final output goals. Production goals can be achieved by a variety of means, and somehow society must make up its mind among them, presumably on the basis of some sort of optimality computation. Planning for the long run cannot be reduced to a simple matter of the solution of a system of simultaneous equations as in the static input-output case.

4. *Some Theorems of Input-Output Analysis*

Before ending the discussion of input-output analysis it is appropriate to describe three noteworthy theorems on the subject and to indicate their function.

1. *The Samuelson substitution theorem:* It will be recalled from the first section of this chapter that a restrictive assumption of the input-output analysis is the premise that there are fixed technological coefficients—that it takes X man-hours, Y units of raw material of a given type, and so on, to produce each unit of an output, and that there is no possibility of any other input proportion. The firm has no choice of using or rejecting, e.g., labor-saving devices.

Professor Samuelson has proved that in some circumstances this restriction is not as serious as it appears.[5] He has shown that even where variation of input proportions is possible, *it will never be advantageous* provided that there are constant returns to scale, only one scarce input (labor, in the discussion of Section 2), and no joint products. In other words, the input-output proportions may be fixed as is assumed, but they will then be fixed by considerations of productive efficiency rather than immutable technological requirements. For each commodity there will simply exist one most efficient capital-labor ratio (e.g., 17 men per $1000 of equipment), and no changes in the level of output of that commodity will affect this ratio.

There is really a simple logic behind this result. We saw in Section 8 of Chapter 9 that with *fixed input prices* and a linear homogeneous production function it will never pay to change input proportions no matter what the level of output. Suppose that there is only one scarce factor, labor, and nothing else preventing the indefinite expansion of national output. This means that the real cost to society of the manufacture of any output or any other input must be calculated in terms of the amount of labor required to produce it. The real price of input A will be, say, two man-hours per unit, that of input B will be twelve man-hours, and given the state of technology these labor "prices" cannot change. It follows that any output should always be produced in a manner which uses the same input proportions. The most efficient input proportions will in fact be those which make the smallest (direct and indirect) drains on the economy's scarce labor supply.

Unfortunately, if there is more than one resource in limited supply this substitution theorem no longer holds, and so we are then back to our original problem. If the fixed input-output proportions assumption is to be accepted at all, it can only be as an approximation to the technological facts of the case.

2. *The Hawkins-Simon conditions:* Let us now turn to a second theorem of input-output analysis, one which is somewhat more abstract but of more general applicability than the one which was just discussed.

After collecting the data for an input-output table it is conceivable that the solution of the corresponding input-output equations will yield one or more negative numbers. This would imply that negative outputs of some commodities are required in order to achieve the final consumption targets! Clearly something has gone seriously wrong in such a case.

Hawkins and Simon have derived mathematical conditions which tell us

[5] See Chapters VII, VIII, and IX (written respectively by Paul A. Samuelson, Tjalling C. Koopmans, and Kenneth J. Arrow) in Tjalling C. Koopmans, ed., *Activity Analysis of Production and Allocation*, Cowles Commission Monograph 13, Wiley, New York, 1951.

the circumstances that will lead to such a pathological phenomenon and help us to understand it.[6] These conditions are useful as a check on input-output data to see whether a mistake has been made in collecting them. More important, these conditions provide us with mathematical requirements which must be met by any acceptable input-output system, and the conditions can therefore be used as a basis for further theoretical analysis.

In intuitive terms, what the Hawkins-Simon conditions show is that if, say, our solution calls for a negative coal output, this must mean that more than one ton of coal is used up (directly and indirectly) in the production of every ton of coal output. If we have such an unfortunate productive situation, only a negative amount of coal will be left over for consumers' use, and this deficit in consumer coal supplies will be smaller the smaller is the economy's total production of coal. In such a topsy-turvy production system, the only way to meet consumer targets is to produce negative coal outputs—an obvious nonsense possibility.

In the dynamic Leontief model the situation is only slightly less serious. If the Hawkins-Simon conditions are violated by the numbers in the input-output table, it may be possible, for a time, to meet consumer demands out of inventories. But, eventually, these inventories will be used up and it will be impossible to build them up again because an attempt to produce more will only hasten the drain on stocks since more of the items in question must be used up by the production process than it is able to turn out.

The nature of the Hawkins-Simon conditions can perhaps be made more specific with the aid of a graph. Consider a very simple two-industry (steel-coal) input-output model in which neither the steel nor the coal industry uses up any of its own product. Then we have the input-output equations

(1) $$S = \quad aC + T_s$$

(2) $$C = bS \quad + T_c$$

where S and C are steel and coal output respectively, T_s and T_c are the final net output targets for steel and coal, and a and b are constants. The first equation, the demand curve for steel, may be represented by a straight line (drawn as the flatter line) in Figure 1. Similarly, the second equation, the demand for coal, may be solved for S in terms of C, and rewritten as

$$S = (1/b)C - (1/b)T_c.$$

This curve can then also be plotted in Figure 1 (the steeper line). The intersection point, B, gives us the solution to the input-output equations,

[6] See D. Hawkins and H. A. Simon, "Some Conditions of Macroeconomic Stability," *Econometrica*, Vol. 17, July–October 1949.

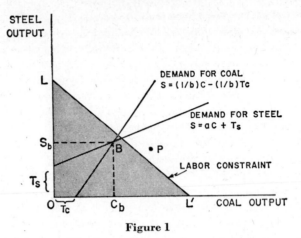

Figure 1

the required outputs of coal and steel thus being OC_b and OS_b respectively.[7]

But suppose the two lines were parallel or that the steel demand curve were steeper than the coal demand curve. In that case, the two lines would not intersect in the positive quadrant. The input-output system would have no solution, and the Hawkins-Simon conditions must be violated. What are those conditions in this case? To prevent the problem of nonsolvability, the slope of the coal demand equation $(1/b)$ must exceed that of the steel demand equation (a) so that we must have $1/b > a$. That is the Hawkins-Simon condition for this simple model.

The economic implication of these conditions which was given above is now easily shown to apply in this case. Substitute the coal demand Equation (2) into the steel demand Equation (1) to eliminate the coal output variable, C, and obtain

$$S = a(bS + T_c) + T_s = abS + aT_c + T_s.$$

This last equation tells us that if steel output increases ΔS units, the amount of steel needed to produce the coal which is used to produce that additional steel will be $ab\Delta S$. But if the Hawkins-Simon conditions are violated so that $(1/b) \le a$, we must have $ab \ge 1$, i.e., more than a ton of steel (i.e., ab units) will be used up in the course of producing an additional ton of steel!

3. *Series approximation to the solution:* A final theorem to be discussed

---

[7] Note the role of the limited labor supply in the input-output system. Its limited availability means that only input combinations represented by points below the labor constraint line, LL', can be produced (shaded region). Points like P, which lie beyond this line, represent outputs which cannot be produced because the requisite labor is not available. Fortunately, in the case shown, the solution point B is feasible. Note also the similarity to the linear programming diagrams.

here arises out of the need for computationally efficient methods of solution of the simultaneous equations of the static Leontief system. Since the work of numerical computation in the solution of a set of simultaneous equations grows so complex as the number of equations increases, it becomes highly desirable to find labor-saving methods. One method[8] which has received much attention involves an approximate solution which is analogous with the computation of the first few terms in the multiplier series $1 + c + c^2 + c^3 + \ldots$ as an approximation to the value of the multiplier $1/(1 - c)$. As we know, in the multiplier case this will work if the marginal propensity to consume, c, is less than unity. In the Leontief computation we have a similar condition which states that this procedure will work if the sum of the first n elements in any column in an n-industry input-output table is less than unity. We may generally expect this to be the case for an operating industry in a profit economy because this total is the sum of the costs of all the inputs except the labor input going into the production of a dollar's worth of any commodity, and the costs of these inputs must usually be no greater than one (dollar), for otherwise it will not pay to produce the item.

Again, there is a simple piece of intuitive logic to the procedure. The purpose of the input-output computation is to answer questions such as "How much steel production is needed to satisfy consumer demands?" And the answer can be given in the form of the following infinite series:

The economy will have to produce
as much steel as consumers will use directly

plus   as much steel as is needed to produce other final consumer products

plus   as much steel as is needed to produce the inputs for these final consumer products

plus   as much steel as is needed to produce the inputs which are in turn used to manufacture those inputs which go into those final products

plus   as much steel as is needed for the inputs to make the inputs to make the inputs for the final products
and so on, ad infinitum.[9]

[8] See, e.g., Frederick V. Waugh, "Inversion of the Leontief Matrix by Power Series," *Econometrica*, Vol. 18, April 1950.

[9] This is readily illustrated with the aid of a trivial one-industry (steel) model, in which aS tons of steel are used up in producing one ton of steel. Here we have one input-output equation

$$S = aS + T$$

where T is the final output steel target. This equation has the obvious solution

$$S(1 - a) = T \quad \text{or} \quad S = T/(1 - a).$$

But the same solution can be arrived at by the multiplier argument used above. To end

The idea in the series-approximation formula is to compute the total steel requirements involved in several such stages (say the first fifteen of these rounds), and to take this subtotal, after some upward adjustment, as an estimate of total required steel production.

REFERENCES

Chenery, Hollis B., and Clark, Paul G., *Interindustry Economics*, Wiley, New York, 1959.

Conference on Research in Income and Wealth (National Bureau of Economic Research), *Input-Output Analysis: An Appraisal*, Princeton University Press, Princeton, N. J., 1955.

Dorfman, Robert, Samuelson, Paul A., and Solow, Robert M., *Linear Programming and Economic Analysis*, McGraw-Hill, New York, 1958, Chapters 9–12 (relatively difficult reading).

Leontief, Wassily W., *The Structure of American Economy 1919–1939*, 2nd ed., Oxford University Press, New York, 1951.

———, and others, *Studies in the Structure of the American Economy*, Oxford University Press, New York, 1953.

Morgenstern, Oskar, ed., *Economic Activity Analysis*, Wiley, New York, 1954. Contains both expository material and some rather difficult mathematical papers.

---

up with T tons of steel we need to produce the T tons plus aT tons (to be used up in producing the T tons) plus $a(aT) = a^2T$ tons (to be used in producing the aT tons), etc. Thus we have the infinite geometric series

$$S = T + aT + a^2T + \ldots$$

which has the well-known solution $S = T/(1 - a)$.

CHAPTER SIXTEEN

Activity analysis

The term *activity analysis* may be taken to refer to the applications of linear programming methods to general equilibrium *theory*. The last few years have seen a new burst of effort devoted to this area which, at least until the '30's, had remained pretty much as it was left by Walras. The three outstanding developments relate to the solvability of the Walrasian equations, the development of general equilibrium growth models, and the application of general equilibrium theory to welfare economics. In all three cases the main advance has consisted in the development of powerful methods rather than in the discovery of surprising new theorems. For this reason much of the discussion which follows is devoted to the description of mathematical arguments and analytic techniques, and its economic content may on first reading leave one rather disappointed.

1. The Existence and Uniqueness Problems

Walras was much concerned with the solvability of his equation system. That is, he wanted to be sure that the system of equations he had set up sufficed to determine the values of his variables—the prices and quantities of the economy's outputs and inputs. Some writers approached this by counting the number of his equations and unknowns. They found he had the same number of equations as unknowns and assumed that the problem was solved.

Unfortunately, the matter is much more complicated. We usually expect a supply and a demand equation (curve) to determine a single equilibrium price-quantity combination, but this is certainly not true of either of the following pairs:

$$\text{Demand:} \quad Q = 1000 - 5P \qquad Q = 1000 - 5P$$
$$\text{Supply:} \quad Q = 900 - 5P \qquad 2Q = 2000 - 10P$$

where P is price and Q is the quantity sold. The pair of equations on the left has no solution (no solution *exists*)—any price-quantity combination which satisfies the one cannot possibly satisfy the other because $Q + 5P$ cannot be both 1000 and 900 at the same time. The trouble here is that the supply and demand curves are parallel straight lines and never intersect. In this case we say that the equations are *inconsistent* and the system is *overdetermined*.[1] By contrast, the other set of equations offers us an embarrassment of riches. It is compatible with an infinite number of price-quantity combinations. (The solution is not "unique.") In fact, since negative prices and quantities have not been excluded, every price can be an equilibrium price. In this case the difficulty is that the supply and demand curves coincide, so that at every point of this single-curve demand will equal supply. Here we say that the equations are *not independent* and the system is *underdetermined*.[2]

If there are scarce resources the Walrasian system may get into trouble in yet another way—the solution to the equations simply may not be feasible because the available resources do not suffice to produce it. It may rightly be suspected that this is where programming enters in, for we are almost[3] back at the production-with-limited-capacity problem.

An *existence theorem* (a theorem which states that some equation or set of equations possesses at least one solution) does not tell us anything about the operation of the economy—rather it tells us something about the operation of the Walrasian model. We know by observation that the market somehow determines unique prices and quantities. Thus the market's "solution" always exists. An existence analysis can serve only as a test for a general equilibrium model, in that if it turns out that the model

---

[1] Just as it might be if we had three well-behaved equations in two unknowns.

[2] As would ordinarily be the case where a system consists in one equation in two unknowns.

[3] But not quite—because we have not found anything to maximize. It should be recalled that this capacity problem also occurred in the input-output analysis where the labor requirements of any output target had to be checked against the available labor supply. Incidentally, note that if resources are available in the wrong proportions it may be impossible to use them up completely, i.e., to satisfy the resource-use equations of the Walrasian system. For example, consider a world of only one output, a unit of whose production requires 2 hours of labor and 3 pounds of raw material. If the available amounts of labor and raw material are 400 hours and 300 pounds respectively, the two equations $2Q = 400$ and $3Q = 300$ clearly cannot be solved. They must be replaced by inequalities which indicate that some labor or raw material will be left unused.

possesses no solution we will perhaps want to reject it on the grounds that it may therefore be neither very helpful analytically nor very realistic.

An existence theorem is a rather esoteric idea. It assures us that a problem can be solved but it may tell us nothing about how to go about solving it. Nevertheless, it is more important—even to an economist—than it may at first appear to be. We know that a system which has passed the test of an existence theorem can contain no contradictory elements since, clearly, any contradictions within the system would make a solution impossible. This may even have some direct economic implications. For example, an existence theorem for a system which postulates both full employment and an "ideal" allocation of resources proves that these two desiderata are not incompatible goals. In other words, such a theorem can tell us whether we are pursuing aims which involve having our cake and eating it.

An existence theorem or a *uniqueness theorem* (a theorem which states that the system has no more than one solution) can have further economic relevance in another way. Often it will turn out that we can prove an existence theorem or a uniqueness theorem for a system only if it satisfies some special requirements. For example, we shall see later how such a restriction on the nature of consumer demand is used to prove uniqueness in a general equilibrium model. Now these requirements can be highly suggestive in indicating conditions which may be necessary for such an equilibrium to occur in the real world. This will become clearer in our discussion of the uniqueness problem below.

2. Solution of the Existence Problem

Existence theorems are closely tied in with the so-called fixed-point theorems. First, let us see what is meant by "a fixed point." Suppose we have some functional relationship $Y = f(X)$ which associates different values of Y with X. Then a fixed point is a specific value of X, say $X = X^*$ (some number), for which $Y^* = f(X^*) = X^*$, i.e., for which the value of Y is equal to the value of X. The reason such a value of X is called a fixed point can be made clear with the aid of the following illustrative table which gives Y as a function of X:

X	1	2	5	6
Y	9	7	5	11

These data may be given the following geometric interpretation: We have four markers (e.g., paper clips) on a rule, one at each X figure, i.e., one at the 1-inch mark, one at the 2-inch mark, etc. The function gives us directions for moving these markers. It tells us to move the paper clip at the 1-inch mark to the 9-inch mark, the one at the 2-inch mark to the 7-inch mark, etc. Note, however, that the instructions tell us not to move the paper clip from the 5-inch mark. That is, $X = 5 = Y$ is a fixed point for this function. As another example, we note that $X = 1$ is a fixed point for the equation $Y = 3 - 2X$ because for $X = 1$, $Y = 3 - 2 = 1$.

But how are fixed-point theorems involved in existence proofs? The answer is that for a wide class of problems they are practically one and the same thing. Suppose, for example, we want to prove that there exists a root for the equation $f(X) - 5 = 0$. This is the same as finding a fixed point for the equation $Y = f(X) - 5 + X$. For if $X = X^*$ (where X^* is some number) is such a fixed point we have $Y = X^*$ so that the equation becomes $X^* = f(X^*) - 5 + X^*$. Subtracting X^* from both sides, we see that $0 = f(X^*) - 5$; i.e., X^* must be a root of our original equation. More generally, we see that X^* is a root of the equation $0 = G(X)$ if and only if it is a fixed point for the related function $Y = G(X) + X$.

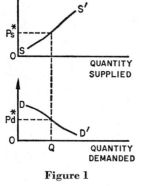

Figure 1

There is another way in which we can see the relation between a fixed-point theorem and an existence proof, this time for the solution of a pair of simultaneous equations. Suppose we are, for example, trying to find a solution to the standard supply-demand problem. A clumsy way to go about it is to draw the demand and supply curves one above the other as in Figure 1. We then pick some price, OP_d, on the Y axis of the demand diagram, see what quantity, OQ, buyers are willing to buy at this price, and then, by moving vertically to the supply curve, we find the price, OP_s, at which sellers are willing to supply that quantity. In this way we obtain a relationship which gives supply price as a function of demand price, $OP_s = f(OP_d)$. If it turns out for some particular demand price, OP_d^*, and its associated supply price, $OP_s^* = f(OP_d^*)$, that we have $OP_d^* = OP_s^*$, it is clear that price OP_d^* is a fixed point for this function. But it is also obvious that OP_s^* and OP_d^* are the equilibrium supply and demand prices. We see, then, that if the function which relates supply price to demand price has a fixed point there must exist a solution to the supply-demand equations. This, as we shall see presently, is in essence an outline of the McKenzie proof of the existence of equilibrium in the general equilibrium system.

The proofs for fixed-point theorems are generally very deep and complex. However, there is one very simple case which is usually used as an illustration. This simple theorem states that in *any* two-variable equation,

$Y = f(X)$, if $f(X)$ is continuous (roughly, if there are no breaks in its graph—kinks, though, are permitted) and if Y is never negative and never larger than some (any prespecified) number N, the function will possess a fixed point. This is shown in Figure 2, which plots the function $f(X)$ as FF' between $X = 0$ and $X = N$. The graph also contains a 45° line through the origin, and it is clear that any point such as P where FF' intersects the 45° line is a fixed point, for there we will have $Y = X$. There are two possibilities: If $Y = 0$ at $X = 0$, this is our fixed point. On the other hand, if $Y \neq 0$ at $X = 0$ so that FF' starts out above our 45° line, it can "try to avoid" the 45° line by staying above it. But since, by assumption, Y can never be greater than N, FF' will be kept from rising above the upper dotted line and the 45° line must catch up to it and corner it at $X = N$, if not sooner.

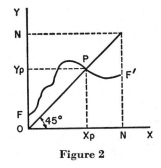

Figure 2

The first proof of the existence of a solution to the Walrasian system was published by A. Wald in 1933. His proof was exceedingly difficult. Like the authors of the more recent proofs, Wald had to impose further assumptions on the Walrasian model. Several of Wald's assumptions have been considered excessively restrictive and economically unjustified. Since then several alternative proofs have been offered involving much weaker and more plausible assumptions.

Without going into details we can now very briefly outline one of these proofs, that of Lionel McKenzie. His model contains two sets of inequalities and one set of demand equations. The first set of inequalities states that production takes place under constant returns to scale, and uses up no more than the physical resources which are available. The second set of inequalities states that since we are dealing with a case of perfect competition, profits will be zero.[4] All products sell at a price which is no higher than the cost of production. (Processes which involve a cost greater than the price of the commodity will, of course, not be used.) The problem is, then, to show that there exists a set of factor prices, commodity prices, and outputs which are consistent with those resource limitations, profit limitations, and the market demand relationships.

We now proceed exactly as in the discussion of Figure 1, only here we must deal with many prices and quantities at once. Pick some arbitrary set of prices and find the quantities which the demand functions tell us

[4] It turns out, surprisingly, that these two sets of inequalities are the respective inequalities of the primal and dual programs in the linear programming production model of Chapter 5!

consumers will buy at these prices. Suppose that these quantities are producible within the given resource limitations.[5] Then use our second set of inequalities to see what supply prices are just compatible with these output plans and the no-profits perfect-competition requirement. In this way we deduce a set of supply prices from any assumed set of demand prices exactly as we did in Figure 1. As in the discussion of that diagram, to show that an equilibrium price-quantity combination exists, it is necessary to prove that the assumed demand prices and the deduced supply prices can coincide. It is here that we must appeal to a fixed-point theorem. It can be shown that there is such a theorem which applies to our problem and proves that there is one set of demand prices which is the same as the set of supply prices deduced from it. At these prices and quantities, then, the demand conditions, the production conditions (resource limitations), and the profit conditions are all satisfied. This, in outline, is the McKenzie proof of the existence theorem for a general equilibrium model.

3. Solution of the Uniqueness Problem

Uniqueness is mathematically somewhat simpler to prove, though perhaps it is less plausible economically. There is really no good reason to believe that there will be no multiple intersections of supply and demand curves and hence a multiplicity of equilibrium points.

Further, the demand assumption which is used to prove uniqueness, although plausible enough for an individual consumer, is, at best, questionable when applied to the economy. This premise, which is employed in the uniqueness proof, turns out to be the basic assumption in Samuelson's revealed preference analysis which we now review briefly (Chapter 8, Section 12).

Suppose that an individual buys a collection of commodities A rather than some other collection B which is also available on the market. Presumably he will have made this choice either because he likes A better than B or because A is cheaper than B. If, in fact, A is more expensive than B when the consumer buys A, then the second possibility is ruled out —our consumer must have bought A because he actually prefers it to B. We therefore say, when a consumer buys the more expensive of these two collections, that A has been *revealed* preferred to B. Suppose that a different set of prices could have led the consumer to change his mind and buy B. If his tastes do not change so that he still prefers A to B, he presumably will not buy B when it is more expensive than A. At least this will be the case if his tastes are consistent, for otherwise his buying of B rather than

---

[5] It can be shown that at the prices which finally emerge, the quantities demanded will indeed be feasible. Their production will require no more than the available resources.

A when *B* is the more expensive collection reveals that he also prefers *B* to *A*! That is the basic revealed-preference premise. In sum, it states that consumer tastes are consistent in the sense that if one set of prices reveals *A* to be preferred to *B*, then there exists no other set of prices which can reveal *B* to be preferred to *A*, i.e., which makes *B* more expensive than *A* and yet leads the consumer to buy *B*.

Now although this is a plausible requirement for consistent consumer behavior, it has much less intuitive appeal when applied to market demand. It may be perfectly consistent for the *community* to buy *A* rather than *B* when *A* is more expensive and yet buy *B* rather than *A* when prices change so that *B* is the more costly. This is because the price change redistributes real income among consumers whose expenditure patterns differ. Thus *different* consumer groups may foot the bulk of the bill in the two cases.[6] Despite these reservations, let us examine the line of reasoning which shows that the revealed-preference premise for the market is violated if we have a multiplicity of equilibria. But, before the argument can be completed, one more preliminary theorem must be explained. This preliminary result will also be needed in the discussion of a later section.

At any *fixed level of input and output prices*, competitive outputs will tend to maximize total net profits; e.g., if there is any opportunity to increase profit by increasing some output at the expense of another, individual businessmen will make this switch until the opportunity disappears.[7] But it shall be argued now that this also means that *the value of the final products* (at these fixed prices) *will also be maximized*.

To make the argument clearer, consider a simplified production arrangement in which the economy's fixed resources are used only by the producers of raw materials who sell their entire product to the makers of finished goods. The total profits in the economy are given by:

The profits of finished-goods producers =	1. The value of finished products. 2. Minus the cost of produced raw materials.

plus

The profits of raw-materials producers =	3. The value of produced raw materials. 4. Minus the cost of the economy's fixed resources.

But the cost to finished-goods producers of their raw materials is exactly the same as the value of the product (revenue) of the raw-materials producers. Hence, in adding items 1 through 4 on the right above, to obtain a figure for the total profit of the economy, items 2 and 3 must cancel out.

[6] For a fuller discussion see J. R. Hicks, *A Revision of Demand Theory*, Oxford University Press, London, 1956, pp. 54–58.

[7] What goes wrong with this argument in the presence of external economies or diseconomies? (See Chapter 13, Section 9.)

We see then that the total profit earned in the economy will equal the value of the output of finished products minus the cost of the economy's fixed resources.

With a given set of positive prices for all products and resources, what can businessmen do to increase the economy's total profit? Since, by definition, the quantities of the various fixed resources are fixed, then with the prices of these items given, nothing which businessmen do will affect the cost of society's scarce resources. Hence, anything which can be done to add to the total value of final output will add an equal amount to total profits (equals the value of final output minus the cost of fixed resources). It follows that businessmen will have maximized the total profits of the economy if, and only if, they have maximized the total value of finished products. And, as we saw at the beginning of the discussion, with any given set of positive prices, the maximization of total profit may be expected in competitive equilibrium. Therefore, *competitive equilibrium will involve maximization of the total value of all finished commodities produced in the economy.*

We are now only one step from the end of the uniqueness argument. Suppose, on the contrary, that equilibrium is not unique—that there are two alternative equilibrium output combinations A and B, each with its own equilibrium prices. We have just seen that, at the prices which lead to the manufacture of A, the value of final outputs will be maximized, i.e., A will be at least as expensive as B. Similarly, at the prices at which B is produced, B will be at least as expensive as A. But if A and B are competitive equilibria, demand must match supply, that is, A must be demanded in the first situation (when it is most expensive) and B must be demanded in the second (when it is the most costly). A is then revealed preferred to B and vice versa. This clearly violates the revealed-preference assumption for the market, so that if that assumption is to hold, there cannot be two equilibrium outputs, A and B. The equilibrium output must be unique.

4. The Von Neumann Model of an Expanding Economy

From existence and uniqueness theorems we turn now to the second of our activity-analysis topics: general equilibrium growth models. Two years before Wald published his existence proof, von Neumann delivered a paper which is perhaps the most remarkable virtuoso performance in the literature of mathematical economics. In this article von Neumann developed what is presumably the first general equilibrium analysis of economic growth. In this respect (though not in some of its other properties) the model is more complicated than the Walrasian system. Nevertheless, von Neumann developed an existence theorem for this model using a fixed-point theorem in a way which is somewhat similar to the later existence theorem for the Walrasian economy. Moreover, in the course of this argument there are clearly discernible features of both linear programming and game theory,[8] and, in particular, of the duality theory of linear programming.

The structure of the model itself can be outlined fairly briefly. Von Neumann describes an economy characterized by a linear homogeneous production function and in which all outputs serve only as raw materials for further production. Consumption can be interpreted as the process whereby finished goods are used as inputs in the production of labor. Thus consumption also becomes a purely technological phenomenon and ordinary demand relationships disappear from the model.[9]

The production function is described as a set of processes each of which turns some inputs into outputs, all in fixed proportions. To make sure his economy is completely integrated so that it is not decomposable into unconnected subsectors, von Neumann also assumes that each commodity is either an input or an output in every process, e.g., it is assumed that *every* process either produces size 7-B brown moccasin style shoes or uses them as a raw material![10]

Suppose now that this economy is expanding; the manufactured outputs of the production processes taken together exceed the outputs of the preceding period (which are the inputs for the current period's products). Moreover, assume with von Neumann that there are no limited supplies of land, labor, or other factors to put an end to this expansion. Von Neumann then asks whether there is a constant equilibrium rate of growth of the economy which will yield no profits, as required by perfect competition, and which satisfies the technological requirement that the process intensities during any period require no more than the available raw-material inputs (the outputs of the preceding period).

Equilibrium is defined as a constant proportionate rate of growth of all outputs, inputs, and process intensities which satisfies the profit and technological conditions just described. (Here a proportionate rate of

[8] As we shall see in the chapter on game theory, every zero-sum, two-person game can be interpreted as a pair of dual linear programs (and the converse is also true), so it is really not so surprising that elements of *both* of these are involved in the von Neumann model.

[9] Actually, the absence of any demand functions removes a major difficulty in the proof of the existence theorem. In this respect the problem of the existence proof is considerably simpler than that for the Walrasian system.

[10] This is not as ridiculous as it may sound—probably some steel worker wears out such shoes somewhere in American steel production. Moreover, there have been two recent articles which analyze the behavior of a von Neumann economy without the use of this assumption. See John G. Kemeny, Oskar Morgenstern, and Gerald Thompson, "A Generalization of the von Neumann Model of an Expanding Economy," *Econometrica*, Vol. 24, April 1956, and David Gale, "The Closed Linear Model of Production," in *Linear Inequalities and Related Systems*, H. W. Kuhn and A. W. Tucker, eds., Annals of Mathematics Studies 38, Princeton University Press, 1956.

growth, P, means that in every period each output is *at least* P per cent higher than it was in the previous period.)

Let α be the equilibrium rate of expansion of the slowest-growing item of the economy, i.e., the production of each item grows at a rate greater than or equal to α per cent per year. Let the money rate of interest be β dollars per annum. The no-profit condition then can be restated as follows: The money outlay on the inputs of any process plus the interest cost of that money for one period must be greater than or equal to the value of the outputs of that process. Similarly, the technological condition can be formulated as follows: The sum of the current inputs of any item in all processes (which is α per cent greater than the amount used in the preceding period) must be less than or equal to the output of that item in the preced ng period. That is, the amount of coal used during the current period [equals $(1 + \alpha)$ multiplied by the amount of coal used last period] must not exceed the coal made available by last period's output. We see, then, how inequalities play a fundamental role in this model as they do throughout activity analysis.

Von Neumann then proves the following results:

1. There exists *one* such equilibrium rate of growth α (existence and uniqueness).

2. This equilibrium rate of growth will equal the interest rate so that the rate of increase of output will just exactly suffice to cover the interest cost of investment in inputs. This is an intuitively obvious consequence of the no-profit condition. Thus, there will be a unique value for both α and β. However, it should be noted that a von Neumann model can be consistent with many equilibrium output-price combinations—in this respect, then, the solution is not unique.

3. There may be some processes whose employment involves a financial loss. These processes will not be used—i.e., all processes actually operated will yield exactly zero profits, as the theory of perfect competition has always taught us.

4. Some outputs may grow at a rate greater than α per cent per period. There will be a surplus of such an item over and above what is required as input in the next period for the equilibrium growth of the economy. Because there will be an excess supply of each such commodity, it will be a free good; that is, its marginal utility and hence its price will be zero.[11]

5. There will be no sustainable rate of growth greater than the equilibrium rate of growth α. For if there were available alternative processes capable of yielding a higher growth rate, α', then the α growth rate would not be consistent with equilibrium. Entrepreneurs would switch to these alternative processes because with interest at the old rate, β, they would

[11] Results (3) and (4) are directly related to the second duality theorem of linear programming which is described in Section 12 of Chapter 5.

make a profit. With the interest rate then raised to $\beta' = \alpha'$, to eliminate this profit the old nonmaximal growth-rate processes would only be operable at a loss.

The extreme abstraction involved in the von Neumann model hardly needs to be pointed out. Later work has removed some of the more unpalatable assumptions. The conclusions are of considerable interest in themselves. Nevertheless, primary interest in the model continues to reside in the analytic tools which were developed and exhibited with its aid.

5. *Activity Analysis and Welfare Economics*

Doubtless the best-known theorem of elementary welfare analysis asserts that a long-run, perfectly competitive equilibrium will yield an optimal allocation of resources. Not only is the theorem elementary and well known—as has already been shown in Chapter 13—it is also, strictly speaking, untrue, or rather, true only under some fairly restrictive assumptions.

In recent years there has been much work devoted to the development of an alternative activity-analysis proof of this theorem. It may well be asked why this has been thought to be necessary. For one thing, activity analysis has made no attempt to dispute the restricted validity of the result. In fact, no way has even been found to apply the methods of activity analysis to external economies and the related difficulties which are incompatible with the optimality of perfect competitive equilibrium. Rather, the new approach has been helpful in another way.

The standard welfare economics deals only with commodities which are actually bought in the market and not with those which are free goods or for which no customers can be found at a profitable price. For old-fashioned welfare theory leans heavily on the marginal conditions of equilibrium, e.g., the condition of equality of price ratios to the marginal rates of substitution. But these conditions need not hold for free or unsalable goods. In old-fashioned terms, if each consumer chooses not to buy a commodity, the marginal utility of that item may well be *less* than its price (note the inequality again). Moreover, the cost of production of such an unsalable good must be greater than its price. For free goods the ratio of prices is not even defined. It follows that the standard version of the theorem which we are discussing must be restated to read that (where the theorem is valid) a competitive economy will allocate resources optimally *among commodities which are salable without loss and which are not free.* But which commodities will these be? We cannot assume we know the answer in advance, for the answer is an economic question of costs of production and demand patterns. Moreover, though our intuition may tell us that this is so, we must prove rigorously that there can be no preferable allocation of resources to free or unsalable goods.[12]

Old-fashioned welfare theory, by taking marginal utility to equal price, may end up requiring negative consumption of an unwanted commodity since even with zero consumption its marginal utility may turn out to be less than its price. Similarly, it cannot preclude the economic absurdity of negative prices for "free goods." But since activity analysis can cope with inequalities, it can specify that (1) prices and quantities exchanged must all be greater than or equal to zero, (2) the average cost of production must be equal to price for all items which are produced, and greater than the price at which any item that no one considers worth producing can be sold, and (3) production must not exceed the levels made possible by the available resources of society. Subject to these and the limitations of competition, businessmen and consumers are then taken to do the best they can for themselves. Marginal equalities and inequalities do not even make an explicit appearance.

Before outlining the proof of the theorem, let us first recall two related concepts. A productive arrangement is called *efficient* if any alternative productive arrangement which increases the output of some commodity must also involve a decrease in the output of some other commodity. The motivation of the definition is obvious. Any productive arrangement which is not efficient in this sense requires that the economy forego the opportunity to get something for nothing—the opportunity to increase the output of some item, X, without giving anything up in exchange. Related to efficiency is the concept of *Pareto optimality* (cf. Chapter 13, Section 11, for the reason for this nomenclature). A situation is said to be "Pareto-optimal" when it is impossible to effect a change which benefits some individual without any deleterious effects on someone else. Efficiency is then a purely technological concept whereas Pareto optimality is the corresponding concept for individuals as consumers and in their other economic roles.

Let us now see how activity analysis can be used to prove that every competitive equilibrium is technologically efficient and that every efficient output combination is a competitive equilibrium, i.e., that for each efficient point there can be found a set of prices which would under perfect competition produce the efficient output combination in question. This part of the theorem amounts essentially to the standard result that a competitive output can occur at and only at any point on the *production-*

---

[12] Pigou long ago pointed out that the production of some items which it would be unprofitable to produce under pure competition can conceivably yield a net benefit to society. See *The Economics of Welfare*, 4th ed., Macmillan, London, 1938, pp. 283, 810–11. However, Pigou's case requires decreasing costs, and these cannot be handled by the activity-analysis approach as developed to date.

possibility locus (transformation surface), the graph which shows the various output combinations which society can produce with its available resources (curve TT' in Figure 3). For the production-possibility locus is the locus of all efficient points. For example, we see that, with output OX_1 of X, the largest possible output of Y is OY_1 so that point C is efficient. But, on the other hand, a point like A which lies inside the transformation locus TT' represents an inefficient combination of output X and Y because it is possible to move to an efficient point like B which lies on TT'

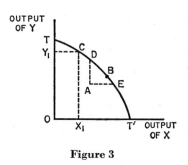

Figure 3

northeast of A, so that B involves greater outputs of both commodities. Note that although C is also efficient, as we have just seen, activity analysis as so far described has not settled whether it is or is not more desirable socially than is A.[13]

How do we know that a competitive output is technologically efficient? The answer is simple. With fixed prices, an inefficient output cannot involve a maximum money value of output. For we can increase the output of, say, X without decreasing that of any other commodity and end up with an output combination whose money value is obviously increased. Thus, with fixed prices, the money value of E in Figure 3 is clearly higher than that of A. But we have seen earlier (Section 3) that a competitive equilibrium necessarily involves a maximum value of output when valued at the equilibrium prices. Hence, no competitive equilibrium can be inefficient.

More difficult is the proof of the converse, which states that every efficient output combination is a competitive output. However, the method of proof is interesting in and of itself. This employs an "intuitively obvious" mathematical theorem whose proof is, in fact, rather difficult. The theorem states that, given an (N-dimensional) convex geometric figure (convex set) and any point R on the boundary of or outside this figure, it is always possible to draw at least one line (N-dimensional hyperplane) through R in such a way that the convex figure lies entirely on one side of

---

[13] We see then that there will usually be many efficient output combinations represented by the points that make up the transformation locus. The locus can be found with the aid of programming techniques. The trick is to choose any output of X, say OX_1, and find the *maximum* output of Y permitted by the resources left over from the production of that quantity of X. This is clearly a programming computation, and it will show that OY_1 is the maximum amount of Y then producible. In this way point C on the transformation curve will have been located, and, by starting with other values of X, other points on TT' can be found in the same way. For the details of the analogous derivation of the contract curve equation, see footnote 2 of Chapter 13.

this line.[14] Thus, in Figure 4 the shaded region is convex. Through points
A, B, and C on its boundary, and point D outside the figure, lines have
been drawn which have the required prop-
erty. Such a line through a boundary
point like A, B, or C is called a *supporting
line* (plane) of the convex set. Such a line
can be taken to divide the plane into two
half-planes (*half-spaces*) and in each case
the shaded figure lies entirely within one of
the half-spaces produced by the lines in the
figure. Supporting lines represent a generalization of the concept of tangency to cover
the case where the boundary curve has a
kink (e.g., at point B—note that there are
many supporting hyperplanes at such
points).

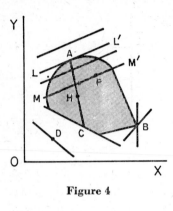

Figure 4

Consider now one of the supporting lines of the convex set, e.g., line
LL' through point A in Figure 4. Since the convex set lies entirely on one
side of such a line, then (if the line is not vertical) either no portion of the
convex set will lie above this line or no part of the set will lie below this
line. Suppose the convex set does not lie above the supporting line in
question (as is the case with LL'). Then any point of the set (e.g., point P)
must lie on or below LL', and any line parallel to LL' which goes through
a point in the convex set (e.g., line MM' through point P) must either
coincide with LL' or lie entirely below it. In other words, *such a supporting
line must be the highest of all the lines which are parallel to it and which meet
the convex set at any point.* We shall employ this result by interpreting the
family of lines parallel to our supporting line as a set of price lines which,
as usual, involve price ratios that are given by the (constant) slope of these
lines. Then the italicized result may be translated to read as follows: If
only output combinations which are represented by points within the convex region are attainable, the highest attainable price line goes through
A, the point of tangency with the convex region. Of course, this final
statement sounds at least vaguely familiar.

Now to get back to our theorem that every technologically efficient
point is a competitive equilibrium. We note first that the set of points
representing all the feasible outputs in a linear program must form a
convex geometric figure.[15] Suppose now that some output is efficient. We
have seen that the point which represents this output combination must lie

---

[14] For the definition of a convex set, see Chapter 6, Section 4. The theorem does not
hold for nonconvex regions as can be shown with the aid of Figure 5b in Chapter 6,
where any line through point E must intersect the nonconvex shaded figure.

[15] See footnote 1 of Chapter 6.

on the upper boundary of the feasible region (compare curve TT' in Figure 3). Moreover, we know that through every such point there passes (at least) one supporting line. This line can be interpreted as a price line giving the value of the output through A, and its slope can be taken to represent the ratio of the prices of X and Y. In other words, for any efficient point there will always exist relative prices at which the efficient point maximizes the value of output.[16]

With these prices, moreover, businessmen under pure competition will (in the absence of external economies and diseconomies) be motivated to produce the technologically efficient output in question; for, as we have argued, it will pay them to maximize the value of output. Thus any such efficient output combination is a competitive output combination; at some set of prices competitive businessmen will produce it.

This, then, proves the theorem about the efficiency of competitive equilibrium. There is some similarity between this proof and the proof of the Pareto optimality theorem which will not be described in detail. Clearly the latter theorem must take into consideration consumer demands, and this involves a number of complications. In effect, what we want to prove is that every competitive equilibrium involves tangency between the transformation locus and some sort of consumers' community indifference curve (an indifference curve which, in some sense, represents the tastes of all consumers taken together), and that any such point of tangency is a competitive equilibrium. For then society will have attained the highest state of welfare compatible with the available production possibilities. The tangency can be assured by the tangency of both the transformation curve and the community indifference curve with the same price line.

Here too we have a theorem on convex sets which comes to our assistance. The theorem states that if two convex sets meet only at boundary points, there will be at least one line such that one convex set lies in one of the half-spaces generated by the line and the other convex set lies in the line's other half-space.

Consider all output combinations above and to the right of some indifference curve, i.e., all the points which involve outputs that are preferred to or indifferent with the outputs at some point, R, on the indiffer-

---

[16] The economic interpretation requires that the price line have a negative slope. But we can show that at an efficient point the slope of the price line must be negative. For we know that if all prices are positive the slope of a price line will be negative. (Indeed this is why we want the price line to have a negative slope.) But suppose the contrary, that one of the "prices" deduced from the supporting price line is negative. We can then increase the value of output by decreasing the quantity of the commodity whose price is negative, which means that we can increase output value by leaving the efficient point, contrary to what has just been shown, i.e., that the value of the efficient output with this price line will be a maximum.

ence curve QQ' (Figure 5). Such a preferred point is defined in the Pareto sense as one that involves an output combination which can make some

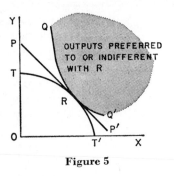

Figure 5

consumers better off than they were at R, without hurting anyone. It can be argued that the set of points preferred to or indifferent with R (shaded region in Figure 5) is convex. The set of feasible output points (the points in region OTT' which lie on or beneath the transformation curve, TT') also constitutes a convex set, at least in cases involving constant returns (linear programming) or diminishing returns (see Chapter 6, Sections 4 and 5). There will then be a line, PP', which separates these two regions. If, in addition, point R lies on the transformation locus, PP' will be a supporting line for both sets and R will be a feasible efficient point which lies on the highest possible indifference curve.

6. Dual Prices and Decentralized Decision-Making

Section 8 of Chapter 13 discussed a pricing scheme which was designed to achieve the results of central planning without detailed centralized direction. The idea is simply to establish such a set of prices that the individual plant or company manager is forced to make the "right" decisions in order to maximize his profits.

Some light can be thrown on the nature of this sort of arrangement with the aid of the analysis of the preceding section and the duality theorems of linear programming (Section 12 of Chapter 5). It will be recalled that one of the properties of the dual program is that the optimal values of its variables can be interpreted as accounting prices of the scarce resources in the primal production problem. Moreover, these accounting prices have the following properties:

1. The cost of the scarce resources used by the firm when evaluated at these accounting prices will be exactly equal to the firm's total profits.

2. If the firm is charged these dual prices whenever it uses its scarce resources, any output or process which should, optimally, not be employed by the firm will actually involve the firm in a loss—i.e., only negative profits can be earned on a commodity which the firm should, optimally, not be producing or on any process which the firm should, optimally, not be using.

Suppose, now, that the economy's production function is linear and homogeneous, and that the central authority were to look for a set of commodity prices and input prices which will lead individual businessmen to produce some efficient combination of outputs. As we saw in the previous section, for every such output combination, Q, there exists some set of prices, P, such that Q is the output combination of maximum value when evaluated at these prices, P. In other words, this output combination would be the solution of a mathematical programming problem: maximize the value of output subject to the constraints imposed on the economy by its scarce resources. Moreover, since the production function is, by assumption, linear and homogeneous, this will be a *linear* programming problem. Such a problem will therefore have a dual whose solution will be a set of accounting prices, R, for society's scarce resources.

The planning authority now can proceed as follows: (1) set prices P for all final products; (2) set accounting prices R for all scarce resources, meaning by this that whenever a plant or company manager uses any such resource he will be required to pay to the government the dual price of this item for every unit he uses.

In that case every business firm will find it unprofitable to produce any outputs or to use any processes which are not included in the optimum (efficient) output combination, Q, for by the standard properties of the dual prices every nonoptimal output or process will incur a loss.

Moreover, if every businessman expands his output to capacity (as he can do without loss since the dual prices just permit zero profits), the result will be the production of exactly the efficient output combination, Q. For as we have seen in Section 3, with fixed input and output prices, businessmen can only maximize their profits by maximizing the value of outputs, and the officially enforced prices P have been chosen so as to make Q the output whose value is a maximum. Thus by choosing output prices P and dual input prices R, businessmen will be forced by the pursuit of self-interest to make decisions which are socially optimal. No detailed central output directives will be required to achieve this optimal result.

7. Integer Programming and Welfare Economics

Most of the preceding results hold for cases involving linear or other convex relationships (constant or diminishing returns to scale) and where there are no problems of indivisibilities (a steam shovel is indivisible because we cannot produce one-half or one-fourth of a steam shovel). However, the presence of indivisibilities and increasing returns complicates the situation, and we shall see now that in these cases things do not work out so well.

These problems can be treated with the aid of integer programming analysis in which the answer is always required to contain no fractional parts (see Chapter 7, above). Its relevance to the indivisibilities case is clear since we desire an analysis which can avoid nonsense answers involving fractional parts of steamships, or drill presses. It was also shown in Section 3 of Chapter 7 that, at least in principle, the increasing-returns case can be reduced to an integer programming computation. Let us see, then, what follows for our welfare theorems from the integer programming analysis.

As in ordinary linear programming, it remains true in the integer programming case that every value-maximizing (competitive) output will also be efficient. This can be shown by exactly the same argument as that of Section 5. Unfortunately, the converse does not hold. There may be efficient outputs which are not competitive, i.e., for which there exist no prices at which this output combination maximizes the total value of output. This is easily proved by counterexample, as shown in Figure 6. Here the shaded triangle, OBC, contains all of the feasible lattice points (the points representing all possible solutions with no fractional coordinates). Point A, with coordinates $(2, 1)$, lies in the interior of this triangle. But (because the feasible points are isolated) it is possible for such an interior point to be efficient. This is in fact the case with A, for there is no feasible lattice point which "dominates" A, i.e., no point which lies directly above it, directly to the right of it, or above it and to its right.

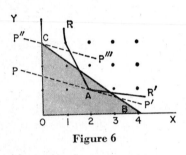

Figure 6

Now consider any straight (price) line, such as PP', through A. Any such line must lie below either lattice point B or lattice point C. This means that there must exist another parallel price line such as $P''P'''$ which lies above PP' and goes through one of these corners of triangle OBC. In other words, in the case shown in Figure 6, at the prices involved in the price (iso output-value) lines shown, the value of output at point C exceeds that at A. And, similarly, at any other possible set of output prices the value of output at A will be smaller than that at B or that at C. This shows how, in the discrete programming case, there are likely to arise efficient outputs which are not competitive (value-maximizing) outputs and which therefore cannot be enforced by the standard type of decentralized control procedure of the economic literature, in which the central authority makes only simple price decisions.

It is to be noted, however, that it is possible to find families of non-linear or piecewise linear price curves such as RR' for which the value of output is maximized at A. This has a simple interpretation. The prices which are set up are discriminatory and vary with the magnitude of output. Output combinations which are close to A are given relatively high prices, but as outputs move further and further from A prices are made increasingly unfavorable to the seller so that there are sharply diminishing returns to departures from A. In other words, an output, t_1, of any commodity at A is broken arbitrarily into a sum of sub-outputs

$$t_{11} + t_{12} + \ldots + t_{1n} = t_1$$

and each of the sub-outputs t_{1i} is assigned a different price, P_{1i}, as just described. Such an arrangement could, in principle, be enforced by government fiat. But it is difficult to see much advantage to a decentralized control procedure when it becomes so complicated, and in any event it would never result from the spontaneous operation of competitive market forces which preclude the existence of different prices for different units of a homogeneous product.

The so-called basic theorem of welfare economics runs into even more serious trouble in integer programming. It is in this situation not generally possible to attain a Pareto optimal point by means of a price system.

This is obviously so for the case of interior efficient points such as A in Figure 6. For let RR' now represent a community indifference curve so that A is now the optimal feasible point. There obviously exists no line which separates the remainder of the feasible lattice points from the region socially preferred to or indifferent with A (the region above RR'). This means that with any fixed price arrangement producers will find it more profitable to manufacture either output combination B or C than to turn out the social optimum combination, A.[17]

Let us summarize the results of this section:

1. Every competitive output combination is efficient and any such point can be attained by a system of fixed prices set by central authority, all other decisions being left to the individual firms in the economy. This is no different from the result for the ordinary linear programming case.

2. However, unlike the ordinary linear programming case, not every efficient output can be achieved by simple centralized pricing decisions or by competitive market pricing processes.

3. Moreover, it is possible in the integer programming case that there exists no hyperplane which separates the feasible lattice points from those which are preferred to or indifferent with the optimal lattice point. In other words, there may exist no set of prices which simultaneously makes the optimal point, Q, the most profitable among those which can be produced and the cheapest among those which consumers consider to be at

[17] Moreover, it can be shown in the three-or-more variable case that even if the optimum point, Q, is a competitive efficient point (a point on the boundary of the convex hull of the feasible points), there may well exist no hyperplane which separates the feasible (producible) points from the lattice points which are preferred to or indifferent with Q.

least as good as Q. That is, at any set of prices either producers will try to make, or consumers will demand, some other output combination.

It should be observed, in conclusion, that these limitations on the price system in the integer programming case should not be entirely surprising. For, as has already been indicated, cases of increasing returns to scale can, at least in principle, be reduced to integer programming problems. And in such cases it has long been recognized that the price system runs into difficulties.

REFERENCES

Expository Material

Dorfman, Robert, Samuelson, Paul A., and Solow, Robert M., *Linear Programming and Economic Analysis*, McGraw-Hill, New York, 1958, Chapters 11–14.

Hicks, J. R., "Linear Theory," *Economic Journal* (forthcoming).

Koopmans, Tjalling C., *Three Essays on the State of Economic Science*, McGraw-Hill, New York, 1957, especially Essay I.

Source Materials

Arrow, Kenneth J., "An Extension of the Basic Theorems of Classical Welfare Economics," *Proceedings of the Second Berkeley Symposium on Mathematical Statistics and Probability*, University of California Press, Berkeley, 1951.

Arrow, Kenneth J., and Debreu, Gerard, "Existence of an Equilibrium for a Competitive Economy." *Econometrica*, Vol. 22, July 1954.

Debreu, Gerard, "The Coefficient of Resource Utilization," *Econometrica*, Vol. 19, July 1951.

Kemeny, John G., Morgenstern, Oskar, and Thompson, Gerald, "A Generalization of the Von Neumann Model of an Expanding Economy," *Econometrica*, Vol. 24, April 1956.

Koopmans, Tjalling C., ed., *Activity Analysis of Production and Allocation*, Cowles Commission Monograph 13, Wiley, New York, 1951, Chapters II and III.

Koopmans, Tjalling C., and Beckmann, Martin, "Assignment Problems and the Location of Economic Activities," *Econometrica*, Vol. 25, January 1957.

McKenzie, Lionel, "On Equilibrium in Graham's Model of World Trade and Other Competitive Systems," *Econometrica*, Vol. 22, April 1954.

——, "On the Existence of a General Equilibrium for a Competitive Market," *Econometrica*, Vol. 27, January 1959.

Von Neumann, John, "A Model of General Economic Equilibrium," *Review of Economic Studies*, Vol. 13, 1945–46.

Wald, Abraham, "Über die eindeutige positive Lösbarkeit der neuen Produktionsgleichungen," *Ergebnisse eines Mathematischen Kolloquiums*, Vol. 6, 1933–34.

CHAPTER SEVENTEEN

Neumann-Morgenstern cardinal
utility

1. Utility, Risk and Game Theory

We have already seen (Chapter 8) that the neoclassical economists con-structed a cardinal utility theory as part of their analysis of consumer demand. This cardinal utility measure was designed to convey information about the psychological state of the consumer (or the businessman and the worker)—the magnitude of his desires, and the psychic gains and losses incurred by the alternative actions which are available to him.

We also saw that it is possible to dispense with this utility analysis in much of the theory of consumer behavior and in the analysis of economic decision-making in general. A large class of decision processes can be explained simply with the aid of information about the individual's preferences, with no attempt to assign magnitudes to them.

Game theorists have had no dispute with the resulting ordinalist (indifference curve) analysis, so far as it goes. However, in their work they have found it exceedingly useful to go beyond an ordinal utility measure wherever questions of risk arise.[1] The outcomes of the alternative choices available to the decision-maker are sometimes known only in probabilistic form, e.g., if he does A he has a 1/3 chance of ending up with $1000 and a 2/3 chance of ending up with only $40. In such a case it is essential

---

[1] The role of this utility analysis in game theory will be indicated in the next two chapters in the discussion of the concept of "mixed strategies."

in game theory to do more than just examine the decision-maker's ranking of A as against his other similar alternatives, B, C, $\ldots$, etc.

In the course of their work on game theory, von Neumann and Morgenstern were therefore led to construct their much-discussed cardinal utility measure for the ranking of situations involving probabilities (risky situations). This nomenclature turns out to have been highly unfortunate. The resemblance between the Neumann-Morgenstern construct and the neoclassical utility measure ends largely with the use of the term "cardinal" to designate both analyses. Much misunderstanding and unnecessary controversy can be traced to this usage.

Let us now turn to a general discussion of the mathematician's use of the term "measurement" and its varieties to make clear what is meant by the term "cardinal utility" in the N-M (Neumann-Morgenstern) sense. Only then will it be possible to explain its relationship to the neoclassical analysis.

2. Classes of Measures and Their Strength

A measure, in its most general sense, is simply a device which is designed to convey information about the phenomena to which it refers. Normally the information is conveyed by means of numbers. This requires a linguistic convention which indicates the meaning of the number "105" when we say that the measure of some feature of an object is 105. For example, if this number represents length or temperature its meaning has been well defined (once the system of measurement—say, Fahrenheit vs. centigrade—is specified).

It is sometimes desirable that such a number convey a great deal of information whereas in other circumstances very little needs to be communicated by a "measurement." As a result, one encounters measures which vary considerably in power to convey information. Let us examine three such classes of index, starting with the least powerful and describing them in order of increasing information content. It will then be shown that an ordinal utility index and the N-M utility index belong, respectively, to the second and third classes.

Class 1. *Associative measures:* The weakest type of index (one which conveys very little information) is one which serves only to *associate* items in two different collections. For example, persons in a newspaper group photograph are sometimes identified by placing a number next to each face and the same number beside the corresponding name in a list printed underneath. Here we set up the linguistic convention that any one man's name and face are given the same number. The numbers themselves do not matter and can be transformed in any way we like (we can exchange any number for another), provided no two faces bear the same number.

Class 2. *Orderings or rankings:* A ranking is a measure which assigns an ordering to a set of items—it tells us which of two items is higher on the scale. To take the standard illustration, in a hardness scale, harder minerals are given higher numbers.

Note that such a ranking measure also contains associative information—two rocks with the same ranking number must be equally hard. Thus a ranking index does carry more information than an associative index. The former does everything which is done by the latter and more besides.

Suppose we assign a set of numbers in such a ranking. We may note that the same information can be conveyed just as well by any other set of numbers provided that we still satisfy our linguistic convention. Of two rocks the one with the higher number in the initial numbering (the harder rock) must also bear the higher number in any new index which is assigned.[2] We describe this by saying that the index which measures, or rather describes, a ranking is *unique up to a monotone transformation.* Thus, while we still have quite a bit of choice in the assignment of numbers, we have considerably less option than in the case of an associative measure. That is because a ranking conveys far more information, thus the meaning of the numbers must be far more rigidly specified by the linguistic convention.

It is clear that an ordinal utility measure is a ranking, so that it falls into this second class of indices.

Class 3. *Cardinal measures:* Finally, we come to "cardinal measurement," which conveys still more information than did either of the other types of measure. It permits us, from what we know about two items in isolation, to *predict* something about them in combination. Consider the problem of finding two pieces of cloth in a shop which together are large enough to cover a table at home. We wish to *predict* which two pieces will do this *without having to take them home and try them* (and return them for exchange if they turn out to be too short). A measure of length can help us here. We know that a table 3 yards long can easily be covered by two cloths whose lengths are $1\frac{1}{2}$ yards and $2\frac{1}{4}$ yards.

It will be observed that a length index can be used to rank and to associate as well as for this sort of prediction. For example, we know just from the numbers and their standard interpretation that a 7-foot board is longer than a 3-foot board (ranking) and that all 3-foot boards are of equal length (association).

Because we want a cardinal measure to be capable of making the sort of prediction which has just been described, we have very little choice in the numbers which are to be used. We wish to convey the prediction that whenever two items, A and B, are combined, we obtain some item, C, as a

---

[2] Clearly other linguistic conventions might do—*softer* minerals might be given higher numbers.

result. For this purpose it is customary to represent the process of combining A and B by the *addition* of the index of A to the index of B. For example, if A is a 6-foot board (a board of length index 6) and B is an 8-foot board, we employ the linguistic *convention* that the length which is obtained by laying these two pieces of lumber end to end (item C) is $(6 + 8)$ $= 14$ feet long.[3] That is why some cardinal measures are called *additive*.

The convention that we make our prediction by adding leaves us very little option in choosing the numbers of any such measure. Indeed, we have no more than two numbers which are up to us (two degrees of freedom)[4] and the rest are then beyond our control—they are automatically dictated to us by our linguistic convention. For example, because we add lengths, we know that the length of two pieces of cloth must sum up to the number which we assign to the length they cover together. A cloth as long as a 3-foot piece and a 1-foot piece *must* be assigned the number "4 feet"; and the three pieces together *must* be called "8 feet," etc.

The N-M utility index is cardinal in this very specific sense—it is intended to be used for making predictions. It is employed to predict which of two lottery tickets (or which of two other risky alternatives) a person will prefer. We are given this individual's ranking of the alternative prizes offered by the lottery tickets and the odds on each prize. From this we wish to be able to infer by numerical calculation, and *without actually asking the person*, which lottery ticket he will choose.

In N-M utility measurement we want to assign to lottery-ticket *prizes* utility numbers which, when they are processed arithmetically in accord with the linguistic convention which is described in the following section, will assign a utility number to the *lottery ticket itself*. This lottery ticket utility number should have the property that it ranks the lottery ticket

---

[3] Here again we might use other conventions. Any process which uniquely assigns a third number to any pair of numbers will do the trick. We might, for example, use logarithmic rulers with slide-rule scales and get used to multiplying lengths—10 in. and 5 in. = 50 in. But the point is that to convey information we must start off with some sort of language. We must first set up our linguistic conventions in any convenient way and then find the numbers which correctly convey the information in this language.

[4] Actually a length measure conveys even more information than this, and so we have only one choice in assigning numbers to lengths—we can only decide on a unit of length—whether we will measure in centimeters or inches. The point is that in a length measure we have a well-defined zero. Mathematically, zero is defined as a number which, when added to another, leaves the latter unchanged. A nonexistent piece of cloth (a piece of zero length) has an analogous (the mathematicians call it "isomorphic") property. Hence, in measuring length we have only one degree of freedom, the choice of units of measurement, and a length measure is said to be *unique up to a proportionate transformation*. When measuring utility or temperature (without an absolute zero) we have two degrees of freedom—the choice of unit and the zero (freezing of water, or some other point, as in Fahrenheit measure), and hence these measures are said to be *unique only up to a linear transformation*.

correctly in relation to any other possible ticket. That is, lottery ticket A should be assigned a higher utility number than is given to B by this calculation if and only if the person prefers A to B. In sum, the N-M utility index is intended as a calculator of lottery ticket preferences. (The term "lottery ticket" is of course meant to denote any alternative involving risk.)

Here again, once we pick such utility numbers for any two alternatives, we will see that we are left no choice on the numbers to be assigned to other alternatives. This, then, is the sense in which the N-M utility measure is cardinal—it is richer in that it conveys more information than does an ordinal utility ranking obtained, for example, by directly asking any individual to state all his preferences. In effect, the N-M index is an economy device which requires an interviewer only to ask the subject to state *some* of his preferences—his ranking of lottery ticket *prizes*. With the aid of the N-M utility index (if it is applicable to this person) the interviewer can then *deduce* by himself the person's ranking of all other alternatives from the answers he has already received.

3. Construction of an N-M Index

If an individual exhibits some degree of consistency in his preferences it is possible and convenient to construct an index which describes these preferences numerically. This "utility index" does so by assigning a higher "utility" number to some item, a, than to another item, b, if the individual happens to prefer a to b. However, for their purposes von Neumann and Morgenstern required a somewhat stronger index than this—one which would enable them to make the sort of deduction which has just been described. For this purpose it was necessary to make a few more assumptions about the consistency of the preferences of the individual in question. These assumptions are described in Section 5, below. First, however, let us examine the mechanics of their special utility index.

Consider a lottery ticket which offers two prizes: the first prize is a Cadillac and the booby prize is a pair of roller skates. Suppose the odds are one in one thousand of winning, that is, the probability of winning is 0.001 so that the probability of losing is 0.999. Suppose also that, somehow, we obtain some information about our individual's attitudes toward the two prizes, and that, by a method to be described presently, we express this psychological information by means of the statement that he values the Cadillac at 2000 utils and the skates at 1 util. Then the N-M utility convention requires us to evaluate the lottery ticket at

$$0.001 \times 2000 + 0.999 \times 1 = 2.999 \text{ utils.}$$

More generally, if a lottery offers two prizes, A with probability P and B

with probability $(1 - P)$,[5] and if their respective utilities are $U(A)$ and $U(B)$, then the utility of the lottery ticket, L, is defined to be

(1) $$U(L) = PU(A) + (1 - P)U(B).$$

This simple calculation is all there is to the N-M evaluation of the utility of a lottery ticket, *once we know the person's evaluation of its prizes*. The crucial question is, then, how do we find the utility of these prizes?

In principle, this is accomplished by an extension of the preceding convention (1). For this purpose we design a special (artificial) lottery ticket which will serve as a standard of comparison. Consider two extreme prizes, E and D. These are chosen so that E is, in his opinion, as good as anything our individual is likely to end up with (mnemonic device: E = eternal bliss) and D is as unpleasant as anything he may plausibly expect (D = damnation).[6] Our standard lottery ticket, which we designate as $S(P)$, offers our individual E with probability P and D with probability $(1 - P)$, where the probability number P is not specified (it is left free to vary). Let us assign any two arbitrary utility numbers to E and D, say $U(E) = 100$ and $U(D) = 1$.[7]

Now consider any ordinary prize, A, and let us see how a utility number is assigned to A. For some values of P in the standard lottery ticket, $S(P)$, the individual will prefer $S(P)$ to A, and for other values of P the reverse will be true. For example, if $P = 1$ (certainty of eternal bliss) he will surely prefer $S(P)$ to A, and if $P = 0$ (certainty of damnation) he will prefer A to $S(P)$. It is therefore plausible that there will be some in-between value of P_a, at which our individual is indifferent between A and $S(P_a)$. Once we have found this in-between probability number, P_a (say $P_a = 0.3$), there is no difficulty in finding the utility of A. For A must have the same utility number as $S(P_a)$ since they are indifferent. But the utility of this standard lottery ticket, $U[S(P_a)]$, is easily calculated with the aid of our N-M linguistic convention Equation (1). We have

$$U[S(P_a)] = P_a U(E) + (1 - P_a)U(D) = 0.3 \times 100 + 0.7 \times 1$$

$$= 30.7 \text{ utils}$$

i.e., $$U(A) = 30.7 \text{ utils}.$$

To summarize, in order to find a utility number which represents some individual's attitude toward any prize, X, we interview or observe the per-

---

[5] If one or the other of A and B is certain to occur, their probabilities must, by definition, sum up to unity. Thus, if the probability of A is P, that of B *must* be $(1 - P)$.

[6] Actually it is not necessary to employ such extreme prizes—any two arbitrarily chosen prizes will do the trick. However, the E and D concepts make the logic of the construction easier to follow.

[7] This is where we use up our two degrees of freedom. There is, of course, one restriction on our choice of these numbers. By convention, we must have $U(E) > U(D)$ since E is preferred to D.

son to find out the probability P_x at which he is indifferent between the standard lottery ticket, $S(P_x)$, and X. We then evaluate the utility of X by using the standard N-M rule, Equation (1), to determine the utility of $S(P_x)$. That is all there is to it.

But where does the N-M prediction come in? Suppose we have two lottery tickets L_1 and L_2 and we wish to predict which of these our individual prefers. If ticket L_1 offers alternative prizes A and B, and L_2 carries with it prizes C and D, we find the utilities of each of these prizes in turn by the procedure which has just been described. From these figures, in turn, we can evaluate, by the N-M calculation [Equation (1)], the respective utilities, $U(L_1)$ and $U(L_2)$, of L_1 and L_2. We then have the prediction that the person will prefer the lottery ticket with the larger *calculated* utility number.

Observe what has happened here. In order to assign utilities to the (riskless) prizes, we did have to interview or observe the person in question. But once he has committed himself on these we need ask him no further questions in order to predict his ranking of any lottery tickets in which only these prizes are involved. We do not have to ask him how he feels about the odds involved in these tickets—this can be determined for him from our computation.

4. *Expected Utility vs. Expected Payoff*

One feature of the N-M utility convention (1) should be pointed out. According to this rule a lottery ticket is evaluated at the actuarial (expected) value of its *utilities*, not at the actuarial value of the prizes themselves, as one might more usually be tempted to do. This assertion, which may not be clear to the reader, is most easily explained by example. Consider a lottery ticket whose prizes, A and B, are amounts of money. Let these amounts and their respective utilities be the figures shown in the following table:

	A	B
Prize (dollars)	500	2
Utility of Prize (utils)	40	2
Probability	P	$1 - P$

A standard actuarial evaluation of this lottery ticket is

$$500P + 2(1 - P),$$

so that, e.g., if $P = \frac{1}{2}$ (50-50 odds) this ticket's *actuarial value* will be

$$\tfrac{1}{2} 500 + \tfrac{1}{2} 2 = 251 \; dollars.$$

But in Neumann-Morgenstern utility analysis it is necessary to translate the prizes into utility terms before one can evaluate the ticket. In N-M analysis the ticket would then be valued at $40P + 2(1 - P)$ or

$$\tfrac{1}{2}\,40 + \tfrac{1}{2}\,2 = 21 \; utils.$$

There is something inherently attractive in the latter procedure. The rational individual may be taken to be interested not in the money value of a prize, but in just how much winning it will mean to **him** (its utility). For example, a prize of $10,000 is ten times as large as a $1000 prize, but if he needs the $1000 very badly the utility of $10,000 may, in some sense, not be quite ten times as high. In evaluating the lottery ticket he should surely take this into account.

In fact, diminishing (or increasing) marginal utility can easily affect the person's attitude toward a lottery ticket. Suppose that $0 is evaluated at 0 utils by some individual, that $50 gives him 60 utils, while a second $50 yields him only 40 more utils. We have the following utility table which thus clearly involves diminishing marginal utility:

Prize (dollars)	0	50	100
Utility (utils)	0	60	100

Now consider a lottery ticket which offers a 50-50 chance of zero or $100. Its actuarial value is, of course, $(\tfrac{1}{2})100 + (\tfrac{1}{2})0 = \$50$. But to an expected utility-maximizer it is worth only 50 *utils*, which according to the table is far less than the value of $50. That is, this person will be willing to pay much less than $50 (its actuarial value) for the lottery ticket. Actually, this makes good common sense. If the ticket costs him $50 he stands a 50-50 chance of either winning or losing $50. But, if to him the marginal utility of money is diminishing, an added $50 is worth less (40 utils) than the disutility of a $50 loss (60 utils). Hence, he should never accept the ticket in exchange for $50. This is an old observation which has been made a number of times by economists and mathematicians. It illustrates how results which are more plausible intuitively can be obtained from expected utility rather than from actuarial (dollar) calculations.

Another example from a totally different field may help to bring out the difference between utility and nonutility calculations. Suppose we are trying to evaluate two alternative bombing strategies. One of them offers a 1 in 10 chance of getting through and destroying 80 per cent of the enemy's productive capacity. The other, more conservative strategy offers an 8 out of 10 chance of destroying 10 per cent of this productive capacity. On a straight actuarial evaluation the two strategies are equivalent $(0.1 \times 80 = 0.8 \times 10)$. But in terms of a doubtless more relevant utility analysis, this is not necessarily so. For example, experience suggests that a ten per cent loss in productive capacity is easily made up and will result in no real long-run difference in enemy military strength, so that it may be almost worthless. On the other hand, an 80 per cent loss is likely to weaken him very substantially and may be of crucial military value, and a utility analysis might therefore definitely recommend this latter strategy over the other. We see, then, that in decision-making it seems more appropriate to use a calculation based on the utilities of the alternative outcomes rather than on the magnitudes of the outcomes themselves. It seems much more appropriate to maximize expected utilities than expected prize values.[8]

5. *Psychological Premises Behind the Prediction*

Let us return now to our main theme, the prediction which is obtained from a N-M utility calculation. We have seen how from a purely numerical manipulation we are able to make a forecast of human behavior—to predict which of two lottery tickets our individual will prefer.

Clearly such a prediction need not always turn out to be correct. Its validity must rest on some sort of psychological assumptions, for only people of some particular psychological constitution will behave in accord with the N-M predictions. Those who have worked with the index are fully aware of this, and various sets of psychological premises have been formulated for the analysis. Let us now examine briefly a set of five assumptions which suffice to produce an N-M psychology. The appendix to this chapter contains a proof which shows that someone for whom these five premises are valid must always do as the N-M calculation predicts.

ASSUMPTION 1. *Transitivity:* If our individual is indifferent between two prizes A and B, and he also happens to be indifferent between B and C, then he will be indifferent between A and C. As we have seen in Chapter 8,

---

[8] Some critics, notably Professor Allais, have argued that although these calculations should be based on utility, they should include all the facts about the utility calculation and not just the expected value. For example, 50-50 odds of 100 and 200 (utils) have the same expected utility (150) as do 50-50 odds of 125 and 175. However, it may be argued that since the former pair of utility payoffs is more widely spread out (dispersion = 200 − 100 = 100) than is the latter (175 − 125 = 50), the former lottery ticket subjects the player to greater risk, and that, therefore, he need not be indifferent between the two. Expected value does not tell the whole story!

However, it has been answered that the utility calculation already takes the dispersion of the prizes into account. That is, if one lottery ticket offers a greater risk than another, its utilities are calculated in such a way as to discount for this fact. The utility of the riskier lottery ticket has already been reduced to take the risk into account. Hence if we make a second adjustment for the risk involved in dispersion of *utilities* we would be double-counting. Those who take this position say that this is why the psychological assumptions described in the next section can be shown (see Appendix) to *require* the person always to pick the lottery ticket with the highest expected utility, no matter what the dispersion of utility payoffs. Since Allais disputes the appropriateness of these assumptions, of course this argument carries no weight with him.

this assumption also plays a role in indifference-map analysis, so that it is no more restrictive than the usual ordinal utility analysis.

ASSUMPTION 2. *Continuity of preferences:* This is, in effect, the plausible assumption (which has already been employed) that if our standard lottery ticket, $S(P)$, is preferred to some prize, A, when $P = 1$, and if on the other hand, A is preferred to $S(P)$ when $P = 0$, there exists some in-between value of P at which $S(P)$ and A are indifferent.

ASSUMPTION 3. *Independence:* If our player is indifferent between a Ford and a Chevrolet, he will be indifferent between two lottery tickets which are identical in all respects except that one of them offers a Ford as a prize while the other offers a Chevrolet instead. This assumption is also taken to hold for lottery tickets, e.g., if the person is indifferent between the Ford and a lottery ticket, R, which offers him a chance at a Rolls Royce he must also be indifferent between two lottery tickets one of which offers a Ford and the other of which offers as a prize (the lottery ticket) R.

ASSUMPTION 4. *Desire for high probability of success:* Given two lottery tickets with identical prizes, our individual will prefer the lottery ticket with the higher probability of winning. This assumption is so persuasive that it hardly seems worth stating but it has been pointed out that there are exceptions even to this premise. Players of Russian Roulette and, sometimes, mountain climbers seem to *prefer* to live dangerously! Finally we have

ASSUMPTION 5. *Compound probabilities:* If the person is offered a lottery ticket whose prizes are, in turn, other lottery tickets, his attitude toward this compound lottery ticket will be the same as though he had gone through all the probability calculations to find out what ultimate odds of winning and losing this compound ticket really offers him. (Luce and Raiffa cite Kuhn's example of very real compound lottery tickets which is worth recalling here. All over Paris one sees wheels of chance whose prizes are, in turn, tickets in the French National Lottery.)

Some controversy has arisen out of the third and fifth premises. It is, of course, clear that few people will, or even can, go through the elaborate calculations envisaged in the last assumption, and no one has ever claimed otherwise. But the question which has been raised is whether they even *ought* to do so as a matter of self-interest. To illustrate the sort of objection which has been raised, let us consider one which has been advanced against the 3rd (so-called independence) assumption. Many, if not most people will offer considerably less than $500 for a lottery ticket, T, which gives them a 50-50 chance of $1000 or zero. Let us say that to one person T is worth $200 (he is indifferent between T and $200). Why is it worth so little to him? The answer, this argument asserts, is that he wishes to avoid risk. Two hundred dollars is a sure thing whereas T is not, so that he is willing to forego the difference between the $500 actuarial value of T and the $200 in hard cash to avoid the gambling element involved in taking T.

But suppose we consider two lottery tickets L_1 and L_2 which differ only in that T is a prize in L_1 and $200 is the corresponding prize of L_2. Should he necessarily be indifferent between L_1 and L_2 as Assumption 3 requires? The answer, says this argument, is no, because the $200 is no longer a sure thing—it has become a prize in a lottery ticket. In this case since the person is gambling in any event, he may well prefer L_1, which offers T (actuarial value $500) as one of its prizes, to L_2, in which the corresponding prize is only $200. For the second choice—the $200 option—no longer keeps him safe from risk. In other words, this argument maintains that the relative value of T and $200 is *not independent* of the context in which they are offered. They will be indifferent in one case but not in the other.

It is not intended here to offer any judgment on the acceptability of the N-M psychological premises. Many economists consider them to be rather attractive assumptions but, as we have just seen, they have not gone unchallenged. The main thing to be recognized is that the validity of the N-M predictions must rest on this or some other set of psychological assumptions.

6. N-M Versus Neoclassical Cardinal Utility

There remains one more subject to be explored—what relationship, if any, does the N-M cardinal utility theory have to that of the neoclassical utility theorists? It is generally (though not universally) agreed that there is none—the two utility measures have nothing in common insofar as their cardinality is concerned.

It is *not* the purpose of the Neumann-Morgenstern utility index to set up any sort of measure of introspective pleasure intensity. Such a measure of "strength of feelings" is totally unnecessary in the theory of games for which the N-M utility theory was constructed. Rather, the utility measure was set up for purposes of calculation, or rather of prediction (in the subtler sense of the word) to permit the theorist to *determine in the absence of the player* which of several risky propositions the player will *prefer*. For the solution of a duopoly game must predict which strategy each player will choose (prefer), and the theory must therefore be able to predict how each player will *rank* risky strategic decisions.

Then where does the "cardinal utility measurement" enter this matter? The answer is that the word "cardinal" has been used, misleadingly, to mean two entirely different things. One denotation is the neoclassical, introspective, *absolute* marginal pleasure measurement. The other, game-theoretic, use of the word "cardinality" is entirely operational. The pre-

diction as to which of the two lottery tickets will be chosen is most con-
veniently made with the aid of a numerical calculation. We are given the
person's ranking of the prizes and intend to predict from these data which
ticket he will choose. For this purpose N and M have constructed an index
far more powerful than the ordinalists'.

But note that this is not cardinal utility in the old-fashioned sense.
Not a word has been said about successive increments of some item yielding diminishing (or increasing) marginal joy. Indeed, to a strict neo-
classicist the N-M index is a sheep in wolf's clothing—to him (but not to
the mathematician) it is nothing but an ordinal measure! For while it can
be used to predict, it can predict only *rankings* of lottery tickets!

It is true that once we have derived a numerical N-M utility index we
can use it to compute numerical marginal utilities[9] and some of the other
measures encountered in neoclassical utility theory, measures which disappear in the ordinalist's analysis. But this kinship between the two cardinal theories is also illusory. It will be recalled that the ordinalist is
perfectly happy to use a concept of marginal utility of X measured in
terms of money (he calls it the marginal rate of substitution between X
and money), or, for that matter, marginal utility of X measured in terms
of any other commodity. He objects only to an introspective evaluation
of marginal utility in absolute psychological units.

But the marginal utility which can be derived from a N-M measurement is just this sort of marginal rate of substitution. To evaluate the
marginal utility of apples in money terms we would ask, "How much more
money are you willing to pay for an additional apple?" In N-M theory we
ask, instead, "How much of an increase in the probability, P, of winning
E in our standard lottery ticket, $S(P)$, is worth the same as an additional
apple?" The N-M marginal utility of X therefore ends up as no more
than the marginal rate of substitution between X and the probability of
winning the prespecified prize (E) of the standard lottery ticket. This is
surely not cardinal measurement in the neoclassical sense.

Appendix: The Psychological Premises and the Index

Let us now prove that the calculation of Section 3 of this chapter will
predict correctly the lottery ticket preferences of any person who satisfies
the psychological assumptions of Section 5.

First, it is necessary to restate these assumptions in somewhat greater
detail. For this purpose it is convenient to employ the following notation:
For any alternatives A and B let AIB mean A is indifferent with B, and
for any alternatives A and B and any (probability) number P where

---

[9] For example, if $U = f(M)$ is the N-M measure of the utility of money, M, to our
individual, we can compute the marginal utility of money to him as $\Delta U/\Delta M$ or dU/dM.

$0 \leq P \leq 1$, let $[P{:}A, B]$ represent a lottery ticket which offers the probability P of obtaining prize A, and $1 - P$ of obtaining prize B. Using this notation, our assumptions become:

ASSUMPTION 1. *Transitivity:* If for this person AIB and BIC, then AIC.

ASSUMPTION 2. *Continuity of preference as a function of P:* For any three outcomes, E, A and D, if E is preferred to A and A is preferred to D, there exists a (probability) number P_a such that $0 < P_a < 1$ and $AI[P_a{:}E, D]$.

ASSUMPTION 3. *Independence:* For any four prizes A, B, C, and F, if AIB and CIF then $[P{:}A, C]\ I\ [P{:}B, F]$ for any probability P.

This states that if two investments (lottery tickets) involve equal probabilities of attaining outcomes which are different but which are valued equally, then the two investments will be equally attractive.

ASSUMPTION 4. For any alternatives E and D, and any probability numbers r and r', if E is preferred to D, then $[r{:}E, D]$ is preferred to $[r'{:}E, D]$, if and only if $r > r'$.

This states that, other things being equal, we will always prefer the investment opportunity with the greater probability of a favorable outcome.

ASSUMPTION 5. *Compound probability arithmetic:* For any alternatives E and D and any probability numbers P, P_a, and P_b,

$$[P{:}[P_a{:}E, D], [P_b{:}E, D]]\ I\ [r{:}E, D]$$

where r is a probability number given by $r = PP_a + (1 - P)P_b$.

This requires some explanation. The long bracketed expression to the left of the I represents a compound lottery ticket which offers the probability P of winning. If the ticket holder wins, however, rather than a definite prize he obtains another lottery ticket $[P_a{:}E, D]$. If he loses, he is given, instead, the inferior lottery ticket $[P_b{:}E, D]$, with the same prizes but poorer odds. What is the probability of eventually coming out of all this with the grand prize, E? There is a probability P of winning the better lottery ticket which offers E with probability P_a, so the probability of getting E in this way is PP_a. However, if he loses the first draw, a loss which will occur with probability $(1 - P)$, the ticket holder still has the probability P_b of getting E, so that there is a probability $(1 - P)P_b$ of his obtaining E in this way. The total probability of obtaining E is then $PP_a + (1 - P)P_b$, which we have called r.

We may now interpret this last assumption to say that the person's psychology is such that he will evaluate a compound lottery ticket in terms of the probabilities of winning the ultimate prizes.

Let us now choose the lottery ticket to be used as a standard against which other alternatives can be evaluated. It is still convenient (but not necessary) to assume that this ticket offers to the winner eternal bliss (E) and to the loser damnation (D), so that any alternative, A, which we bring to be evaluated against this standard ticket will presumably be no better than E and no worse than D.

By Assumption 2, for any such A, there will be a probability number $P_a(0 < P_a < 1)$ such that $AI[P_a:E, D]$. We can now prove the following:

THEOREM 1. *Possibility of predicting:* Given any two lottery tickets $[P:A, B]$ and $[P':A', B']$ and a person whose preferences never violate Assumptions 1–5, if we obtain (say by his introspection) the four probability numbers P_a, $P_{a'}$, P_b, and $P_{b'}$ chosen so that

(2) $\qquad\qquad AI[P_a:E, D] \quad \text{and} \quad BI[P_b:E, D]$, etc.

then *from these numbers it is possible to predict which of the two lottery tickets will be preferred.*

Proof: We begin by evaluating our first lottery ticket in terms of E and D. This we can do by replacing A and B by their equivalents in terms of our standard lottery ticket, to obtain

$$[P:A, B]I[P:[P_a:E, D], [P_b:E, D]] \qquad \text{(by Assumption 3)}$$
$$\therefore \quad [P:A, B]I[r:E, D] \qquad \text{(Assumptions 1 and 5)}$$

where r is the probability number $PP_a + (1 - P)P_b$. Similarly, the second lottery ticket can be evaluated in terms of E and D as

$$[P':A', B']I[r':E, D] \quad \text{where} \quad r' = P'P_{a'} + (1 - P')P_{b'}.$$

Therefore, by Assumption 4, the individual must prefer $[P:A, B]$ to $[P':A', B']$ if and only if

(3) $\qquad r = PP_a + (1 - P)P_b > P'P_{a'} + (1 - P')P_{b'} = r'$

and he will be indifferent between these tickets if and only if $r = r'$. But by hypothesis, P, P' are numbers given by the terms of the two lottery tickets, and P_a, P_b, $P_{a'}$, and $P_{b'}$ were found out by observing or questioning our individual. Then r and r' can be evaluated directly and the higher of these two numbers must, by Assumption 4, correspond to the preferred lottery ticket.   (Q.E.D.)

Let us now see how the N-M index is constructed and prove that it can be used to predict correctly the choice of lottery ticket. As already indicated, we employ the following linguistic convention (definition) for evaluating the utility of a lottery ticket in terms of the utilities of its prizes:

(4) $\qquad\qquad U[P:A, B] = PU(A) + (1 - P)U(B).$

That is, if $P = \frac{3}{4}$ so that the odds of winning are 3 to 1, we evaluate the utility of the lottery ticket at $\frac{3}{4}$ the utility of victory plus $\frac{1}{4}$ the utility of defeat. But we note again that this is only a convention. To show that it is usable we must first restate, in terms of our present notation, how these utility numbers can be found, and then we must prove that they must always assign a higher utility number to the preferred lottery ticket.

To find the utility of any alternative, A, we first assign arbitrary "utility" numbers

(5) $$U(E) > U(D)$$

to eternal bliss (E) and damnation (D) in our standard lottery ticket. Now we find $U(A)$ by recalling (2) and defining

(6) $$U(A) = U[P_a:E, D], \; U(B) = U[P_b:E, D], \text{ etc.}$$

so that by (4)

$$U(A) = P_a U(E) + (1 - P_a)U(D), \text{ etc.}$$

Hence by finding P_a in (2) the utility number $U(A)$ can be computed.

Finally, let us prove

THEOREM II: *Validity of the prediction:* These utility numbers rank lottery tickets correctly so that $U[P:A, B] > U[P':A', B']$ if and only if the former is the preferred lottery ticket, i.e., if and only if (3) holds.[10]

Proof: The utility of the first lottery ticket is

$$U[P:A, B] = PU(A) + (1 - P)U(B) \qquad \text{[by convention (4)]}$$
$$= PU[P_a:E, D] + (1 - P)U[P_b:E, D] \qquad \text{[by (2) and (6)]}$$
$$= P\{P_a U(E) + (1 - P_a)U(D)\}$$
$$\qquad + (1 - P)\{P_b U(E) + (1 - P_b)U(D)\} \qquad \text{[by(4)]}$$

which gives on multiplying out and rearranging terms

$$= \{PP_a + (1 - P)P_b\}U(E)$$
$$\qquad\qquad + \{P(1 - P_a) + (1 - P)(1 - P_b)\}U(D)$$
$$= \{PP_a + (1 - P)P_b\}U(E) + \{1 - PP_a - (1 - P)P_b\}U(D)$$

(7) $$= rU(E) + (1 - r)U(D)$$

where r is defined as in (3), above. Similarly, the utility of the second lottery ticket is

(8) $$U[P':A', B'] = r'U(E) + (1 - r')U(D).$$

Thus comparing (7) and (8) we see that since by (5) $U(E) > U(D)$, the first lottery ticket will have the higher utility number if and only if $r > r'$. But we have just seen (3) that this condition also guarantees that that lottery ticket will be preferred. Thus we have proved that convention (4)

---

[10] The proof can easily be extended to the case of indifference.

will always assign a higher utility number to the preferred lottery ticket, as we require.

REFERENCES

Alchian, Armen A., "The Meaning of Utility Measurement," *American Economic Review*, Vol. XLIII, March 1953.

Ellsberg, Daniel, "Classical and Current Notions of Measurable Utility," *Economic Journal*, Vol. LXIV, September 1954.

Friedman, Milton, and Savage, Leonard J., "The Utility Analysis of Choices Involving Risk," *Journal of Political Economy*, Vol. 56, August 1948, reprinted in American Economic Association, *Readings in Price Theory* (J. G. Stigler and K. E. Boulding, eds.), Irwin, Homewood, Ill., 1952.

Luce, R. Duncan, and Raiffa, Howard, *Games and Decisions*, Wiley, New York, 1957, Chapter 2.

Strotz, Robert, "Cardinal Utility," *American Economic Review*, Vol. XLIII, May 1953.

More Difficult Readings

Allais, Maurice, *Fondements d'une théorie positive des choix comportant un risque et critique des postulats et axiomes de l'école américaine*, Imprimerie Nationale, Paris, 1955.

Herstein, I. N., and Milnor, John W., "An Axiomatic Approach to Measurable Utility," *Econometrica*, Vol. 21, April 1953.

Marschak, Jacob, "Rational Behavior, Uncertain Prospects and Measurable Utility," *Econometrica*, Vol. 18, April 1950.

Samuelson, Paul A., "Probability, Utility, and the Independence Axiom," *Econometrica*, Vol. 20, October 1952.

Von Neumann, John, and Morgenstern, Oskar, *Theory of Games and Economic Behavior*, 2nd ed., Princeton University Press, Princeton, N. J., 1947, Chapter 1 and Appendix.

CHAPTER EIGHTEEN

Game theory[1]

1. Taking Account of Competitive Decisions

One of the most vexing and persistent problems of the businessman is that of outguessing his rival. If only he could calculate in advance what the competition was going to do, his planning would become far easier and more effective.

As we have seen in Chapter 11, this problem can be dealt with in a variety of ways. The simplest approach is applicable where experience with the behavior of a competitor makes it relatively easy to predict his strategies. Where such information is available, it is, in effect, possible to choose that decision which maximizes the firm's expected return after the effects of the rival's countermoves are taken into consideration. Procedures which resemble this are frequently encountered in business practice.

But it is often against the competitor's interests to permit this sort of a calculation. Management may therefore avoid too obvious a pattern in its decision-making in order to keep the opposition guessing. When it succeeds in this goal, no such simple prediction of competitive behavior will be possible. At best, one may be able to say something such as, "The odds are about two to one that he will match our price cut, but if he doesn't, there's a fifty-fifty chance that he will do nothing or try to underbid us,"

[1] There is a considerable literature on this subject. The classical source is, of course, John von Neumann and Oskar Morgenstern, *Theory of Games and Economic Behavior*, 2nd edition, Princeton University Press, Princeton, N. J., 1947. For superb exposition and further references, see R. Duncan Luce and Howard Raiffa, *Games and Decisions*, Wiley, New York, 1957.

and even the validity of the estimate of these odds is apt to be questionable.

It is also possible to approach the analysis of competitive behavior by a more deductive route. Instead of asking, inductively, what we can infer from the competitor's past behavior, one seeks to determine a rival's most profitable counterstrategy to one's own "best" moves and to formulate the appropriate defensive measures. This is the approach which game theory has adopted.

2. The Zero-Sum, Two-Person Game

Consider a competitive struggle for share of the market by two firms (a duopoly). Here, every percentage point gained by one of the firms is necessarily lost by the other. This situation is called a *two-person, zero-sum game*. It is called "zero-sum" because, no matter what is done by either competitor, the total gain in market share to the two players is zero, so that the interests of the competitors are diametrically opposed. There is nothing to be gained by collusion. In our example, so long as their number remains unchanged, the share of the market which the two firms have between them is necessarily 100 per cent.[2] But the game is zero-sum only because of the nature of the company objectives. Decisions which are taken by the firms may very well increase or reduce both the absolute size of their market and the total profits of the two taken together. Increased advertising outlay and price-cutting may, for example, increase their combined sales volume and reduce their profits, and if the firms' objectives were maximization of either profit or sales rather than market share, the game would not be of the zero-sum variety.

Returning to the "battle for share of market" case, let us view the situation from the point of view of one of the firms, company A. Suppose that it has three strategy choices under consideration. A new package for its product is being investigated and the choice has been narrowed down to a red, yellow, or blue package, which we call strategies 1, 2, and 3, respectively. Suppose also, that its competitor is considering four alternative strategy moves involving, say, four different combinations of advertising media. Thus in an extreme, unrealistic case, these might involve exclusive use of television, radio, newspaper, or magazine advertising (e.g., strategy 4: put all advertising money into magazine ads).

---

[2] Strictly speaking, this is a "constant-sum" rather than a zero-sum game because the sum of the two market shares is the fixed number 100 (per cent), not zero. However, there is no significant analytic difference between the constant-sum and the zero-sum games. This is because there is no change in strategic possibilities from a given game to another game in which some constant amount that cannot be changed by the players is added to the original payoffs.

Consider now any pair of strategies open to the two players (e.g., player A employs strategy 2, a yellow package, and B uses strategy 3, newspaper advertising). Such a pair of decisions will (other things being equal) determine A's market share. Say, it will result in a 9 per cent share of market for this firm. This figure is called A's *payoff*.

All the information of this variety can be summarized in a *payoff matrix* such as the following, which shows what A will receive as a result of each possible combination of strategy choice by himself and by his competitor:

		B's strategy			
		1	2	3	4
A's strategy	1	50	90′	18*′	25
	2	27	5*	9	95′
	3	64′	30	12*	20

Thus we see the number 9 recorded in the space which is at the junction of the second row and third column, indicating that if A chooses strategy 2 and B chooses strategy 3, A will receive a payoff of 9. Since in a constant-sum game one competitor gains only that part of the fixed total prize which the other fails to obtain, there is no need to record B's payoff separately. It is obvious that if A has 9 per cent of the market, then B's payoff from this strategy-counterstrategy combination must be 91 per cent.

We assume that both A and B are acquainted with all the information contained in this table. Using these data, each player must decide on a best strategy without knowing the countermove which will be made by his opponent.

3. Maximin and Minimax Strategies

The cautious approach to this problem is to assume the worst and act accordingly. Thus, in terms of the preceding payoff matrix, if firm A employs strategy 1, its management would, on this approach assume that firm B will employ its strategy 3, *thereby reducing A's payoff from strategy 1 to its minimum or security value*, 18, which is therefore marked with an asterisk. Similarly, the fatalistic view of A's strategy 2 is that B will employ its strategy 2 and so A will obtain a payoff of 5 per cent of the market, the lowest figure in the second row of the matrix, which records the possible payoffs of A's strategy 2. Finally, the corresponding security payoff level for A's strategy 3 is 12.

With this dyspeptic view, A can make the best of the situation by aiming at the highest of these minimum payoffs. That is, management will choose that one among its strategies for which the starred figure is highest. It will seek the *maximum* among these minimum payoffs. This decision rule is, for obvious reasons, called a *maximin* strategy.

Firm B can, of course, employ a similar strategy. Only for B to assume the worst means that A receives a very *large* payoff, so that B is, residually, left with very little. Thus if B plays its strategy 1, its worst possible (security) payoff level is 64, which is therefore marked with a prime. The worst possible payoff for each of B's other strategies (the highest figure in each column) is marked in the same way. The best of these (pessimistic) payoffs for B is, of course, the lowest of these figures, the 18 in column 3. Hence the best of these choices, which is called B's *minimax* (not maximin) strategy, is strategy 3.

4. Equilibrium (Saddle) Points

In the example which has been chosen, A's security payoff from its maximin strategy 1 is exactly the same as the amount which B expects A to receive when B employs a minimax strategy 3. That is, the starred entry in the first row coincides with the primed entry in column 3. In such a case the payoff matrix is said to possess an *equilibrium point*, 18 (which, for geometric reasons that will be described presently, is also called a *saddle point*). It is to be emphasized that this coincidence of maximin-minimax strategy payoffs does not always occur. What happens in cases where the payoff matrix possesses no equilibrium point will be discussed later.

The maximin or minimax strategies have a number of important properties, some of which hold only if the payoff matrix possesses an equilibrium point:

PROPERTY 1. *The protective power of maximin strategies:* By definition, a strategy of this variety offers both parties a measure of protection in that A's maximin strategy gives him the largest share of market which B can be prevented from reducing any further, and B's minimax strategy offers B the lowest share of market for A which A can be prevented from increasing any further. A has set up the highest absolutely defensible floor under his earnings. Thus, when A plays strategy 1, anything B does will either leave his market share at its maximin level, 18, or raise it above that figure. Similarly, B's use of his minimax strategy, 3, places the lowest possible ceiling over A's payoffs.

By contrast, suppose A had chosen strategy 2 instead of his maximin strategy 1. It is true that if B miscalculates and plays strategy 1 or 4 this offers A a greater market share than the maximin payoff, 18. But B then has available a better counterstrategy. He can choose strategy 2 which (with A using his strategy 2) will confine A to a 5 per cent share of market.

In other words, by choosing a strategy other than his maximin strategy, A has left himself unprotected against a countermove by B which gives him, A, less than his maximum-security-level share. Thus the maximin or minimax strategy is designed to offer both sides maximum protection—it may well be described as the coward's (or if one prefers, the prudent man's) strategy.

PROPERTY 2. *The minimax-maximin combination and equilibrium:* Where the payoff matrix possesses an equilibrium point, a maximin strategy also has the attractive property of being a most advantageous strategy available to the one firm *if the other firm chooses a minimax strategy.* Indeed, this is why the coincident payoff matrix entry of the minimax-maximin strategy combination is called an *equilibrium point.* That is, if one of the two firms plays its minimax (maximin) strategy, the other is motivated to employ its maximin (minimax) strategy because that is how it can achieve its largest market share. Equilibrium points therefore possess an element of inner stability in that if one player adopts a strategy consistent with the attainment of such a point, the other player is also motivated to do so.

This property can be illustrated with the aid of our payoff matrix. If B plays its minimax strategy 3, the most which A can obtain is an 18 per cent share of the market, which he gets by playing his maximin strategy 1. The reason this is so is that since 18 is also B's minimax payoff, it must represent the largest figure in column 3 (the worst market share for B when he plays strategy 3). Similarly we see that if A employs his maximin strategy 1, the best B can do in response is to employ his maximin strategy 3, because any other strategy will give A more than 18 per cent of the market.

PROPERTY 3. *All equilibrium pairs are minimax-maximin strategies:* A pair of strategies a and b (where a is *any* one of the strategies open to firm A and b is one of those open to B) is defined as an *equilibrium pair* if, whenever firm A chooses a, B's most profitable countermove is b, and vice versa.

The previous property of minimax strategies, stated in this terminology, is that the minimax-maximin strategy combination constitutes an equilibrium pair. In addition, we may now assert that the converse of that proposition is also valid: i.e., that any equilibrium pairs of strategies are necessarily minimax-maximin strategies.[3]

---

[3] For if b is B's most profitable move against a, this combination of strategies must yield to A his smallest possible return from a, i.e., his security-level evaluation of strategy a, call it $S(a)$. Now, consider any other one of A's strategies, and call it a'. The security value of a', that is, $S(a')$ is the minimum yield of a' so that the combination of strategies a' and b must yield a payoff, $c(a', b)$, which is at least as large as $S(a')$. Hence $c(a', b) \geq S(a')$. Moreover, since a is A's most profitable countermove to b, the combination (a, b) must pay A at least as much as does combination (a', b), i.e., we must

PROPERTY 4. *Equality of payoffs of different equilibrium pairs:* A payoff table may possess more than one equilibrium pair of strategies. Suppose we call them (a, b) and (a', b'). However, since by the preceding property, both a and a' must be maximin strategies for A, they must yield the same security payoff to A. Similarly b and b' must yield the same security value to B. In other words, any of the *four* strategy combinations (a, b), (a', b'), (a, b'), and (a', b) must yield the same payoffs. Therefore if there are several equilibrium pairs of strategies, if one of the players picks any such strategy, then the other player can achieve the same degree of protection (minimum payoff) no matter which of these he chooses.

PROPERTY 5. *Maximin strategies may be poor countermoves to non-minimax strategies:* The minimax strategy also has an important unattractive feature. Suppose one of the firms is run by managers who are poorly informed or are not very clever, or who simply are willing to take risks, and who, for any of those reasons, do not employ a minimax strategy. Then, the maximin strategy is likely to be unprofitable to the other firm. For example, if B employs strategy 1, then it will be strategy 3 which yields A its highest market share (64 per cent) and A's maximin strategy, 1, will not do as well. In other words, the prudent maximin strategy is only guaranteed to be good when playing against another prudent man!

5. Geometry of Equilibrium Points: Saddle Points

A's payoff as a function of his and B's strategy choices can be represented in a three-dimensional diagram such as shown in Figure 1. In order

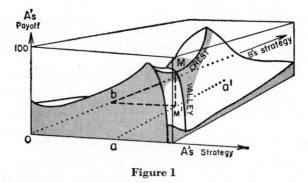

Figure 1

to obtain a smooth diagram it has been necessary to assume that both A and B have entire (continuous) ranges of strategy choice open to them,

---

have $S(a) \geq c(a', b)$. Comparing the two inequalities, we see that $S(a) \geq S(a')$, i.e., no other strategy, a', has a security value greater than that of a. Hence a must be A's maximin strategy. A similar argument shows that b must be B's minimax strategy.

involving decisions such as the prices to be charged for their projects or the amounts to be spent on advertising. Thus either player has an infinite number of choices open to him (one corresponding to each point on his strategy axis). This contrasts with situations involving only a finite number of strategy possibilities (such as the three strategies assumed available to A and four to B in the previous payoff matrix) to which most theorems of game theory refer.

In this diagram A's market share is shown directly by the height of the surface above any point on the floor of the diagram (representing a combination of strategy choices by A and B). B's market share can be inferred just as easily, since whatever per cent of the market is not held by A must be in B's hands. B's share of market surface is thus what is left of the three-dimensional cube in the diagram after A's share of market surface has been removed.

It will be noted that A's surface has been drawn to involve two very special characteristics. It has the crest of a hill running roughly north to south and the trough of a valley running roughly east to west. The valley is the locus of security levels for A's strategies. For example, if he chooses strategy a in the diagram, the worst payoff he can possibly receive is $M'M$, the payoff at the point where line aa' (the line which represents strategy a) falls under the trough or valley line of the payoff surface. Similarly, the crest line is the locus of B's minimum payoffs (i.e., the maximum payoffs to A for any of B's possible strategy choices).

The altitude of the point of intersection, M, between the trough and the crest lines is A's payoff from the combination of A's maximin strategy a, and B's minimax strategy b. A's maximin strategy a is his maximin strategy because that is where the trough line reaches it highest point, i.e., where it crosses the crest of the hill. For similar reasons b is B's minimax strategy. Thus, M is an equilibrium point and M' represents the equilibrium pair of strategies a, b.

Because the graph of the payoff surface has the shape of a somewhat distorted saddle, a point such as M, which is the intersection of a hill crest and a valley trough, is called a *saddle point*.

6. *Payoff Matrices Without Equilibrium Points*

We have yet to deal with the case where A's share of market payoff matrix has no saddle point. An illustration is provided by the following payoff matrix for A:

	1	2
1	80′	20*
2	40*	100′

Here A has a maximin strategy, 2, because 40 is the maximum of the lowest numbers in the two rows. Similarly, B has a minimax strategy 1 which will guarantee that A obtains a market share no larger than 80 per cent. This is not a saddle point because the maximin strategy combination (2, 1) and the minimax combination (1, 1) do not coincide. The lowest point on the crest of the surface is at a different location from the highest point in the valley. Note that if the maximin-minimax combination of strategies is employed, A will obtain 40 per cent of the market so that B will be pleasantly surprised.

Even in this case, the maximin-minimax procedure will still be the coward's strategy. By definition, it provides maximum protection against one's competitor.

But now this strategy pair lacks the second attractive feature which it possessed in the saddle-point case. It is no longer an equilibrium pair. That is, *if B is certain to employ his minimax strategy* 1, A is better off employing his *non*maximin strategy 1 which will raise his market share from 40 to 80 per cent. It is also easy to see that B will want to change his strategy if A changes from his maximin to his nonmaximin strategy, and that A's best counterstrategy will depend, equally, on B's strategy choice. Thus, in the absence of a saddle point, the choice of strategies becomes a highly unstable affair.

This does not mean that maximin or minimax strategies are now necessarily undesirable. Especially when A and B are highly uncertain of one another's plans, they may still both prefer to play it safe and to stick to this decision no matter what the risky temptations.

7. *Mixed Strategies*

There is another interesting type of strategy alternative open to A and B. Its analysis will require the aid of the utility theory developed in Chapter 17. It turns out that if the number of possible pure strategies with which we began is finite, this alternative type of strategy has the effect of replacing A's share of market payoff matrix with another which has the following remarkable property: If the original share of market surface had a saddle point, the new surface will also have one at the same location. And even if the original share of market surface had no saddle point, the new one *always* will!

The way in which this additional set of strategic possibilities enters can be indicated in a somewhat roundabout manner. It was remarked at the beginning of the chapter that good business policy will often seek to prevent the competition from predicting one's own strategy. One way of doing this is to choose one's strategy randomly, e.g., to pick two fairly good strategies and choose between them by the toss of a coin or some other chance device such as a spinner. The combination of the two strategies and the probabilities assigned to the two strategies[4] is itself called a *mixed strategy*, as compared with the *pure strategy* which involves no such random elements.

Mixed strategies can easily be shown to have a very interesting property. They can often increase the security levels available to both competitors when the pure-strategy payoff matrix has no saddle point. This is easily demonstrated with the aid of the preceding payoff matrix.

Suppose that the payoffs in the table, instead of representing share of market, are measured in utility terms. We can then compute the (expected) *N-M* utility of a mixed strategy to compare its value with that of a pure strategy.

Consider the mixed strategy which offers *A* a 1-to-3 chance of having to employ strategies 1 and 2, respectively. If *B* employs his strategy 1, the expected value of the utility of the outcome to *A* will be $\frac{1}{4}80 + \frac{3}{4}40 = 50$. On the other hand, if *B* employs his other strategy, 2, the expected value of *A*'s payoff is $\frac{1}{4}20 + \frac{3}{4}100 = 80$. Either of these outcomes exceeds the 40 guaranteed to *A* by his maximin pure strategy, and so, simply by turning his decision into a gamble, *A* has increased the level of protection which is available to him. In the same way, *B* can also increase the value of his minimum payoff by the use of mixed strategies.

There appears to be an element of sleight of hand in this procedure, and some writers have questioned the value of mixed strategies except as a means of confusing the competition. It can at least be charged that the businessman in question must be a split personality who always assumes the worst in situations in which the odds for the different alternative strategies open to *B* are unknown and who yet accepts a more temperate evaluation when his own decision is also made into a gamble. If the individual were to adopt as pessimistic a view of the outcome of a mixed strategy as he does for a pure strategy, he would act as though he were always sure of losing and a mixed strategy could not increase his degree of protection.[5]

Mixed strategies have proved advantageous to *A* by enabling him (*only in his anticipations*) to take his eggs out of one strategy basket. Actually,

---

[4] The odds can be set any way the player prefers to have them. For example, if the pointer in a spinner can fall on any number from 1 to 12, the odds are set at 2 to 1 in favor of strategy 1 by deciding to play strategy 1 if the pointer falls anywhere on 1 through 8 and to play strategy 2 otherwise. Since there is an infinite number of possible sets of odds, the number of mixed-strategy alternatives open to a player is infinite.

[5] Such a person, in fact, would not possess the second characteristic of the expected-utility maximizer as listed in Chapter 17. To him the value of a gamble will not vary with the magnitude of the probability of winning. A ten-to-one chance of making $50 or $5 would be worth exactly the same to him as a similar bet at 50-50 odds—both would be worth exactly $5. This again suggests that the extreme pessimism of a minimax strategy may not always be appropriate.

however, by using such a strategy he has opened himself to the worst of contingencies. If luck is against him, and B uses strategy 2 while against 3-1 odds he is led to employ 1, his payoff will be only 20, the lowest possible payoff in the table which is well below the 40-util payoff to his maximin pure strategy. The mixed strategy has really provided him with no absolute protection in the ultimate outcomes, unlike his pure maximin strategy. But, in return, the mixed strategy has permitted him the luxury of anticipating far more desirable outcomes, e.g., the 100 payoff which the maximin pure strategy approach would have required him to keep out of his calculations altogether.

8. Optimal Mixed Strategies and the Saddle-Point Theorem

The theorem that there must be a saddle point on the surface which represents the payoffs from a finite number of pure strategies and, in addition, all possible mixed strategies into which these can be combined, was first proved by J. von Neumann. It has been called the fundamental theorem of two-person, zero-sum game theory.

To discuss the derivation of this theorem the concept of the *optimum* mixed strategy must first be described. The odds attached to the different pure strategies which make up the mixed strategy need not be chosen arbitrarily. By changing the odds in our previous illustrative computation, it is easy to show that different mixed-strategy odds yield different maximum security levels for a player. He should therefore look for a set of probabilities for his own mixed strategy which will make his security level as large as possible.[6] This so-called *optimum* mixed strategy will set the highest possible floor, L, under A's expected earnings. If A plays this mixed strategy, the best B can hope to do is keep A's *expected* earnings down to level L.

If we go back to the first payoff matrix in this chapter for an illustration, the probabilities which constitute this optimal mixed strategy can be found with the aid of the following linear program: let q_1, q_2, and q_3 be the probabilities which player A will assign to the pure strategies one of which is to be chosen by his random device. Then he seeks those values of the q's which maximize L, the floor to his payoff. Since the q's are proba-

---

[6] This is the point where the Neumann-Morgenstern utility theory is required. We wish to find which of the infinite number of possible mixed strategies is preferred by the minimaxing player. But the utility axioms tell us that he will prefer the one for which the *expected* security (utility) value is highest. We therefore compute the general expression for this expected value in accord with the procedures of the utility theory, and are then in a position to use linear programming methods to find the odds which maximize this expected value, in the manner described below.

bilities, their sum must equal unity and none of them may be negative. We also require (in order to be sure L is a floor) that no matter what his opponent does, A's expected payoff is at least L. The symbol q_1 represents the probability that A will be told by his random device to employ his pure strategy 1, so that, if his opponent plays his strategy 1, A will have the probability of q_1 of receiving the corresponding payoff which we denote by $P_{11} = 50$ (see the payoff matrix). If his opponent plays strategy 1 he can also expect payoff $P_{12} = 27$ with probability q_2, etc.

Considering all these possibilities together, we see that if B plays his strategy 1, A's payoff must turn out to be one of the numbers 50, 27, or 64 ($= P_{13}$) and A's *expected* payoff will then be 50 multiplied by the probability, q_1, that he will end up with strategy 1 plus 27 multiplied by the odds on strategy 2, q_2, plus $64q_3$. A will seek q's which guarantee that this sum is no less than L. Similarly, if B were to play his strategy 2, A's expected payoff would be $90q_1 + 5q_2 + 30q_3$, and this, too, must be no less than L. Similar conditions must also take care of A's expected payoff if B should employ either strategy 3 or 4. Taking all of these constraints into account, we see that the determination of A's optimum mixed strategy constitutes the following linear programming problem:

Maximize L (the floor to A's payoff) subject to

$$\left.\begin{array}{l} 50q_1 + 27q_2 + 64q_3 - L \geq 0 \\ 90q_1 + 5q_2 + 30q_3 - L \geq 0 \\ 18q_1 + 9q_2 + 12q_3 - L \geq 0 \\ 25q_1 + 95q_2 + 20q_3 - L \geq 0 \end{array}\right\}$$

These conditions state that A's expected earnings are never less than L, i.e., that L is truly a floor.

$$\left.\begin{array}{l} q_1 + q_2 + q_3 = 1 \\ q_1 \geq 0,\ q_2 \geq 0,\ q_3 \geq 0 \end{array}\right\}$$

These conditions must be satisfied for the q's to be probabilities.

Since whatever B gains A must lose, B will be equally anxious to minimize A's expected payoff. His optimum mixed strategy will impose on A's expected maximum payoff (the most A can get for himself) a ceiling, S, which is as low as possible. It is easy to check that the probabilities, v_1, v_2, v_3, and v_4, which accomplish this are found with the aid of the dual of the preceding program:

Minimize S subject to

$$50v_1 + 90v_2 + 18v_3 + 25v_4 - S \leq 0$$
$$27v_1 + 5v_2 + 9v_3 + 95v_4 - S \leq 0$$
$$64v_1 + 30v_2 + 12v_3 + 20v_4 - S \leq 0$$
$$v_1 + v_2 + v_3 + v_4 = 1$$
$$v_1 \geq 0,\quad v_2 \geq 0,\quad v_3 \geq 0,\quad v_4 \geq 0.$$

We can now apply the two duality theorems of Chapter 5, Section 12, to this zero-sum, two-person game.[7] Theorem I tells us that if both players employ their optimal mixed strategies, then L, the highest floor which A can set under his payoff, will be equal to S, the lowest ceiling which B can place over A's earnings. This means that there will always exist a pair of *mixed* strategies which constitute an equilibrium pair in the sense that neither player can do any better for himself when the other employs his optimal mixed strategy. A can guarantee himself no more than $L = S$, and B cannot force him to take less. This is the fundamental theorem of the zero-sum, two-person game. This theorem paved the way for most further game-theory analysis. It may be added that von Neumann's original proof is much more complicated than that which was just outlined.[8]

Our Duality Theorem II also has an interesting game-theoretic interpretation. Since both players know the payoff figures, player B can, of course, compute A's optimal mixed strategy and its expected yields just as well as can A. We would, therefore, expect B not to play any strategy which offers to A more than his minimum expected return, $L = S$. Duality Theorem II tells us that this is precisely how he will behave if his strategy is optimal. For suppose the probabilities of A's optimal mixed strategy are such that strategy 1 turns out to be a poor one for player B; that is, if B plays strategy 1, A's expected earnings will be greater than the minimum, L, to which B can force them. This means that in the first constraint condition in A's linear program the expected value of A's payoff, $50q_1 + 27q_2 + 64q_3$, will actually be *greater than* L. Duality Theorem II then tells us that the optimal value of v_1, the corresponding variable in the dual problem, will be zero. But, it will be recalled, V_1 is the probability that when B spins his mixed-strategy spinner it will tell him to play pure strategy 1. In other words, Duality Theorem II tells us that the linear programming calculation will assign such odds to B's mixed strategy that he takes no chance on his random device leaving him stuck with undesirable strategy 1. More generally, we see, then, that Duality Theorem II *always* assigns probability zero to an inferior pure strategy. An optimal mixed strategy will automatically insure the player against any risk of employing a pure strategy which enables his opponent to do well.

The programming view of the two-person, constant-sum game yields one other significant observation. We would normally expect that in an

---

[7] The duality theorems of Chapter 5 must be extended somewhat for the present purpose since our pair of dual programs contain not just inequality constraints but also the equations

$$q_1 + q_2 + q_3 = 1 \quad \text{and} \quad v_1 + v_2 + v_3 + v_4 = 1$$

(which, as they stand, contain no slack variables).

[8] Actually, for this argument to constitute the outline of a proof, it is necessary to show that the pair of dual programs in question possess optimal solutions.

optimal solution a number of slack variables will take zero values. The corresponding constraints must then become equalities, i.e., the corresponding expected yields are all exactly equal to L. The economic interpretation is that a player picks the odds in an optimum mixed strategy in a way which offers his opponent little real choice—the opponent can choose among a number of strategies, but, typically, *most of these offer him exactly the same payoff* (the rest offer him even less since they give the first player *more* than L).[9]

9. Strategy; the Extensive and Normal Form of a Game

There is a matter of interpretation which it is well to take up before proceeding further. The term "strategy choice" has been employed in a way which makes it appear to denote a single move. However, as the concept is used in game theory it has been interpreted to mean a great deal more. The strategy really becomes an extensive book of rules indicating what the player intends to do, in every contingency, from the beginning of the game to the end. Thus the strategy commits the player to an entire sequence of moves which is contingent in a fully specified manner upon what is done by the other player.

This clearly artificial device serves to collapse the entire game into two strategy choices, one by each player. Once these choices have been made, the subsequent history of the game is completely determined. One can, in principle, figure out all the rest. Of course, only in the simplest of game situations can a player even be conceived of as thinking in terms of strategies in this extreme sense.

Some studies have been made of games considered move by move.

---

[9] Where the payoff matrix has exactly two rows and two columns and has no equilibrium point containing any pure strategy, it is clear that the equilibrium pair must consist of mixed strategies, i.e., all four numbers q_1, q_2, v_1, and v_2 must be positive. Hence, in a *basic* solution to such a problem all four slack variables must be zero. This states that the expected payoff to a player must be the same for both of his pure strategies if his opponent uses an optimal mixed strategy.

This observation yields an easy method for the determination of the optimal mixed strategies in such simple (2-row, 2-column) games. For example, in the second payoff table of this chapter the expected payoff to B's strategy 1 is $80q_1 + 40q_2$, and that to B's strategy 2 is $20q_1 + 100q_2$, where $q_1 + q_2 = 1$, i.e., $q_2 = 1 - q_1$. If these expected payoffs are to be equal we must have

$$80q_1 + 40q_2 = 20q_1 + 100q_2$$

or

$$80q_1 + 40(1 - q_1) = 20q_1 + 100(1 - q_1)$$

that is,

$$80q_1 + 40 - 40q_1 = 20q_1 + 100 - 100q_1 \quad \text{or} \quad 120q_1 = 60$$

so that $q_1 = \frac{1}{2}$ and the optimal mixed strategy for A involves $q_1 = \frac{1}{2}$, $q_2 = \frac{1}{2}$. The reader can check for himself that the optimal mixed strategy for B involves $v_1 = \frac{2}{3}$, $v_2 = \frac{1}{3}$.

Such an analysis is said to deal with games in their *extensive form*. However, the bulk of the literature discusses games in the collapsed form that uses the strategy concept, referred to as games in *normal form* (meaning that the games have been rewritten in accord with this convenient mathematical norm—not that games are normally played in this way!).

10. *Two-Person, Nonconstant-Sum Games*

So far the discussion has dealt only with constant-sum games, i.e., only with games in which the behavior of the players has no effect on their combined payoff. Real economic problems are usually of the nonconstant-sum variety. For example, collusion can normally increase the total profits of a pair of duopolists, and two countries can usually do better by getting together than by declaring war on one another. Unfortunately, the theory is in a far less satisfactory state outside the area of the two-person, constant-sum game.

In the literature, nonconstant-sum games are divided into two classes: *cooperative* and *noncooperative*, i.e., into games where collusion does and those where it does not occur.

In the cooperative case the game theorists have tended to argue that the players will be sufficiently rational to discover and make full use of all opportunities which can be mutually advantageous. That is, the players are taken to cooperate on any and every action which can increase the payoff of either player (provided it does not, at the same time, reduce the payoff of the other). In the terminology of Chapter 11, Section 9, this states, then, that they will always end up somewhere on the contract curve.

Of course, it is doubtful whether players are really so rational in practice. Moreover, the problems involved in arriving at an acceptable division of the "take" may well prevent the players from maximizing their total loot as this rationality assumption requires! It is noteworthy that most of the novelty in the cooperative-case analysis occurs in investigation of the division of the spoils between colluding players. Nash has supplied a criterion for a reasonable or "fair" division which has been the subject of considerable attention and some criticism.[10]

[10] The Nash criterion states that if the *status quo* is (as a matter of convenience) evaluated at zero for both players, and if the players' payoffs are evaluated by the recipients at u_1 and u_2, then a fair division is one which maximizes the product of these utilities, u_1u_2. Nash derives this rather surprising arbitration formula from a set of axioms which are set up as reasonable criteria for a fair division of the spoils. A Zeuthen-Harsanyi model, which assumes that the bargainer who makes a concession is always the one whose percentage utility loss is the smaller, has also been shown to lead to the Nash solution. See John C. Harsanyi, "Approaches to the Bargaining Problem," *Econometrica*, Vol. 24, April 1956.

Noncooperative, nonconstant-sum games will also be discussed briefly. They possess a number of interesting features:

1. If such a game possesses several equilibrium pairs of strategies, they need not all yield the same payoff. Moreover, if (a, b) and (a', b') are equilibrium pairs, neither (a, b') nor (a', b) need be equilibrium pairs. Thus two properties of the zero-sum case no longer hold (cf. Section 4, above). This can greatly complicate the planning problems of both players since, if they do not aim for the same equilibrium pair, both may lose out.

2. In the noncooperative, nonconstant-sum case it will often pay a player to publicize his plans, in marked contrast with the rather obvious advantage of secrecy in the zero-sum case. Disclosure may be useful either as a threat or as a means for transmitting information which permits a degree of tacit collusion:

(a) *Threat information:* To a player who announces that he will drop a jar of nitroglycerine which will blow everyone up if he does not have his way, disclosure of this information is necessary for him to win his point. Curiously, a reputation for stupidity and stubbornness can be useful to the player who poses a threat because it will help convince the others that he really means it! Many mundane economic examples, such as strike threats, are easily cited.[11]

(b) *Information for quasi-collusion:* A company will often make certain that any price increases are well publicized in the hope or even the confident expectation that this move will soon be followed by other firms in the industry, to their mutual advantage. Other examples will doubtless occur to the reader.

3. Another peculiarity of the nonzero-sum, noncooperative case is that both players will often be led by self-interest to take decisions which are mutually disadvantageous. This has been illustrated sharply by a game called "the prisoners' dilemma" which is attributed to A. W. Tucker. Two prisoners are brought in and interrogated separately. Each knows they will both get off if neither prisoner "talks." However, they are both told that if one confesses and the other does not the one who fails to confess will receive a particularly heavy penalty. In this situation both players may well decide to protect themselves by confessing.

This point is of considerable economic importance. It shows why citizens may not contribute taxes voluntarily even though each wants the government to function—the citizen sees nothing to be gained by paying taxes unless there is some guarantee that others will contribute too, just

[11] For a highly suggestive analysis of this and other related problems, see T. C. Schelling, "Bargaining Communication, and Limited War," *Conflict Resolution*, Vol. I, March 1957, and "The Strategy of Conflict: Prospectus for a Reorientation of Game Theory," *Conflict Resolution*, Vol. II, September 1958.

as one prisoner will confess unless he has some assurance that his fellow prisoner will not do so. Similarly, many storekeepers will keep their shops open on Sunday although they all prefer a holiday, each fearing that if he does not do so he will lose customers to his competitors. This argument is involved in the logic behind conscription and rationing in wartime, governmental anti-inflationary measures, etc. All of these measures are designed, at least in part, to achieve the cooperation which alone can prevent the loss to each player from his trying to protect himself when he has no assurance that others will behave as required for their mutual interest.[12]

11. n-Person Games: Some Concepts

Of most widespread potential economic application is the theory of many-person games, for most industries contain more than two firms, most real international trade problems involve more than two countries, and so on. But n- (many-) person games have so far proved rather intractable to analysis. Writings on the subject and results have been much fewer than in the case of the two-person, zero-sum game. Certainly there is nothing in n-person theory resembling the well-rounded analysis of the two-person case.

Nevertheless, the literature is rich in suggestive ideas—definitions and concepts rather than theorems. Some, but not all of these concepts are matters of common sense and common observation and it is only remarkable that they were given little attention in pre-game-theoretic economic theory. So far, in economic application, such suggestive concepts have been the most fruitful aspect of game theory—they have served to provide an illuminating way of looking at difficult problems rather than a source of cut-and-dried calculations. For these reasons the discussion of n-person games which follows is little more than a description of concepts and definitions, and it is organized accordingly. These will, however, enable the reader to form an impression of the present state of n-person theory.

In this theory, games are again divided into the cooperative and noncooperative varieties. Only one result will be reported for the noncooperative case. Nash has proved that *every* noncooperative game in which each player has only a limited number of strategy alternatives open to him has at least one (mixed or pure strategy) equilibrium point. In other words, there exists at least one combination of mixed or pure strategies $(a, b, c, \ldots, n)$ such that, if they are employed by players $(A, B, C, \ldots, N)$, respectively, it will be unprofitable for any one of these players to switch to any other strategy. Thus there exist strategy combinations which have

---

[12] Indeed, I have suggested that this argument is central to the rationale of governmental control in a democratic society. See my *Welfare Economics and the Theory of the State*, Longmans, London, 1952, esp. Chapters 7–9 and 12.

this self-policing feature: If all players but one follow this pattern the self-interest of the remaining player will also lead him to stick to the equilibrium pattern.

However, an n-person game may possess more than one equilibrium point, and there may then arise the difficulties which were mentioned in the two-person, nonconstant-sum case: Different equilibrium points may yield different payoffs to the players, and if some players aim for one equilibrium point and the remaining players aim for another, they may all end up at a nonequilibrium point! Hence, in the absence of coordination of their plans, if a game possesses a number of equilibrium points, the players may find it difficult to attain any one of them.

We now turn to a listing of the central concepts of the theory of n-person cooperative games:

1. *Coalitions.* In the two-person game there is no possibility of several players combining against the rest. Such collusive arrangements can obviously arise in a many-person game. In game theory this sort of combination of players is called a *coalition.*

Obviously there are many cases where a coalition can add to the "take" of its members by successfully exploiting the remaining players. However, there are some games in which coalitions offer no net advantage to their members (an economic example might involve the costs of administration eating up the profits of any coalition). A game of the relatively uninteresting variety in which there is no motivation for coalition formation is called an *inessential game*, as contrasted with *essential games* in which its members can benefit from the formation of a coalition.

2. *Side payments.* Sometimes, in order for a coalition to maximize its returns, it may be necessary for a member to undergo some sacrifice. For example, a cartel may find it profitable to close the inefficient plant of one of its members rather than getting every member to reduce his scale of operations. In this case, in order to induce the short-changed individual to serve the interests of the coalition it is necessary to set up an equalization payment (bribe) for him. In game theory such a redivision of the spoils is called a *side payment.*

3. *Imputation.* Any assignment of payoffs to the players is called an *imputation* if it meets two acceptability requirements:

(a) Each player must receive at least as much as he can get for himself when all other players are arrayed against him. If this condition is not met, any player who receives the short end of the payoff allocation can refuse to go along with the coalition structure from which these payoffs result. Obviously, he can always hold out for at least the amount which he can obtain for himself without anyone's help.

(b) A second requirement for an imputation is that the total of all the payoffs to all of the players combined equals the maximum amount they can get by forming one grand universal coalition in which every member is included.[13] This second condition of group rationality is, in fact, widely violated in practice. When farmers do not get together and voluntarily restrict their outputs, they end up with a reduced total take. The same is true when several countries adopt restrictive tariff policies and all of them end up poorer as a result. In other words, an imputation may be described as a set of payoffs which could be achieved by the players in a game if they were more rational than they are in reality.

4. *The core.* Some imputations may satisfy a condition of group rationality which is even stronger than (b) above. This more stringent condition requires that the members of *any potential* coalition, S, jointly earn at least as much as they can by getting together and forming coalition S. Of course, people do not, in fact, think out every possible coalition they can possibly form and what they may hope to earn by joining it, so that this condition is certainly not met in practice. The set of all possible coalitions which meets this difficult requirement is called the *core* of a game. However, many games have no core. Indeed, it has been proved that any zero-sum game which has a core, i.e., for which such imputations exist, must be inessential!

5. *Characteristic function.* But how does one determine how much will be paid to each player in different circumstances? Given the coalitions which are formed, what payoffs will be received by the members of each coalition? Von Neumann and Morgenstern approached this question by describing lower limits to these amounts. Given any coalition C, the worst that can possibly happen, from its point of view, is that all other players will combine against it in one grand countercoalition. But if the total take of the two coalitions is *fixed* at its maximum possible value (group rationality requirement (b) of an imputation) this transforms the problem into a constant-sum, two-person (two-coalition) game. Since such a game can always be solved by the linear programming methods described in Section 8, above, we can calculate how much will be earned by our coalition C in these unfavorable circumstances.

In this way a minimum-earnings figure can be computed for every possible coalition. If payoffs are measured in utility terms, the relationship $R = v(S)$ which gives this minimum payoff, R, for every possible

---

[13] This implies that any imputation must be Pareto optimal (cf. Chapter 13, Section 11, and Chapter 16, Section 5), for otherwise it would be possible to make a change which was advantageous to some of the players and disadvantageous to no one, i.e., the group would initially not have obtained the maximum "take" as rationality condition (b) requires. It also follows that a Neumann-Morgenstern n-person game solution (defined below) must be Pareto optimal.

coalition S, is called the *characteristic function* of the game. The Neumann-Morgenstern analysis of the n-person game is based largely on the characteristic function. However, such an analysis is bound to leave out much relevant information about the game because it concentrates exclusively on the worst outcomes for each coalition.

The following plausible result is among the theorems on characteristic functions: If two coalitions combine, the value of the characteristic function for the combination will equal or exceed the sum of the values for the uncombined coalitions, i.e., the combined coalition will earn at least as much when the rest of the world is against it, as the two subcoalitions can earn for themselves in similar circumstances.

6. *Domination.* An imputation, I, is said to dominate another imputation, J, if there exists at least one coalition C which can be sure (in terms of the characteristic function) of earning for its members an amount, $v(C)$, which is at least as large as that prescribed for them by imputation I and if, in addition, every member of C receives more from imputation I than from imputation J. In other words, J is dominated by I if a set of players who are in a position to prevent imputation J from supplanting I find it profitable to prevent J. It is, of course, possible for two imputations to dominate one another if coalition S prefers I to J and can prevent J, and if coalition T prefers J to I and is in a position to prevent I.

7. *Solution.* Von Neumann and Morgenstern define a solution of an n-person game as a *set* of imputations which has the following characteristics:

(a) If I and J are any two of the imputations in a solution, then neither I dominates J nor J dominates I.

(b) If K is an imputation which is not included in the solution set then there is at least one imputation, K^*, which dominates K and which is included in the solution. Thus, a solution consists of a set of imputations none of which dominates any other, and which can among them dominate any excluded imputation.

There are several difficulties involved in this concept. First of all, a solution usually includes a number—sometimes an infinite number—of possible imputations. That is, a solution only lists for us a number of possible outcomes to a game. Thus it does not usually tell us how the game will or should end up. It only confronts us with a list, and sometimes a very large list, of possible alternatives.

The situation is even worse than this suggests, because a game may, and often does, possess a number of alternative solutions (each with its multiplicity of imputations). It is clear, then, that the solution concept does not permit us to calculate any unique outcome for the general game.

Moreover, although it is known that the number of solutions in the three-person game is usually embarrassingly large, it is not known whether there are games which do not possess even a single solution even where the number of players is restricted to a number as low as five. Shapley has also shown that there are games for which the solutions constitute strange and unpredictable sets, that is, cases which make it very difficult to set up general rules about the nature of solution sets.[14]

Because the solution concept permits so much indeterminacy and is not fully satisfactory in other respects, a number of alternative concepts have been explored. Milnor has set up several sets of criteria which, he suggests, an imputation should meet in order to be considered reasonable. These criteria are designed primarily to get rid of some of the possible imputations on the ground that they are in some sense not "reasonable." Vickrey has proposed a concept which he calls a *strong solution*, consisting only of imputations and coalitions such that if anyone defects from one of the included coalitions he is apt to regret it because there exist alternative imputations which tempt his new partners to "double-cross" him in turn. Luce has constructed a theory which takes into account the fact that there are institution constraints on the formation and breakup of coalitions. That is, it recognizes that social mores may well prevent the formation of certain types of coalition. This points up what is admittedly the main weakness of game theory in its present stage of development—the relative lack of specific sociological, psychological, and economic content in its premises. Until such material is supplied, it is unreasonable to expect the mathematics to yield the empirically applicable results which are not contained in its assumptions.

This concludes a rather disjointed discussion of concepts of n-person theory, which should nevertheless at least offer the reader a hint of its flavor.[15] At any rate this section should suggest both the strength and weaknesses of game theory from the points of view of the economist and the operations researcher—its weakness as a source of devices for the calculation of categorical answers to competitive problems, and its strength as a suggestive frame of reference within which the structure of these problems and the alternatives available to the decision-maker may be seen more clearly.

[14] The solution concept has also been criticized for its reliance on the characteristic function. That is, in practice, one imputation, I, may in effect "dominate" another, J, even though the characteristic function indicates that no coalition C can prevent J profitably. For the characteristic function gives only the most conservative estimate of what C can hope to achieve, and in practice C may often be expected to do much better than that.

[15] For further details the reader is again referred to Luce and Raiffa, *Games and Decisions*, Chapters 7–12.

REFERENCES

Luce, R. Duncan, and Raiffa, Howard, *Games and Decisions, Introduction and Critical Survey*, Wiley, New York, 1957.

McDonald, John, *Strategy in Poker, Business and War*, Norton, New York, 1950 (very elementary).

McKinsey, J. C. C., *Introduction to the Theory of Games*, McGraw-Hill, New York, 1952.

Tucker, A. W., *Game Theory and Programming* (mimeographed), Oklahoma Agricultural and Mechanical College, Stillwater, 1955.

Von Neumann, John, and Morgenstern, Oskar, *Theory of Games and Economic Behavior*, 2nd edition, Princeton University Press, Princeton, N. J., 1947.

Williams, J. D., *The Compleat Strategyst*, McGraw-Hill, New York, 1954.

CHAPTER NINETEEN

Decision theory[1]

1. The Subject Matter of Decision Theory

Contemporary theory follows Knight's distinction between risk and uncertainty.[2] Risk refers to situations in which the outcome is not certain, but where the probabilities of the alternative outcomes are known, or can at least be estimated. Uncertainty is present where the unknown outcomes cannot even be predicted in probabilistic terms, that is, it refers to contingencies against which one cannot protect oneself on ordinary insurance principles.

In game theory, choice problems which involve risk are analyzed with the aid of utility theory, as we have seen in the last two chapters. One makes that decision whose expected utility (the average utility of the alternative outcomes each weighted by its probability of occurring) is highest. Decision theory has been developed to deal with problems of choice or decision-making under uncertainty, where the probability figures required for the utility calculus are not available.

Quite a bit of the games apparatus has been carried over into decision theory. As will soon be shown, the payoff matrix, the strategy concept,

---

[1] As in the last chapter, the reader who wishes to learn more about the theory, or who desires further references, is advised to consult R. Duncan Luce and Howard Raiffa, *Games and Decisions*, Wiley, New York, 1957, especially Chapter 13.

[2] F. H. Knight, *Risk, Uncertainty and Profit*, Houghton-Mifflin, Boston, 1921. Reprinted by the London School of Economics, series of reprints of scarce tracts in Economics No. 16, 1933.

and the minimax approach all make their appearance again. But there is one fundamental difference between the problems of game and decision theory which cannot be overemphasized. In game theory, at least in the zero-sum, two-person case, there is a major element of predictability in the behavior of the second player. He is out to do everything he can to oppose the first player. If he knows any way to reduce the first player's payoff, he can be counted upon to employ it. In decision theory the second player is not even, strictly speaking, an opponent. Often this second player is referred to as "nature" and the corresponding decision problems are called "games against nature." But our player cannot count upon nature to oppose him. In fact he cannot count on nature to do anything in particular.

This chapter follows the bulk of the decision-theory literature by treating only the so-called *complete-ignorance* case, that is, the case where the player who is to make a decision has absolutely no clue as to what the other player is going to do. Once there is available any information about his rival's likely behavior, however fragmentary, the requirements of the complete-ignorance case are violated.

However, the standard complete-ignorance analysis supposes, at least implicitly, that the player has at his disposal a large amount of other types of information—more, in fact, than a relatively well-informed businessman is likely to have in practice. In assuming that he can describe his problem in terms of a payoff matrix, the player is taken to possess a list of the strategy alternatives which are open to himself as well as those which are available to his opponent. In addition, he is assumed to know the magnitudes of all of the elements in the payoff matrix. This means, for example, that if a businessman player adopts a particular inventory policy and the demand for his product turns out to follow some particular time pattern, say falling at first, subsequently rising sharply, and finally, leveling off (this time pattern is considered "nature's strategy choice"), then the businessman knows, or believes he knows, exactly what payoff he will receive as a result of this (and every other) pair of his and nature's strategy choices. This is the sort of information which is conveyed by the numbers in his payoff matrix.

The player must also be recognized to have at his disposal a very different kind of highly pertinent information, for he knows something about *himself*—his own financial position and his attitude toward taking chances. Together, these must determine to what extent he will desire and can afford to gamble. The validity of any rules for rational decision-making under uncertainty must, then, be contingent upon at least these two elements—the player's psychological makeup and his pecuniary circumstances.

2. *Some Proposed Decision Rules*

Since attitudes toward gambling and financial circumstances differ from person to person, it is clear that there can be no one universally valid rule which tells a player how to choose among the strategies that are open to him. The appropriate decision criterion must vary from person to person and from one situation to another.[3]

It is not surprising, therefore, that a considerable number of alternative decision rules have been proposed. At present, the bulk of the literature of decision theory relates to such decision-rule proposals. Let us now examine in turn the most frequently discussed of these decision criteria.

1. *The maximin criterion.* As in game theory, one of the most conservative of decision rules is the maximin criterion. For each possible strategy the player determines the worst that can possibly happen, and then picks the strategy which is "least worst," i.e., whose most unattractive contingency is least disastrous.

In the present context the maximin strategy is somewhat less attractive than it is in a games situation, where the player has an active opponent whose interests are in direct conflict with his own. In such circumstances there can be good reason for fearing the worst. But where one's opponent is nature, who, at least in calmer moments, cannot be considered a systematic and calculating opponent, the maximin approach is rather clearly a manifestation of pure cowardice. This is not meant to imply that cowardice is necessarily irrational. On the contrary, there is much to be said for the Falstaffian position on self-preservation. There are persons and situations where the maximin strategy is entirely appropriate, but it's well to recognize the criterion for what it is.

As an illustration, consider the following payoff matrix (which is carefully chosen to make the maximin criterion show up badly):

	C	D	E
A	100	2	1
B	99	98	0

If our player employs strategy A his worst payoff is one (1) (which he receives if nature employs strategy E), whereas if he employs strategy B his lowest possible payoff is zero. Hence his maximin strategy is A, because it offers him the larger of the two minimal payoffs.

---

[3] It must be made clear, however, that this relativistic view is my own, and it is not a standard feature of the writings on decision theory. But cf. the Hurwicz α criterion described below.

This table also illustrates an objection which has been raised against the maximin rule whose conservatism will now be shown, in some circumstances, to be somewhat specious. From the point of view of the rational conservative, there is much to be said in favor of strategy B, because its highest and lowest payoff (in case nature employs strategies C or E) are fairly close to those of A, whereas B's intermediate payoff, 98 (if nature's strategy is D), is much higher than A's intermediate payoff, 2. Hence B appears to offer an excellent hedge against the possibility that neither the best nor the worst possible outcome will be realized.

The source of the difficulty is that the maximin criterion disregards most of the information in the payoff matrix. It considers only the worst possibility in each row, and makes its recommendation with complete disregard for the values of the other elements. Hence it is always possible to find cases in which the nature of these other numbers in the payoff matrix casts doubt upon the wisdom of the maximin choice. As will be seen presently, a similar criticism applies to most, but not all, of the other decision criteria which have been proposed.

2. *The maximax criterion.* A second decision criterion, which does not seem to have been put forth seriously anywhere in the literature, is worth describing because it is at the very opposite end of the scale of venturesomeness from the maximin rule. The maximax criterion, which is a decision rule well suited to the temperament of a plunger, considers only the most glittering prize offered by any strategy and is blind to any other contingencies. It calls for the player always to choose that gamble whose first prize is highest, no matter what the dangers in the relative values of the other prizes and penalties.

In terms of our payoff matrix, it is clear that the maximax criterion advises the decision-maker to employ strategy A, whose highest payoff, 100, exceeds the 99 first prize of strategy B. Two observations are relevant: (a) This illustration shows that the extremely gambling-oriented maximax rule can sometimes recommend the same course of action as the maximin rule, the counsel of timidity—their advice will coincide when one strategy carries with it the best of both first and booby prizes; (b) like the maximin criterion, the maximax rule ignores all intermediate prizes and so may suggest to a player that he give up a very great advantage in the less glittering payoffs, for a negligible difference in the highest prize.

3. *The Hurwicz α criterion.* As a (reportedly somewhat tongue-in-cheek) compromise, Hurwicz has proposed that a weighted average of the minimum and maximum payoffs of each strategy be employed as a decision criterion. For example, if we weight the minimum payoff (security value) of any strategy at $\alpha = \frac{3}{4}$, and the maximum payoff $\frac{1}{4}$, then the Hurwicz α criterion would evaluate strategy A in the payoff table at

$$1 \cdot \tfrac{3}{4} + 100 \cdot \tfrac{1}{4} = 25\tfrac{3}{4}$$

and strategy B at

$$0 \cdot \tfrac{3}{4} + 99 \ \cdot \tfrac{1}{4} = 24\tfrac{3}{4}.$$

Hence, it would again select strategy A. This is to be expected, since both the maximin and maximax criteria selected A, and the Hurwicz criterion is, in effect, a weighted average of the two in which the weights are designed to reflect the player's psychology. Like the other two, the Hurwicz criterion clearly ignores a strategy's less extreme payoffs in its computations.

4. *The Bayes (Laplace) criterion.* A criterion whose history is far older than the others that have been described is the Bayes, or equiprobability of the unknown criterion. This states that if we have absolutely no information about the relative probabilities of nature's strategies A, B, and C, we must assign equal probabilities to them in our calculations and then adopt the strategy whose expected payoff is highest.

In our payoff table, this criterion evaluates A at

$$\tfrac{1}{3} \cdot 100 + \tfrac{1}{3} \cdot 2 + \tfrac{1}{3} \cdot 1 = 34\tfrac{1}{3}$$

while B is rated at

$$\tfrac{1}{3} \cdot 99 + \tfrac{1}{3} \cdot 98 + \tfrac{1}{3} \cdot 0 = 65\tfrac{2}{3}.$$

Unlike the others which have been examined, then, the Bayes criterion ranks B ahead of A. It does so because the Bayes rule is the only one of the criteria so far examined which takes all possible payoffs into account. For the first time the 2 payoff possibility of strategy A and the corresponding 98 payoff of strategy B have entered the calculations, and these have turned the tide in favor of B.

In this respect, then, the Bayes criterion is more appealing than the others.

However, the Bayes criterion does suffer from a serious limitation. The difficulty is that it is not clear in advance what unknown possibilities are to be considered equally probable. To illustrate this point, let us consider an economic situation which can lead to a payoff matrix like ours. Suppose our player is considering whether to sell ice cream (strategy A) or hot dogs (strategy B) at a baseball game. We may divide nature's strategies into the three possibilities, C: sunshine, D: cloudiness, and E: rain (or other forms of precipitation). In the complete absence of meteorological information we might consider C, D, and E to be equally probable and assign them each the probability $\tfrac{1}{3}$ as was just done.

Alternatively, however, we might have decided that the major contingencies to consider are rain vs. nonrain. Because we possess no relevant information, it can be argued just as persuasively as before that these two contingencies are equally likely and each should be assigned the probability $\tfrac{1}{2}$. We see, then, that by a simple act of reclassification, the *a priori* probability assigned to the rain contingency (nature's strategy E) has been raised from $\frac{1}{3}$ to $\frac{1}{2}$! In other words, unless we have some advance information on the number of categories into which the alternatives should be classified, the Bayes equiprobability-of-the-unknown approach can leave the relevant probability figure completely ambiguous. By breaking the alternatives down into enough different categories, we can assign any one strategy a probability as low as we like.

A variant on the Bayes procedure is to ask the decision-maker to assign subjective probabilities to nature's possible strategies. If for some intuitive reason he feels that C, D, and E may reasonably be assigned odds of $\frac{2}{10}$, $\frac{5}{10}$, and $\frac{3}{10}$ respectively, the expected value computation can be repeated using these figures instead of the $\frac{1}{3}$, $\frac{1}{3}$, and $\frac{1}{3}$ probabilities of an equiprobability-of-the-unknown calculation. With these figures, strategy A, for example, would be evaluated at

$$100 \cdot \tfrac{2}{10} + 2 \cdot \tfrac{5}{10} + 1 \cdot \tfrac{3}{10} = 21.3.$$

5. *The minimax regret criterion.* The last criterion to be discussed was proposed by Savage. His rule concentrates on the opportunity cost of an incorrect decision. The approach is to protect the player against excessive cost of mistakes. From the original payoff matrix, a second matrix showing the cost of mistakes (the regret) is calculated. For this purpose it is necessary that the elements of the original payoff matrix be expressed in utility terms. Suppose that this is true of the data in our illustrative matrix and that nature's strategy turns out to be D. If the player employs his strategy B he obtains the maximum payoff against D (98 as against 2 utils) and so he has nothing to regret. The corresponding regret figure is, consequently, zero, which is entered in the regret matrix at the juncture of row B and column D as shown. But if our player had

Regret Matrix

	C	D	E
A	0	96*	0
B	1*	0	1

instead employed A against nature's D, he would have earned only 2 utils as compared with the maximum possible payoff of 98, so that his net loss, his degree of regret, is $98 - 2 = 96$. This is entered in the row A, column D space. The rest of the regret matrix is computed similarly from the original payoff matrix as the reader should check for himself. To protect himself against excessive loss, the player may now apply a minimax rule to this matrix. In each row the maximum loss is starred, and that strategy is chosen whose row contains the smallest of the maximum regret elements.

In this case, strategy B is recommemded by a minimax regret rule, because the worst that can happen to the player who chooses B is a 1-util regret.

At first glance it may appear that this criterion, because it recommends strategy B rather than A, overcomes the problem that was raised in connection with the maximin, maximax, and Hurwicz criteria. It is true that the minimax regret criterion can take into account large disparities in intermediate payoffs. In our illustration, nature's strategy D, with its prohibitive 96-util regret figure, assumes a crucial role even though it offers neither the maximum nor the minimum payoff for any of our players' strategies (see the original payoff matrix). However, the minimax regret criterion runs into the same problem in a slightly different manner. Since it is a minimax criterion it considers *only the largest regret figure* in any row, and ignores any other data. Hence low and intermediate regret numbers are disregarded. If one strategy, F, has a very slightly smaller highest regret figure than another strategy, G, the criterion will recommend F even if every other regret figure in G is much lower than the corresponding number in F.

The appropriateness of the measure of regret which is employed by the criterion has also been called into question. It is not clear from the Neumann-Morgenstern utility index that the difference between the utilities of two payoffs is a good measure of the player's regret when he receives the smaller of the two. Perhaps the regret measure can be considered a somewhat crude and arbitrary, though not a totally unreasonable measure of the player's loss in choosing the wrong criterion.

6. *Mixed strategies.* Rather than choosing a pure strategy directly, the decision-maker may prefer to let a random device—a coin or a spinner—make his choice for him. As in the game-theory case, such a decision is called a mixed strategy. As before, the player can, by using the utility calculus, compute the expected utility yield of any mixed strategy corresponding to any one of nature's strategies. For example, if the player employs that mixed strategy which involves 50-50 odds of choosing either strategy A or B, then if nature plays its strategy C, the expected payoff will be

$$\tfrac{1}{2} \text{ the } A \text{ payoff} + \tfrac{1}{2} \text{ the } B \text{ payoff} = \tfrac{1}{2} 100 + \tfrac{1}{2} 99 = 99.5.$$

Continuing the calculation, one obtains the following augmented payoff matrix:

	C	D	E
A	100	2	1
B	99	98	0
$[\tfrac{1}{2}:A, \tfrac{1}{2}:B]$	99.5	50	$\tfrac{1}{2}$

The last row indicates the alternative expected payoffs of the mixed strategy $[\frac{1}{2} : A, \frac{1}{2} : B]$ which represents a 50 per cent chance of either A or B.

By varying these odds, e.g., to three to one, etc., these expected payoffs of the mixed strategy are, of course, changed. It then becomes possible to calculate at which odds the *mixed* strategy will yield the largest maximin value, or, if we prefer, the odds which give the lowest minimax regret figure.[4] Such a set of odds is said to constitute an *optimal* mixed strategy. The decision-maker may then prefer to employ an optimal mixed strategy.

Some comment on the concept of the mixed strategy is called for at this point. It may seem rather irrational for the decision-maker to permit a coin to make up his mind for him, and few if any businessmen are prepared to adopt this as a standard decision-making procedure. However, the maximiner is a fundamentally timid man who fears that his opponent (whether it be nature or another player) will always outguess and outplay him. This is the logic behind his disregard of anything but the least favorable outcome for any pure-strategy choice. A mixed-strategy calculation, however, no longer disregards these more favorable payoffs—rather it deals with their average or expected value. This can be rationalized by the argument that, when the player's decisions are made by a coin or some other random device, he can be sure that no one will outguess him and so those more favorable payoffs which he formerly left out of his calculations now become very real possibilities, and they must therefore appear in his mixed-strategy calculations. Thus, the higher security value of a mixed strategy may be treated as a subtle reflection of the fact that a mixed strategy can prevent the player's opponent from predicting his decision.

[4] Mixed strategies are not helpful to the player who employs a maximax or a Bayes criterion. Since the expected utility figure is a weighted average of the pure strategies, it will give something intermediate between the highest and the lowest of the items being averaged. This process of averaging therefore tends to raise lowest figures (it increases the security level) of a pure strategy, and is therefore useful to the maximiner. However, because it is an average, the expected values will tend to fall short of the maximum figures, i.e., a mixed strategy will tend to reduce the expected return of a maximaxer.

The user of a Bayes criterion never benefits from a mixed strategy for a similar but somewhat more complex reason. On a Bayes criterion, both strategies A and B are themselves evaluated by means of a weighted average of their payoffs. Thus, as we have seen with our payoff matrix, strategy A is evaluated at $34\frac{1}{3}$ and B at $65\frac{2}{3}$. A mixed strategy will in turn be evaluated, on the Bayes criterion, at a weighted average of these two figures (their expected value). This average must be less than the $65\frac{2}{3}$ value of B, so that the pure strategy B will always be preferred to the mixture of A and B. Thus, a Bayes calculation always evaluates a mixed strategy at some figure intermediate between the highest and lowest values of the pure strategies, and so one of the pure strategies will always be preferred on this criterion.

PROBLEM

In the following payoff matrix (constructed by John Milnor) show that strategy A will be chosen by a Bayes criterion, strategy B will be selected by the maximin criterion, C by the Hurwicz α criterion (for $\alpha < \frac{1}{2}$), and D by a minimum regret criterion:

A	2	2	0	1
B	1	1	1	1
C	0	4	0	0
D	1	3	0	0

3. Geometric Interpretation of the Decision Rules

The decision rules which have been described undertake to rank the strategies that are available to a player in terms of the alternative payoffs which they offer him. This suggests that each criterion implicitly postulates some set of indifference curves for the player so that they can rank the strategies for him. As will be shown presently, that is precisely what they do.

First, it is necessary to describe the nature of the indifference map which is involved. To keep the diagram down to two dimensions we shall deal only with pure strategies each of which offers exactly two possible payoffs. That is, the general pure strategy in this set offers our player a payoff which will be designated by V if nature plays some strategy C and some other payoff, W, if it employs its *only* alternative strategy, D. Two such strategies are shown in the following payoff matrix which will provide our illustrations throughout this section:

	C	D
A	6	3
B	2	8

Here pure strategy A has two possible payoffs, $V = 6$ and $W = 3$; for pure strategy B we have $V = 2$ and $W = 8$.

Given the payoffs, a point representing such a strategy can be plotted at once on a diagram which measures off the magnitude of payoff V on its horizontal axis and that of W on its vertical axis. Thus strategies A and B are represented in this way in Figure 1a. Any point in the diagram clearly represents a pair of payoffs and, therefore, some (hypothetical) strategy, and, conversely, every possible strategy with a pair of alternative payoffs can be represented by such a point. If V and W are interpreted as *expected*

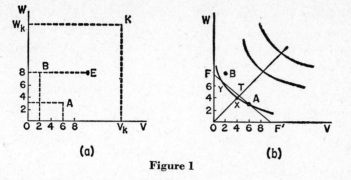

Figure 1

payoffs *such a point can also represent a mixed strategy* whose expected payoffs are the coordinates of the point. We may familiarize ourselves with the nature of the representation by noting the following:

1. If (and only if) one strategy, such as E, has possible payoffs *both* of which are greater than the corresponding payoffs of another strategy, A (we say then that E strongly dominates A), point E will lie above and to the right of A.

2. If and only if one strategy, E, has payoffs no smaller than those of another, B, and if just one of E's payoffs is higher than the corresponding payoff of B (E *weakly dominates* B), point E will lie either directly above or directly to the right of point B.

3. If some strategy point lies directly on the 45-degree line through the origin (point T in Figure 1b), the corresponding strategy will involve no uncertainty, since the two alternative payoffs will be equal. Thus, T has a payoff of 4 utils if nature employs strategy C and (also) 4 utils in the alternative event that nature plays D. At any point, such as A, which is not on the 45-degree line, the two possible payoffs V and W are unequal and we say that there is *dispersion* in the payoffs.

Suppose now that the player's preferences among these possible strategy points can be described by a set of indifference curves drawn through the diagram (Figure 1b). This is a rather strong premise since it means that the player must be able to rank every such possible strategy. However, that is precisely what is done by any one of the criteria which have been described. In any event, it does not seem much less plausible than the corresponding assumption behind the ordinary indifference map construction.

The only difference between this and the ordinary indifference-map construction is that in the usual case the payoffs V and W represented on the axes are received by the player together (at point K he receives V_k *plus* W_k) whereas in our diagram the payoffs are alternatives (he receives either V_k or W_k but not both).

The shapes of the players' pure-strategy indifference curves will vary with their attitudes toward uncertainty. For example, we might expect that the indifference curves of a person who has an aversion to gambling will be convex to the origin like those in Figure 1b (or in the extreme case, like those of Figure 2a). To see why, we note that this shape (a diminishing marginal rate of substitution of W for V) means that successive equal increments in one of the payoffs will compensate the player only for ever smaller reductions in the other payoff. He considers one increasingly glittering prize to be poor compensation for a continued proportionate deterioration in the alternative payoff.[5]

Similarly, the gambler who is anxious to give up the protection of a fairly good, second-best payoff in return for a more glittering first prize may be expected to have pure-strategy indifference curves which are concave to the origin.

It will now be shown that the maximin, the maximax, the Hurwicz, and the Bayes criteria each require that the decision-maker's pure-strategy indifference curves be of a very special shape which varies from criterion to criterion. For example, in the maximin ranking of a strategy, only the smaller of its payoffs is taken into account. This means (Figure 2a) that below the 45-degree line where payoff W (the ordinate of any point) is the smaller of the two coordinates, an indifference curve is any horizontal line $W = $ constant, because the player will never be indifferent between two strategies for which the smaller payoffs, their W's, are not the same. For the same reason, above the 45-degree line the indifference curves must be the vertical lines $V = $ constant. In other words, only for an individual whose pure-strategy indifference curves are like those in Figure 2a will it be appropriate to use the maximin criterion.

Similarly, since the Bayes criterion evaluates strategies at $\frac{1}{2}V + \frac{1}{2}W$, the equation of a Bayes indifference curve is $\frac{1}{2}V + \frac{1}{2}W = K$ (constant), i.e., $W = -V + 2K$. These curves are the parallel straight lines of slope -1 which are shown in Figure 2b. The use of other subjective probability numbers instead of 50-50 odds only changes the slope of these parallel straight lines. The reader can readily show that a maximax criterion

---

[5] The connection between convexity to the origin and desire for a low dispersion in payoffs can be shown somewhat more rigorously as follows. For any probability numbers q and $1 - q$, the straight line $qV + 1 - qW = K$ (FF' in Figure 1b) is the locus of combinations of payoffs, V and W, all of which yield the same expected payoff, K. If the player is averse to gambling he would therefore presumably prefer point T on the 45-degree line, where the dispersion in the payoffs is zero, to either points A or Y on line FF' since all three points represent pairs of payoffs whose expected values are the same. Choose Y to be a point which is indifferent to A. If both points are indifferent also to some point on the 45-degree line it must be a point which is inferior to T, i.e., Y and A must be indifferent to a point such as X nearer to the origin (i.e., of lower payoffs) than T. Thus the indifference curve YXA must be convex to the origin.

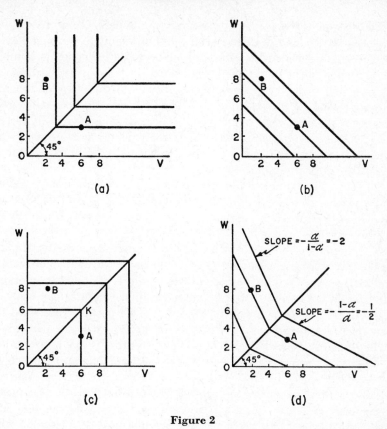

Figure 2

(according to which the larger of the numbers V or W is constant along an indifference curve) and a Hurwicz α criterion [α multiplied by the smaller of the numbers V and W, plus $(1 - \alpha)$ multiplied by the larger of these two numbers = a constant] require indifference maps of the kinds shown in Figures 2c and 2d respectively.[6]

Since there is no reason to believe that every person's indifference map will assume (the same) one or even any of the forms in these figures, it follows that no one of these criteria is a universal prescription for ration-

---

[6] The convexity to the origin of the indifference curves of the extremely conservative maximining player, and the concavity of the extreme gambling maximaxer's curves are in line with the interpretations of convexity and concavity given above.

The Savage minimax regret criterion cannot be represented in so simple a diagram since it involves direct comparison of all the elements in several strategies so that more than two dimensions are required for the indifference map even where each strategy has only two possible payoffs. However, if we deal with the regret matrix rather than the payoff matrix, the indifference map is again that shown in Figure 2a, since Savage applies a minimax (maximin) criterion to the regret data.

ality. Strategies can be ranked, but only by the criterion which happens to be appropriate to the particular decision-maker in light of his psychological and financial circumstances as reflected in the shape of his indifference map.

4. Axiomatization

An alternative approach to the decision problem has employed what is called *the axiomatic method.* By setting up as axioms a number of requirements for an acceptable decision criterion, several authors have been able to come up with unique decision rules, e.g., several writers have shown that the Bayes criterion is the only one which satisfies the sets of axioms which they have proposed. Before we go into further detail, a few preliminary words on the axiomatic method are appropriate.

Axiomatization is one of the mathematician's very powerful and fruitful methods. In using it, the analyst sets out in explicit mathematical form the assumptions which he is willing to use in his investigation. He then employs rigorous mathematical techniques to deduce from these axioms as many of their implications as he can. Often the derived theorems are extremely surprising and bear little *obvious* relationship to the axioms from which they are deduced. The axiomatic method, then, has two very attractive features. It forces the analyst to set his assumptions out explicitly, and it puts him in a position to deduce rigorously the implications both obvious and obscure of his *a priori* notions about the problem as expressed in these axioms.

However, it must be recognized that while mathematical statements are always explicit, they are often not transparent. The literature abounds with axioms whose meaning is in dispute or which turn out to mean something other than what their author intended. It is true that a mathematical axiom must have everything there—the author cannot simply hint at some of its features and keep reservations in back of his head in a fuzzy statement, as he is able to do in a literary discussion. But if the axiom requires a complex mathematical formulation (though simplicity, too, can sometimes be deceptive), the more subtle nuances of its meaning may be obvious neither to the analyst nor to his audience. There are a number of innocuous-sounding premises in the literature whose critical implications belie their apparent innocence. None of this is meant as a criticism of the axiomatic method. It amounts only to the trite injunction that powerful weapons should be used with very great caution.

The axiom systems which have been employed in the decision theory literature are fairly complex and abstract, and there will be no attempt to describe any of them here. Implicitly, such a system must specify something about the needs and desires of the decision-maker if it is to be used to derive some specific decision rule.

The next section describes such a derivation. It is selected for its simplicity and it is unfortunate that it is not one of the standard axiomatic treatments of the literature of decision theory, all of which are too difficult for our expository purposes. Like a number of the standard analyses, this illustrative axiomatization will be shown to rule out all decision rules except the Bayes criterion. However, it does not follow that this is true of any axiom system. Indeed, Milnor has described a set of axioms corresponding to each of the decision rules which this chapter has described.

5. Neumann-Morgenstern Utility and the Bayes Criterion[7]

It will be shown in this section that a simple extension of the Neumann-Morgenstern utility assumptions rules out anything but the Bayes criterion. That is, a person whose psychology is as described by these axioms must, if he is consistent, employ a Bayes decision rule (with subjective *a priori* probabilities assigned by him to nature's strategies, if he prefers).

First it is necessary to discuss the applicability of the utility axioms to the decision problem. Consider a player who is trying to make up his mind between one of two equally priced refrigerators. The theory is willing to assign utility numbers to these objects and to assume that the player will choose that refrigerator whose utility is highest. But suppose, e.g., that refrigerator A is better adapted to storing tall objects and that B is designed primarily for heavy items. Since the consumer cannot be entirely certain in advance what he will be buying over the lifetime of the refrigerator, the choice between A and B must represent a strategy decision against an uncertain future. Similarly, the acquisition of any other durable item, such as a factory, can also be interpreted as a strategy choice.

Generalizing from this we may interpret two strategies A and B in a payoff matrix as two refrigerators, or two factories, or two tickets to a game with fixed prizes but unknown odds. The player may be certain of possessing ticket A and hence he may evaluate the utility of the ticket just as he does that of a refrigerator. Moreover, it is possible to assume that the player's ranking of these strategies satisfies the Neumann-Morgenstern utility axioms. Certainly, casual inspection of the axioms suggests that they are no less persuasive than usual when applied to refrigerators, to factories, or to any other tickets of admission to a game involving uncertainty rather than risk. Thus we adopt for our illustrative purposes

[7] This section is somewhat more difficult than the preceding portions of the chapter.

AxIOM 1: The player's ranking of strategies satisfies the Neumann-Morgenstern utility axioms.

In addition, it is necessary for our purposes to specify explicitly an essential feature of a game against nature—the fact that nature is not a calculating opponent so that the decision-maker has nothing to gain by camouflaging his strategy intention. Thus

AxIOM 2: The utility of a strategy is dependent only on the payoffs and probabilities which it involves. (In particular, its utility is not affected by an attempt to conceal from a competitor the fact that one has decided to play it.)

These two axioms together permit us to make a standard calculation of the utility of a mixed strategy. For, if M is the mixed strategy which chooses A with odds $\frac{3}{5}$ and B with odds $\frac{2}{5}$, we have, by the usual rules: the utility of $M = \frac{3}{5} \times$ utility of $A + \frac{2}{5} \times$ utility of B; or, in symbolic notation[8] (with generalized odds q and $1 - q$ instead of $\frac{3}{5}$ and $\frac{2}{5}$)

$$U(M) = qU(A) + (1 - q)U(B).$$

Finally we adopt

AxIOM 3: The decision-maker is indifferent between any two strategies whose payoffs or expected payoffs are identical.

The theorem about the Bayes rule can now be derived geometrically.

In Figure 3 consider two strategies R and S which are represented by points lying on the W and V axes, respectively, so that for the former strategy we have the payoffs $V_R = 0$ and $W_R = $ length $OR = r$ (some number), etc.; thus the payoff matrix is

	C	D
R	0	r
S	s	0

Any strategy point T which lies on the straight line connecting R and S divides that line into some proportions which we designate $1 - q$ and q. Point T can be interpreted in either of two ways: it can be taken as a

---

[8] Axiom 2 is required for this result. For if the opposition is likely to outguess and outplay the decision-maker unless he employs a mixed strategy, the evaluation of a mixed strategy given by the equation in the text is no longer valid because the values of $U(A)$ and $U(B)$ are changed by the very act of randomization. Strategy A will be much more valuable if there is a fair chance that the enemy will not make the right countermove so that randomization will increase $U(A)$ to, say, $U^*(A)$, and $U(B)$ to $U^*(B)$, and the utility of the mixed strategy becomes

$$U(M) = qU^*(A) + (1 - q)U^*(B) > qU(A) + (1 - q)U(B).$$

(hypothetical) pure strategy T, or as the mixed strategy M, which consists of R with probability q and S with probability $(1 - q)$, whose expected payoffs $V = qr$ and $W = (1 - q)s$ (see figure) are the same as those of T. We can now proceed with our proof in two parts which shows that the in-

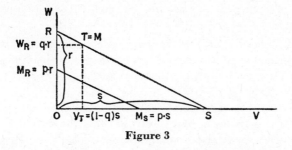

Figure 3

difference curves must be straight and parallel as a Bayes criterion requires (compare Figure 2b, above):

Part 1: Let S be chosen so that it is indifferent with R. Then the in-difference curve connecting them is a straight line.

Proof: By hypothesis, since R and S are indifferent, we have $U(S) = U(R)$, i.e., the utility of S equals that of R. By the usual Neumann-Morgenstern formula, our mixed strategy, M, has the utility

$$U(M) = qU(R) + (1 - q)U(S) = qU(S) + (1 - q)U(S)$$
$$= (q + 1 - q)U(S) = U(S) = U(R).$$

Thus the mixed strategy M is indifferent with both S and R. But by Axiom 3, pure strategy T is indifferent with M (since they have the same expected payoffs). Hence any pure strategy T on the line RS must be indifferent with both strategies R and S.

Part 2: All of the decision-maker's remaining indifference curves are parallel to RS.

Proof: Consider the pure strategy O both of whose payoffs are zero, and which is therefore represented by the origin of the diagram. Form the two mixed strategies M_R and M_S where M_R is defined as R with any fixed probability p and O with probability $(1 - p)$, and where mixed strategy M_S is S with probability p and O with probability $(1 - p)$. We have

$$U(M_R) = pU(R) + (1 - p)U(O)$$
and $$U(M_S) = pU(S) + (1 - p)U(O).$$

Since S and R have been chosen to be indifferent, so that $U(R) = U(S)$, it follows at once that $U(M_R) = U(M_S)$, i.e., that the two mixed strategies are indifferent. Hence by the argument of part 1, the straight line $M_R M_S$

connecting the mixed strategy points is an indifference curve. But (Figure 3) M_S has coordinates $(ps, 0)$, and M_R has coordinates $(0, pr)$. Hence $M_R/M_S = pr/ps = r/s$, that is, the slopes of the two lines are equal, and the straight-line indifference curve $M_R M_S$ is therefore parallel to RS.

This proves our theorem because any parallel straight-line indifference curves satisfy the Bayes criterion. This has already been indicated in the discussion of Figure 2b.[9]

Thus we have proved the theorem that a simple extension of the Neumann-Morgenstern utility axioms requires the rational decision-maker to employ a Bayes criterion. It follows, incidentally, that there is some conflict between the maximin strategy and these utility axioms. The source of this difficulty is the extreme pessimism of the maximin strategy user which is not shared by a person to whom the utility axioms are applied. The former views the worst possible payoff of any strategy as the only possibility worth considering, whereas the utility calculator takes all payoffs into account. As already indicated, this difference in outlook can be rationalized by arguing that a mixed strategy protects the player from being outguessed by his opponent, a possibility which seems doubtful in games against nature, and which is therefore ruled out by Axiom 2 of this section.

6. Decision Theory and the Foundations of Statistics

Before concluding this chapter it is worth indicating briefly how the decision analysis has been used to reorient some of the literature on the foundations of statistics.

To illustrate the nature of this application, consider a simple problem of statistical quality control. A television tube manufacturer has a sample of tubes taken out of each day's production and tests every tube in the sample. Unless too many of the sample tubes are found to be defective, the entire day's production is just packed up and shipped without further examination. The statistical problem is how large a sample should be chosen for inspection and what proportion of defectives in the sample

---

[9] More rigorously, any one of these lines has an equation of the form $W = -kV + c$ where k and c are any numbers and $k \geq 0$. Let r be a number defined by $r = k/(1 + k)$. Then we have $0 \leq r \leq 1$, so that r can be a probability number. Moreover, solving for k in terms of r we have $k = r/(1 - r)$. Substituting this expression for k into the equation of our line, we get

$$W = -[r/(1 - r)]V + c \quad \text{or} \quad rV + (1 - r)W = (1 - r)c = \text{a constant}$$

which is the equation of a Bayes indifference curve with probability r of payoff V and $(1 - r)$ of payoff W.

ought to be considered excessive, i.e., what is the proper borderline between an acceptable and an unacceptable sample.

In conventional statistical analysis it is customary to make some probabilistic calculation indicating the degree of assurance provided by different sample sizes and rejection levels that the number of defectives in the
total output batch will fall short of some specified number. Ultimately,
the sample design decisions are made more or less arbitrarily, after a check
that these decisions can be considered reasonable.

But the statistical problem is really one in which it is meaningful to
look for an *optimal* decision. Too small a sample or too liberal a rejection
level means that the percentage of defectives in the firm's shipments is
likely to be high, and this can prove costly both in the cost of servicing
under the manufacturer's guarantee, and in the loss of customer good will.
On the other hand, as many firms have found to their sorrow, excessively
rigid quality control standards can be very expensive and can force the
manufacturer to price his product out of the market. Clearly, some intermediate quality control standards must be optimal, and an analytic approach to this problem of statistical design must seek such an optimum.

This problem is now readily translatable into standard decision-theo-
retic terms. Each relevant sample-size, rejection-level combination may be
considered a strategy of the quality controller and, for each of these, the
alternative possible payoffs to the firm may be entered in a payoff
matrix. The rest of the analysis can then employ the methods of decision
theory.

The same sort of comment applies to statistical problems more general
than that of commercial quality control. The entire theory of testing of
hypotheses is subject to the same considerations. The customary use of
tests conducted at a 95 or a 99 per cent level of significance is essentially
arbitrary and does not take into explicit account the costs and benefits
(payoffs) of alternative significance levels.

These considerations have, at least as yet, had no influence on the
methods of applied statistics. Rather, they have affected only the relatively
abstract and philosophical discussions of the foundations of statistics. In
part, this is because decision theory is still in a rudimentary state and can
offer no firm and final answers to the questions of statistical design. Among
the sources of the unsolved problems are the difficulties involved in obtaining data for the payoff matrix and the fact that the results of a decision-
theoretic calculation depend on whether one chooses to employ a maximin,
or a Bayes, or some other decision rule, and we have, as yet, no systematic
procedure for making this choice. However, the discussion has served to
call attention to the optimality problem—which is fundamental to most
statistical problems—and to indicate some new and illuminating ways in
which these problems can be viewed.

REFERENCES

Chernoff, Herman, and Moses, Lincoln E., *Elementary Decision Theory*, Wiley, New York, 1959. (Statistical applications of decision theory.)

Luce, R. Duncan, and Raiffa, Howard, *Games and Decisions, Introduction and Critical Survey*, Wiley, New York, 1957, Chapter 13.

PART IV

*Application to Marketing
and Operations Research*

CHAPTER TWENTY

Theory in marketing

1. "Theory" in Popular Language

Words mean different things to different people and there is little point in arguing definitions. But meaningful discussion is only possible if the connotation of a word is the same to all who employ it. This has not been the case in the use of the word "theory," which means one thing to the layman and something entirely different to the theorist. As a result, the public has a distorted view of the goals and methods of theoretical research.

In common parlance "theoretical" is taken to be contradictory of either "factual" or "practical." "A theory" is the term often used to denote an allegation of fact for which no evidence has been presented. Unverified statements about the chemical composition of some compound, or about the behavior of some group of Australian aborigines, or about the nature of the so-called "canals" on Mars are all likely to be labeled theories. However, in the literature of scientific method, the statement, "the canals on Mars contain water," has nothing to do with astronomical, biological, or any other theory. Rather, such an assertion would be referred to as an "unverified hypothesis."

The distinction is no mere quibble. A hypothesis is a pure question of fact whereas theory, to the theorist, is concerned with explanation. The Martian canal hypothesis is either true or false and its validity can be settled one way or another by the first space ship to return from Mars, should one ever succeed in making the trip. Final disposition of the question of the Australians may be even simpler and may be contingent only on the financing of an anthropological expedition by one of the foundations. With

389

theory, as we shall indicate presently, the question of verification is not so simple.

There is also a second common use of the term "theory," characterized by the frequently encountered statement: "That may all be very well in theory, but when we get down to practical matters . . . ." Of course, most theorists prefer to believe that their work can be immensely helpful to the practical man. Whether this is likely frequently to be the case, the reader must judge for himself from the sequel. At this point we only recall the rather hackneyed illustrations which are usually employed to show that in some cases at least theory can have enormous practical implications. We have often been reminded that the well-publicized developments in electronics and atomic energy would not now be possible without the work of the theoretical physicists. Even Edison's work, which itself was totally devoid of theory, depended heavily on earlier theoretical results which by his time had become part of the standard equipment of the technician.

2. *"Theory" as Used by the Theorist*

Roughly, the theorist uses the word "theory" to mean "systematic explanation." A theory is a structure which describes the workings and interrelations of the various aspects of some phenomenon. Philosophers tell us that the word "explanation" has a great variety of meanings, but this need not concern us here. We can avoid this expository difficulty by describing in some detail what the theorist seeks to do.

Essentially, his procedure involves the examination of some aspect of reality and the construction of a simplified small-scale model which behaves in at least some ways like the phenomena under observation. The analyst can understand and trace out the workings of his model whereas reality is far too complicated and chaotic for this to be possible. In practice a particular day's demand for refrigerators may be conditioned by a family quarrel in Abilene, a case of mumps in South Bend, and the statement of a tealeaf-reading gypsy to one of her clients in Jersey City. It is hopeless to seek to take all of these considerations into account in an investigation of the appliance market. Instead, one deals with a simplified make-believe market in which consumer demand is conditioned by income, advertising expenditure, and a few other variables.

This method is well established in the natural sciences. The physicist cannot predict just what path will be followed by a real automobile left free to roll down a real hill or the time a real chestnut will take to pop in a real fire. He can only tell us what will happen in the artificial circumstances described by a controlled experiment, where the elements carefully held constant in the laboratory are the aspects of reality from which his simplified model abstracts. Once he steps out of the laboratory, his conclusions must be treated with extreme caution. That is why the salaries of test pilots are high!

Basically, the need for theory arises because facts unfortunately do not speak for themselves. An inflationary movement in prices or a fall in the sales volume of a shoe manufacturer is compatible with a variety of hypotheses. Facts supply us with correlations, not with structural relationships. At times all of us are prepared to reject conclusions which appear to be implied by the facts because these conclusions conflict with the rudimentary theoretical structures which we implicitly accept. For example, no one ever treated seriously, as an explanation of prosperity and depression, the statistics which showed that at least for a time there was a high correlation between the level of national income and the height of feminine skirt hems. None of the theories of the business cycle to which we more or less unconsciously adhere allows for dictation of the level of America's industrial activity by a Christian Dior.

Perhaps a better example is the relationship between interest rates and industrial construction. Statistics show that they tend to go up and down together and apparently imply that a rise in interest rates encourages the appearance of new factories and equipment. But economic theory usually denies this violently and argues plausibly that a rise in the cost of borrowing increases the businessman's construction costs and serves to deter this type of investment. The economist then accounts for the observed fact by pointing out that a third variable enters in and confuses matters. When national income is high, construction is profitable and the demand for funds to finance it raises interest rates. Which version of the facts is correct, we may never be sure, but the reaction of businessmen to Federal Reserve tight-money policies lends credence to the view that high interest costs are no stimulus to the creation of industrial capital goods.

We see then that since the facts themselves are silent, theory must be invented to describe their workings. If we desire to understand the structure of reality, we desire theory in the sense the theorist employs the term. This does not mean that nontheoretical research is undesirable or even less desirable than the work of the theorist. Their purposes are different—one supplies the data; the other, the explanations.

3. Illustration: An Empirical and a Theoretical "Law"

As an example of an empirical result in marketing, let us consider "Reilley's law." As originally formulated, this states that "Two cities attract retail trade from any intermediate city or town in the vicinity of the breaking point, approximately in direct proportion to the populations of the two cities and in inverse proportion to the square of the distances from these two cities to the intermediate town."[1]

When Reilley presented this result, he marshaled an impressive array of market data in its support but made no attempt at systematic explanation. The assertion was nevertheless useful and illuminating to marketing men.

Let us compare this with a somewhat related theoretical result which we owe to Fetter.[2] Consider two manufacturing centers A and B which produce a similar product at different unit costs. If they both pay the same cost of transportation per mile, what is the borderline between the territories that will be served by A and B? The answer is that if goods are sold at cost plus the same percentage mark-up, and customers buy from the man who sells more cheaply, the borderline will be a hyperbola whose formula is easily written down by a freshman mathematics student. For at every point, X, of equal price (cost), the difference between the distance of X to A and that of X to B will just make up for the difference in manufacturing cost at the two centers. In other words, there will be a constant difference between the distance of a point on the borderline to A and the distance from the point to B. But in analytic geometry, a hyperbola is defined as the locus of all points the difference in whose distances to two fixed points is a constant, and Fetter's conclusion follows at once.

Let us now see what the theoretical result does and what it does not do. Because we understand its workings we can easily see how the conclusion is affected by changes in the circumstances. If transportation cost is not strictly proportioned to the distance a cargo is carried, or if the pattern of pricing is not simply cost plus, or if in some other way the situation is known to differ from that postulated in the derivation of the original theorem, it may not be difficult to modify the analysis to take this into account. Should there be a proposed change in railroad rate structure, we could in advance examine the nature of its effects on competitive market areas with the aid of this theoretical analysis. Here, an empirical generalization would be of very little help because this can only tell us how things stand. Since it offers no clue as to how things work, it cannot tell us what will happen under changed conditions until after the change occurs and its results are observed. This, then, is a major advantage of the theoretical construct. It can help us in this way because it permits us to understand the *structure* of the situation.

On the other hand, the empirical law is—as a result of the way in which it is derived—virtually certain to be in closer agreement with the facts.

[1] William J. Reilley, *The Law of Retail Gravitation*, Pilsbury Publishers, New York, 1931, p. 9.

[2] Frank A. Fetter, "The Economic Law of Market Areas," *Quarterly Journal of Economics*, Vol. XXXVIII, May 1924.

The empirical law *states* the facts. The theoretical law describes not the facts, but a simplified model which at best only approximates them fairly well. We have said that a distinguishing feature of a factual hypothesis is that it is either right or wrong. By contrast, we may assert that a theoretical construct is sure to be more or less wrong in that it oversimplifies and hence distorts or omits some aspects of the circumstances under investigation.

4. Characteristics of "Good" Theory

Though all theory is in this sense wrong, it is not all of one quality. One piece of theoretical work is considered more successful than another. To account for this difference, we may list some of the desiderata of a theoretical model:

1. The model should be a sufficiently simple version of the facts to permit systematic manipulation and analysis. This means that a more realistic model may often be a poorer model. It is, of course, always desirable to make a model more realistic if this can be done without seriously complicating the investigation.

2. On the other hand, the model must be a sufficiently close approximation to the relevant facts to be usable. How close an approximation is necessary and which facts are relevant depend, of course, on the problem under investigation. It follows, and this cannot be overemphasized, that a model which is appropriate for the examination of one problem arising out of a given set of circumstances may be totally useless and even misleading for the investigation of another problem arising out of these same circumstances.

How difficult it is to find a theoretical model which acceptably meets these two criteria is partly a matter of luck. Some problems may just be so complicated that any model which is sufficiently simple to be analytically useful must be too gross a misrepresentation of the situation which it seeks to describe. This observation is sometimes advanced as a partial explanation of the less than spectacular progress that has characterized the social sciences.

It is worth mentioning one more feature to be desired of a theory:

3. Its conclusions should be relatively insensitive to changes in its assumptions. An example which comes to mind is a pricing recommendation which was made to a client on the basis of an operations research analysis. The relevant cost data were not unambiguously indicated by the accounting records, so a wide variety of cost assumptions was investigated. It was shown that these had little effect on the computed optimum price—and the recommended price structure could consequently be regarded with

considerably greater confidence. The basic point is that the assumptions of a model are never more than approximately valid, and if the structure of a model is such as seriously to magnify errors, this inaccuracy in the premises is likely to be translated into thoroughly undependable conclusions.

5. Is There a Place for Marketing Theory?

Even when it is granted that theoretical work can play a useful role, questions are sometimes raised about the possibility of a distinctive marketing theory. It is pointed out that the problems of marketing now fall under the purview of various fields, including psychology, sociology, and economics, each of which already has developed a considerable body of theory. This is true, but it is not entirely relevant. Pursued to its limits, this argument might have economics and sociology as branches of psychology; the latter, in turn, might be labeled a field in biology; and all the sciences might end up reclassified as physics. It seems to me that economics and psychology may more usefully be taken to provide some bricks for the construction of marketing theory rather than constituting its sum and substance. The difference between two disciplines often lies in the point of view with which they view the same subject. Clinical pathology, which makes up so much of the psychologist's subject matter, is of little interest to the marketing man whose attention is focused more on the behavior of groups than of the individuals which constitute them and on behavior which is in some sense normal. The appropriate choice of theory is, as I have emphasized, a matter of the problem in which the investigator is interested. It must surely be admitted that marketing has its special problems and may, therefore, well find it useful to develop further its own body of theory.

CHAPTER TWENTY-ONE

Marketing and operations research[1]

This book has described a number of the techniques which are considered to constitute the equipment of operations research. Mathematical programming, the optimization methods of the differential calculus—in particular as applied to inventory analysis, input-output, game theory, and decision theory have all been considered tools of operations analysis, though, at least so far, these have not all proved equally useful in actual application. However, a very significant group of operations research methods have not even been alluded to in this volume. Largely, these omissions involve the body of techniques based on probability analysis. Since this is not a book on statistics or probability, it is neither appropriate nor convenient to describe any of those methods in detail. But, in the course of the discussion of this chapter, two of these approaches—Monte Carlo and queuing theory—will be described rather briefly and superficially. It is hoped that from this discussion the reader can at least gather something of their flavor.

The main purpose of this chapter is to illustrate some of the applications of operations research techniques to concrete marketing problems. Most of the illustrations are based on factual cases. The discussion is, for the most part, discursive and brief. However, at the end of the chapter a few of the cases are described in greater detail to illustrate the nature of the models that were employed.

Much, if not most, of the work in operations research has been devoted

[1] The first three sections of this chapter are largely a discursive summary of the materials relevant to marketing which have occurred earlier in this book, and the reader may prefer to omit them.

to production problems where detailed quantitative data are more readily available, and mathematical (engineering) analysis is more traditional, than is the case in marketing. Nevertheless, there is much to be gained by examination of marketing problems with the aid of operations research methods.

1. Some Pricing Problems

Every pricing decision involves a process of balancing off cost and demand considerations. Too high a price may, even in prosperous times, drive customers into the arms of direct competitors; or it may lead potential purchasers to turn to substitute products or even to drop out of the market altogether. This is the meaning of the negative slope of a demand curve as discussed in Chapter 8. Obviously, then, the situation calls for some price in between that which drives most customers away and that which does not cover costs; but which is the "best" of these in-between prices?

Let us briefly review an actual pricing problem. The reader will recognize it at once as a direct application of the profit-maximization techniques of Chapter 10. A public utility firm which sold industrial and home heating fuels asked for an examination of its pricing structure. It was found that a small reduction in price would make this fuel cheaper for most uses than the fuel which was its main competitor. An examination of past experience of this firm, and of distributors of the same fuel in other cities, showed that such a price cut was not likely to be met by a reduction in the price of the competing fuel. In addition, there was evidence that a price cut could be expected to lead to increased sales whose magnitude could, within limits, be estimated. Similarly, the costs of supplying different quantities of this fuel were also estimated from the company data.

It was now possible to compute the price which could be expected to yield maximum annual net profits. This might have been done simply by selecting a large number of different possible prices, computing the sales and volume which were to be expected at each price, and using that to plot marginal cost and revenue curves. This would have indicated the price and output combination which would yield the highest profit. The techniques of the differential calculus did essentially that, somewhat more quickly and directly. It showed that a substantially lower price would, indeed, increase profits considerably—both by making this fuel price-competitive and thereby increasing volume, *and* by reducing unit costs.

Operations research analysis does not always call for lower prices. A large seller of a popular beverage found it was losing sales to less expensive, competing brands. It asked whether a reduction in the price of its products to competitive levels was advisable. Given the reduction in mark-up which results from a price cut, it is possible to compute the breakeven level of increased volume—the level of volume increase which, if it is achieved, will just make up for the reduction in margin and result in a zero net profit change after a price reduction.

In the case of the beverage manufacturer, it was possible to show that the proposed price reduction would have been totally uneconomical, at least in the short run. To make up for the reduction in margin, the firm would have required a breakeven increase in volume of approximately 70 per cent. It was highly unlikely that customers would flock in at a sufficient rate to make this possible. But, more important, the manufacturer did not even possess the capacity for a 70 per cent increase in output. Thus, the price reduction would almost certainly have resulted in a serious fall in his annual net profits.

2. The Optimum Use of Selling Effort

We now turn to a second marketing decision area, selling and promotion. The firm must decide on the best use of its salesmen's time, its advertising dollars, its sales managers' efforts, etc. It is not enough to know that a salesman is bringing in sales. If time spent on one class of customer brings the firm $15 per hour of salesman time, while effort devoted to another customer class brings in only $8, then every hour the salesman spends on the latter may, in effect, cost the firm $7.

Most firms do not have the data and have not examined in detail the salesmen's effort, advertising costs of sales by different districts, different products in the firm's line, and different customer classes. But investigation shows that the cost per item sold of a salesman visit to a small distributor, or of an effort to push an unpopular package size of the firm's product, or of a salesman maintained in a sparsely settled rural district, is often phenomenally high. Very frequently it is found that these sales activities actually involve substantial losses to the firm, so that it would serve the interests of the business to effect a substantial reallocation of selling activities.

The technique which investigates in detail the profitability of the use of sales effort, in different districts and by different products and customer groups, is called "distribution cost analysis." To mention only one investigation of this variety, a firm was shown to be losing heavily on sales made during personal visits by company representatives to small retailers. Here mail-order selling offered the opportunity for substantial increase in profits, and any small loss in volume could be made up by a transfer of effort to more profitable accounts.

The first step in a distribution cost analysis is a finer breakdown and a reclassification of the firm's cost and profit data. The over-all distribution costs for the entire business must be allocated, as well as the available information permits, to the specific segments of the business for *which they are incurred*. Once the required information has been collected in sufficient detail in the course of the distribution cost analysis, the optimal allocation of selling effort can be computed by the use of mathematical programming techniques.

Another application of linear programming to sales problems arises out of the allocation of an advertising budget. In practice, advertising budgets are sometimes divided up by the following method among various media such as radio and television programs, newspapers and magazines, etc. Market surveys are undertaken to find the economic and demographic characteristics of purchasers and likely new purchasers of the product in question. For example, it may be found that the product is largely consumed by elderly people who are urban residents and fall in the lower income brackets. Advertising media are then selected for this product in such a way as to reach as large an audience *of the required composition* as possible. Some questions can be raised about the appropriateness of this approach, but it is easy to show that, given the relevant data, such a selection can be performed effectively by a linear programming calculation. The object is maximization of the size of the audience reached, subject to the constraint that the total advertising budget not be exceeded and that the audience be of the required characteristics. A simple example of such an advertising allocation model appears in Section 11 of Chapter 5.

3. Choice of Distribution Arrangement

The choice of distribution arrangement is taken to include such problems as transportation routes and inventory levels. Illustrative is a warehouse location problem for a firm which stores its products in a number of public warehouses located throughout the country. With very little notice, this firm can move its inventory out of any of these to other warehouses. In all, there are about 100 locations at which warehouses possessing the requisite physical facilities can be found.

The problem, then, is this: Should the firm employ 8, 18, or 80 of these warehouse locations? And if it should use, say, 35 warehouses, which of the possible locations should these occupy? This is a complex problem involving considerations of transportation distances, freight rates, inventory levels, and warehousing rates. It is essentially a complicated routing problem in that a decision to employ warehouse A is a triple decision to ship from some factory, B, to some customer, C, along a route via A.

Here intuition and common sense are particularly likely to mislead. In deciding between warehouses A and B, judgment may do a good job. But with so many interrelated possibilities, a decision to move out of the

Denver warehouse may make it desirable also to move from Cleveland to Akron, and to make a chain of other adjustments in order best to serve the customers formerly receiving shipments from the Denver warehouse. Nor can all the possibilities be enumerated and investigated one at a time. The number of possibilities is truly astronomical. As is well known, there are 15 different possible ways of choosing combinations of warehouse sites from just four possible locations (one may pick any of the following: $A, B, C, D, AB, AC, AD, BC, BD, CD, ABC, ABD, ACD, BCD$, or $ABCD$). When the possible location choices go up to 100, the number of possibilities increases enormously—even to levels beyond those which can readily be visualized. This may be dramatized by the following paraphrase of a description of the number of possibilities involved in a somewhat related problem of comparable magnitude: If we had . . . a computer on each square inch of the earth, land and sea, and if each computer could examine a billion of the possibilities per second, we would have to wait a billion-billion-billion centuries for an answer.[2]

Fortunately, mathematical programming techniques can help once more. These can indicate *without a case-by-case examination of all the possibilities*, and within the limitations imposed by the accuracy of the available data, what will be a good choice of warehouses, how much should be shipped through each warehouse, and from which factory and to which customer shipments should be routed through any particular warehouse.

Closely related to the warehouse-location problem is the more common inventory-level problem. In fact, part of the job in computing the cost effect of any warehouse arrangement is a determination of the most appropriate inventory level for each warehouse. Only when the total amounts to be stored have been determined can the storage rates specified by contract with each warehouse be used to calculate the corresponding total storage cost. Since the most economical warehouse arrangement is that which saves most on both storage and transportation costs, it is clear that determination of the best warehouse location must also involve determination of optimum inventory levels.

As in every problem described in this chapter, determination of the best inventory levels involves a balancing-off of advantages and disadvantages. The most obvious disadvantage of a small inventory is the likelihood that it will lead to lost orders. If customers find that a firm cannot provide rapid delivery because the desired items are out of stock, they may turn to the seller's competitor. If this happens too often the firm may lose customers, not just sales. Buyers simply will get tired of having to wait

---

[2] The discussion refers to the number of routes in a 49-city "traveling salesman problem"—what is the shortest total route which permits the traveler to visit all 49 cities? See George A. W. Boehm, *The New World of Math*, Dial Press, New York, 1959, p. 115.

for order after order and will switch their allegiance to a competing seller.

Low inventories also have another disadvantage. It is possible to keep small stocks on hand only if the supplier is prepared to make frequent deliveries to his warehouses. A firm selling 600 refrigerators per 6-day week, from a single warehouse, can either deliver 600 refrigerators from factory to warehouse at the beginning of each week, or deliver 100 each day (or it can make deliveries on some other schedule). The once-a-week delivery schedule involves an average inventory level of 300 (plus whatever inventory is kept on hand for emergencies). But daily delivery never involves an inventory against foreseen sales which is larger than 100 refrigerators. Thus inventories can be kept low, but at the cost of more frequent deliveries. This may involve the costs of additional bookkeeping, higher handling costs, and higher transportation rates because shipments are so small they must go in less-than-carload lots.

It is seen, then, that low inventory levels must result in higher shipping costs and in the increased danger of lost orders and lost customers. But high inventory levels are also costly. Storage costs, insurance costs, tax payments, interest payments on money capital tied up in inventory, pilferage and deterioration costs are all high when inventory is large. It is obvious, then, that inventory levels must be prevented from going too high or too low. In particular, an attempt to keep an inventory so great that no item ever runs out of stock and no customer order is ever delayed is likely to be catastrophically expensive, and it may be futile as well. For any commodity it is likely that occasionally many orders will, by coincidence, be placed at the same time. The cost of providing against such a remote contingency is almost never worth incurring.

The optimum inventory level can be found, as well as the data permit, by the use of standard operations research methods. The various types of inventory costs (storage, handling, taxes, lost orders, etc.) must first be translated into mathematical notation. Once this is done it is usually possible to employ the differential calculus in essentially the same way as it is used in the price-determination problem, to find the inventory level which will yield the highest profits to the firm. A simple case has been described in some detail in Chapter 1.

Another related inventory problem arises out of seasonal swings in the prices of perishable raw materials. It is costly to concentrate production exclusively at the season when raw material costs are low, because this can add substantially to labor costs, require a large plant capacity much of which may have to remain idle the rest of the year, and require the storage of finished-goods inventory between production seasons. On the other hand, production spread evenly throughout the year can involve very high labor costs. Here one must find the best compromise between completely even production and production concentrated entirely during a few months of the year. It may perhaps be surprising that the mathematics of the solution is very closely related to that of the optimum routing problem, but in fact the reason is simple—storage from September to January is a movement through time just as shipment from New York to Dayton involves movement through space. The optimum production inventory schedule involves the choice of optimum routes through time and can be solved by methods simpler than, but similar to, those required for the warehouse location decision.

4. Queuing Analysis

Queuing theory is one of the subjects which has loomed large in the literature of operations research. Any operation in which the objects to be dealt with arrive at irregular intervals, and in which the operating facilities are of limited capacity, is a queuing problem. Automobiles waiting to be serviced in a garage, subway riders waiting to get through a turnstile, and telephone callers waiting for a clear line all constitute queues. Among the real problems to which queuing theory has been applied are the landing of aircraft, the parking of automobiles, the timing of traffic lights, the processing of films, and the servicing of travelers through customs.

One of the key characteristics of a queue is the random pattern of arrivals, which can therefore only be described in probabilistic terms. There will be times, which cannot be predicted precisely, when the number of arrivals will be unusually large, and as a result, it will then take longer to be serviced. For example, in a supermarket, customer delays at the checkout counters may be caused by the arrival of a large number of customers at the same time, or by the coincidental arrival of several customers each of whom has many groceries in her shopping basket, so that the average checkout time is materially increased.

Suppose the manager of the supermarket wishes to know what sort of delays his customers are likely to encounter. The analyst requires information about two frequency distributions, one describing customer arrivals and the other the length of time it takes a clerk to handle a customer's purchases. Once both of these have been found, mathematical analysis permits us, in many cases, to find out such things as the expected average customer waiting time, the expected length of the waiting lines at different times of the day or week, etc.

The basic idea of the calculation is relatively simple, although the details are ingenious and complicated. The probability that there will be, say, 25 customers waiting now is equal to the sum of probabilities of the several alternative series of events which can produce this result. For example, there would now be 25 customers in line if 24 customers were there one minute ago, none has since been serviced, and one more customer has just arrived. Since we know the probability of a customer's having been serviced during any one minute and of a customer's arriving during any one minute, we can find out the relationship between the probability that there were 24 customers a minute ago and the probability that there are 25 customers in line now. Similarly, we can find the probability that the lines will grow from 25 to 26 customers in this way; and we can trace, customer by customer, the expected growth of the queues in the supermarket from the time it opens in the morning with zero customers.

One of the most interesting results of the theory states, in effect, that service facilities must have excess capacity built into them if service is not to break down altogether. More specifically, suppose the service facilities, if they were always kept fully occupied, were just sufficient to meet the needs of all the store's customers. Then queues would just grow longer and longer, without limit, and ultimately the operations would collapse. The basic reason for this result is, of course, that customer arrivals are *not* spread evenly in time, and so during some periods the facility will temporarily be idle whereas at other times it will be overcrowded. But, by assumption, the facilities would be of sufficient capacity only if there were no such oscillations in customer arrival time. To permit them to cope with bunched arrivals, therefore, the capacity of service facilities must be increased.

The theory also permits us, at least in principle, to investigate how much the expected length of queue lines will be reduced when a number of new checkout counters are added in our supermarket. This immediately raises an optimality question—just how many checkout counters should the supermarket have? More counters cost money to install and operate. Too many counters will therefore be wasteful, but too small a number of counters will slow down service and lose customers. The optimality problem, then, is to determine the intermediate number of counters which best serves management's purposes. Unfortunately, these probabilistic optimality calculations are often likely to grow very complex; therefore, instead of a direct approach to the problem, the operations researcher frequently resorts to the methods described in the following section.

5. Artificial Experimentation: Monte Carlo Techniques

Before we can hope to find out the consequences of a course of action, it is necessary to have some sort of data. For example, suppose, as before, that it is desired to test some proposed service facilities to see how often customers will be kept waiting, and how long they will have to wait, on the average. These figures, of course, depend on the fluctuations in the number of customer arrivals—how frequently their number will exceed a particular magnitude.

In solving such a problem, experimentation is not a real possibility. It can be costly in customer relations to try very much more meager service facilities just to see what will happen. It may be that some information can be obtained from the experience of other supermarkets. But this may be too limited in range and in quantity to be of much assistance.

The operations researcher has, however, invented another very effective way to gather the relevant data: that is, to make them up himself, or rather to let the mathematical statistician make them up for him! But one may well ask, how can improvised statistics help us to foresee what will happen in the real world?

The answer is that the numbers are invented in a manner which carefully employs the analytical methods of mathematical statistics in order to stretch as far as possible such few actual data as are available to begin with. At some particular moment in the week we may assume that customers will arrive randomly, in a pattern somewhat similar to outcomes in successive throws of a pair of dice. The pattern of customer arrivals may then be described in terms of a frequency distribution, which indicates how many weeks in a year customer arrivals per hour can be expected to fall between 100 and 110 units, how often the number will lie in the 110 to 120 range, etc.

Now, from the available information *and the nature of the problem*, the statistician can often decide which frequency distribution best describes the pattern of expected customer arrivals. From this frequency distribution it is then possible to construct an artificial history of customer arrivals by choosing randomly among all the possibilities, but in a way which is "loaded" to produce the right frequencies. To give a very simple illustration, suppose we consider two possibilities: *A*, fewer than 100 arrivals per hour and *B*, at least 100 arrivals. If, on some basis, the odds are computed to be 2 to 1 in favor of *A*, we can generate an artificial demand history as follows: Toss the (unbiased) die. If it falls 1, 2, 3, or 4, put down an *A*; if it falls 5 or 6, put down a *B*. This might yield a pattern for weekly demands such as the following:

TABLE 1

"*Week*"	*Face of Die*	Arrival "History" Under 100	100 *or More*
First...........	3	*A*	
Second.........	1	*A*	
Third..........	3	*A*	
Fourth.........	5		*B*
Fifth..........	6		*B*
Sixth..........	2	*A*	
Seventh........	2	*A*	

This, incidentally, indicates the reason for the term "Monte Carlo method."

In practice, it is not actually necessary to toss any dice. Instead, we can use tables called "tables of random numbers" which have been worked out in advance. Moreover, the computations can be made by high-speed electronic computers which are able, in a few minutes or hours, to run off thousands of cases and manufacture data whose collection would, otherwise, require many years. But although this method is economical and powerful, it must be used only with the greatest care and caution. As we have seen, everything depends on the choice of frequency distribution (i.e., the odds of the various outcomes), and unless there is some assurance that these have been picked well, the entire calculation can be worthless.

Once this artificial experience has been generated, it can be used to find approximate solutions to optimality problems such as that of determining the number of checkout counters which was described in the last section—problems where straightforward computational methods are too complex. To illustrate the approach, consider the (unrelated) problem of finding an approximate root of the equation

$$X^2 - 6X + 9.1 = 0.$$

Instead of using the standard formula, we can go about it indirectly by trial and error, first, say, substituting $X = 1$ to find that the expression takes the value

$$(1)^2 - 6(1) + 9.1 = 4.1.$$

Clearly, $X = 1$ is not our root. So we try again, this time using, say, $X = 0$, and we see that this value of X makes the expression equal 9.1— i.e., it has only made things worse. We therefore infer that we have been going in the wrong direction, so this time we go up and try $X = 2$, etc. The results of several such trials can be tabulated as follows:

Trial value of X	1	0	2	3	4
Value of $X^2 - 6X + 9.1$	4.1	9.1	1.1	0.1	1.1

Clearly, this suggests that there is a root located very close to $X = 3$, at which the value of the expression is very close to zero, and we can take this as the approximate value of the root we are seeking.

The finding of optimal solutions in queuing problems and many other difficult operations problems can be approached in somewhat the same spirit with the aid of Monte Carlo methods. A number of alternative possibilities (number of possible checkout counters) can be postulated, and their consequences over a long period can then be simulated and reported on by the computer with the aid of Monte Carlo predictions of customer arrivals. If our objective is to minimize some sort of over-all cost function (which includes the costs of operating additional checkout counters as well as the costs of customer delays), we would take the optimal solution to be approximated by that trial (number of checkout counters) for which the machine reported the lowest over-all expected costs.

Unfortunately, this description, although correct in essence, is somewhat misleading in its simplicity. Particularly where decisions involve the assignment of values to a number of interrelated variables and where the ranges of possible values are considerable, there are difficult problems in deciding on what combination of values to try out next. It is by no means easy to design a procedure which converges with reasonable rapidity toward an optimal solution.

It is to be emphasized that the use of Monte Carlo methods is not limited to queuing problems. They can be used in inventory analysis, replacement analysis (when to stop repairing a piece of equipment and replace it with a new one), and a wide variety of other situations in which a prominent role is played by probabilistic elements such as the timing and magnitudes of customer demands or of the need for repairs.

Simplified Example of a Queuing Calculation: A store is considering whether to install one or two checkout counters. A computer is used to manufacture statistics minute by minute for the 20 busiest minutes of the day. Monte Carlo methods are used to generate customer arrival-time figures (column 2 in Table 2) and figures for the time it takes to service each customer (column 3). Thus, e.g., we see that in the fifth minute under consideration (column 1) one customer arrives to be checked out and it takes 4 minutes to service him. [Note that, as a matter of simplicity, we have chosen our time interval (one minute) to be so short that no more than one customer ever arrives during any such period.]

Columns 4 and 5 are the basic calculations. They show how long each customer must wait before being served. For example, consider the "one checkout counter" case (column 4). In minute number 4 a customer arrives at the checkout counter and finds no one there so he does not have to wait (zero entry in column 4). However, it takes two minutes to serve him, so when another customer arrives one minute later, the new arrival has to wait one minute before the checker is free to serve him (the "1" entered in line 5 of column 4). This customer takes 4 minutes to be served, so that by the time the next customer arrives in minute number 6, the checker is 4 minutes behind (next entry in column 4 is 4); etc. Column 5 is constructed similarly, on the assumption that there are two checkout counters, and that any customer goes to the first unoccupied counter.

We can then total the number of customers who may be expected to arrive in the 20 minutes (11 customers), and the amount of customer waiting time in the one- and two-counter cases (55 minutes and 1 minute, respectively). The average waiting time per customer is then 5 minutes with one checkout counter, and almost nil with two counters. An optimal decision then involves a balancing of the cost of the additional checkout counter against the 5-minute saving in average customer waiting time to see whether, from management's point of view, it is worth installing.

TABLE 2

(1) Number of minutes after beginning of busy period	(2) Number of customers arriving at checkout counters	(3) Service time (minutes)	(4) Waiting time for each customer with one check-out counter	(5) Waiting time with two checkout counters
1	1	3	0	0
2	0			
3	0			
4	1	2	0	0
5	1	4	1	0
6	1	4	4	0
7	0			
8	1	1	6	1
9	0			
10	1	4	5	0
11	1	2	8	0
12	0			
13	1	1	8	0
14	1	1	8	0
15	0			
16	0			
17	1	4	6	0
18	1	3	9	0
19	0			
20	0			

Total: 11   55   1

Average waiting time per customer: $55/11 = 5$ min. $1/11$
                                                                        (negligible)

6. A Pricing Decision Model

The foregoing material should give the reader some feeling for the considerable scope of the marketing applications of operations analysis. The next three sections will describe the models employed in several of these applications in somewhat greater detail in order to convey some of the spirit of the art of model building.

As our first illustration, let us reconsider the pricing problem of the beverage manufacturer which was described in Section 1 of this chapter. What transformed this case from a routine matter of pricing by equating marginal cost to marginal revenue was the incompleteness of the available information. There simply were no usable data on the shape of the demand curve. Prices had not changed in recent times so that there was no experience to indicate, even roughly, the nature of the demand function.

However, we were able to construct a rough marginal cost figure and had some reason to believe that marginal costs would not vary (or, at least, would not decrease) substantially over the relevant range. Our problem was to determine, on the basis of these limited facts, whether a fall in price from current price, call it P cents per unit, to some lower price, P^*, would be profitable. For this purpose the following model was employed:

We were given the following (numerical) data:

Q,   the current quantity of the item sold
P,   the current price
P^*,   the proposed new price
C,   the marginal cost.

Let Q^* represent the *unknown* new quantity which would have been sold at the new lower price. Then current revenue is given by PQ, potential revenue at the new price is P^*Q^*, and to produce this increased quantity, $Q^* - Q$, it would cost (at least) an additional $C(Q^* - Q)$ dollars. The net change in profits resulting from this price reduction is therefore equal to the increase (change) in revenue minus the increase in costs, i.e., it is equal to (or less than) $P^*Q^* - PQ - C(Q^* - Q)$. Obviously, this change in profits must be no less than zero if the firm is not to lose out as a result of the price change. This minimal result then requires

$$P^*Q^* - PQ - C(Q^* - Q) \geq 0$$

which can easily be solved to give

$$Q^* \geq \frac{P - C}{P^* - C} Q.$$

That is, we can now find the *minimal* increase in quantity sold necessary to prevent the firm from losing out, since P, P^*, C, and Q are all known. In this way it was possible to determine, in the case of our beverage producer, that the requisite change in demand, $Q^* - Q$, was a number which, as a practical matter, was completely out of the question.

Before concluding this discussion it is well to indicate two particularly noteworthy features of this solution:

1. It illustrates how the analyst must frequently exercise ingenuity to overcome gaps in his information. In practice, one rarely if ever encounters the mass of refined data called for by the standard textbook models. As was shown, this does not mean that these real cases are completely unamenable to systematic analysis.

2. In this case, as in many operations-analysis applications, it was not possible to use any of the standard models without modification to fit the circumstances. However, *these standard models did provide the method of analysis* by which the problems were solved. It is at least partly for this

reason that this book has placed so much emphasis on methods of proof. Often in economics when theorems are inapplicable to practice, their methods of proof can suggest an extension or modification of the theorems which can be used for the problem at hand.

7. *A Transportation-Storage Model*

This section begins with a description of the standard transportation model of linear programming, at least partly in order to show how its application can be extended and how it can be modified for use in other situations.

The transportation problem deals with a set of m geographical supply points (locations), and a set of q geographical demand points. A quantity of some commodity is distributed among the supply points and is to be shipped to the demand points. Suppose the ith supply point possesses quantity S_i of the item and the jth demand point desires quantity D_j (where the total amount desired by all demand points together is taken to equal the total amount available so that $\Sigma\, S_i = \Sigma\, D_j$). The problem is to determine which supply points should ship to which demand points and in what quantities, in order to minimize the total cost of the operation.

Let $X_{i,j}$ be the amount shipped from supply point i to demand point j. Then the total amount which is shipped by i is

$$X_{i,1} + X_{i,2} + \ldots + X_{i,q}$$

that is, it is the sum of the shipments from i to all demand points. This amount is required to be equal to S_i, the total supply available at point i, that is, all of this supply is to be shipped out. Thus, for every supply point, i, we have the constraint

$$X_{i,1} + X_{i,2} + \ldots + X_{i,q} = S_i.$$

Similarly, for each demand point, j, to receive its required demand quantity, D_j, we must have

$$X_{1,j} + X_{2,j} + \ldots + X_{m,j} = D_j.$$

If the cost of shipping a unit of the item from point i to point j is $C_{i,j}$ dollars, the total cost of shipping all $X_{i,j}$ units is $C_{i,j}X_{i,j}$. Hence the total cost of all shipments must be $\Sigma\, C_{i,j}X_{i,j}$.

Thus the standard transportation problem is, then, described by the linear program[3]

---

[3] Note that there are $q + m$ constraints, but one of these is redundant. Since total supply equals total demand, any solution which gets the right quantity to all but one of the demand points must automatically send the right amount to the remaining demand point as well. Hence, a basic solution will contain exactly $q + m - 1$ positive $X_{i,j}$ values.

$$\text{minimize} \quad \Sigma \, C_{i,j} X_{i,j}$$

subject to

$$X_{i,1} + X_{i,2} + \ldots + X_{i,q} = S_i$$

for all supply points, i, and

$$X_{1,j} + X_{2,j} + \ldots + X_{m,j} = D_j$$

for all demand points, j, where all $X_{i,j} \geq 0$.

This linear programming problem has a particularly simple structure. For example, the coefficients of the $X_{i,j}$'s in the constraints are all unity. There are also many zeros in the simplex tableau (e.g., variable $X_{3,5}$ does not appear in the 6th supply point constraint,

$$X_{6,1} + X_{6,2} + \ldots + X_{6,q} = S_6$$

that is, the coefficient of $X_{3,5}$ in this equation is zero. This simplifies computation considerably. Methods of computation in the transportation problem will not be described here but simple descriptions of the technique are available in the literature.[4]

This transportation model is readily modified into an analysis of the seasonal purchase-inventory-production problem described in Section 3, above. The problem was to decide how much of a perishable raw material, whose price varies seasonally, to buy for immediate processing in each month of the year, and how much of it to keep in inventory for later resale. Here we let i represent the month the material is purchased and j represent the month it is resold so that, e.g., $X_{2,4}$ would represent the quantity purchased in February (month 2) for resale in April (month 4). Let D_j represent the quantity of finished goods needed in month j. Then we require for each month,[5] j,

$$X_{1,j} + X_{2,j} + \ldots + X_{12,j} = D_j$$

and our objective is, again, to minimize $\Sigma \, X_{i,j} C_{i,j}$ where $C_{i,j}$ is the cost of purchasing a unit of raw material in month i *and* storing it until month j.

We thus end up with the following linear program which is even simpler than that of the transportation model:

$$\text{minimize} \quad \Sigma \, C_{i,j} X_{i,j}$$

subject to

$$X_{1,j} + X_{2,j} + \ldots + X_{12,j} = D_j$$

for all months, j, and all $X_{i,j} \geq 0$.

---

[4] For an elementary exposition see A. Henderson and R. Schlaifer, "Mathematical Programming," *Harvard Business Review*, Vol. 32, May–June 1954.

[5] Of course, j, the month in which the raw material is resold, must be no earlier than the month it is purchased, so that $X_{12,2}$ must be taken to represent a purchase in December for use the *following* February.

8. A Warehouse Location Model[6]

Finally, to illustrate further the very great flexibility of the transportation model, let us examine the analysis employed in dealing with the warehouse location problem described in Section 3.

A division of a large corporation asked us to investigate the number and location of its warehouses. Its inventory is kept in public warehouses. Since none of these installations is owned by the company, the division can, with relative ease, move all or part of its operations to other warehouses or change the number of warehouses it employs.

It was assumed in the investigation that sales volume at each geographic customer location is given and is not affected by the choice of warehouse through which shipments to that destination are routed. (This is probably not strictly true because the distance of a warehouse from the market can affect the speed with which a retailer who has exhausted his stock of the product can replenish his inventory, and the warehouse location can, therefore, influence the volume of sales.)

In principle this would appear to be an example of the general *location problem* which is very difficult largely because the set of possible warehouse locations is infinite. But in practice a crucial simplification was made possible by the fact that the company rents space in public warehouses, and that the number of places[7] in this country at which are located warehouses possessing the requisite physical characteristics (including loading facilities, etc.) is relatively small, apparently of the order of magnitude of one to two hundred.

This permitted formulation of the problem as the following (nonlinear) program. Let

X_{ijk} be the quantity shipped from factory i ($i = 1, 2, \ldots, m$) via warehouse j ($j = 1, \ldots, n$), to retailer location k ($k = 1, \ldots, q$),

$C_{ijk}(X_{ijk})$ be the cost of this shipment including the relevant inventory cost,

S_i be the quantity shipped from plant i,

R_j be the capacity of warehouse j,

D_k be the quantity required at destination k.

The problem is to minimize the total delivery cost, i.e., to minimize

$$(1) \qquad \Sigma \, C_{ijk}(X_{ijk})$$

subject to

$$(2) \qquad \Sigma \, X_{ijk} = S_i$$
$$\text{(summing for all } j \text{ and } k\text{)}$$

(all goods must be shipped out of the factory),

---

[6] This section is somewhat more difficult than the remainder of the chapter.

[7] For our purposes a "place" or "location" can designate an entire city, so that all the warehouses in the New York metropolitan area are taken to occupy a single location. This is, of course, the explanation of the small number of relevant warehouse locations.

(3) $\Sigma A_{ijk}(X_{ijk}) \leq R_j$

(summing for all i and k)

(no warehouse capacity can be exceeded), and

(4) $\Sigma X_{ijk} = D_k$

(summing for all i and j)

(all customer demands must be met), where all $X_{ijk} \geq 0$. The expression $A_{ijk}(X_{ijk})$ in (3) represents the amount of inventory that will be held as a result of the flow X_{ijk}.

The resemblance to the standard transportation problem is obvious. There are only three differences: (a) the possible nonlinearity of the cost function (1); (b) the presence of the warehouse-capacity constraints (3); and (c) the need for a three-subscript rather than a two-subscript notation for the variables X_{ijk} arising out of the necessity of routing each flow through a warehouse. Of course, a nonlinear objective function is not necessarily ruled out for the transportation problem, and in fact nonlinearities in the objective function do sometimes occur in practice. Moreover, for practical purposes it transpires that the warehouse capacity limitations in our problem can be ignored because the firm never ends up renting more than a small fraction of the public warehouse space available at any location. This fact eliminates difference (b) between this and the standard transportation problem.

Assume, to begin with, that our objective function (1) is linear, so that difference (a) from the transportation problem also disappears. Then elimination of difference (c), i.e., of the three-subscript notation, becomes a trivial matter. For we have the following rule: *An optimal (least-cost) solution will involve shipment of all goods that go from factory i^* to destination k^* via that (those) warehouse(s) j^* for which*[8] C_{i*j*k*} *is smaller than or equal to any other* C_{i*jk*}. In other words, it will always pay to make any shipment via the warehouse that offers the lowest delivery cost.

The solution of the linear program is now very simple. For each factory-destination combination, i^*, k^*, select the least-cost warehouse. That can be done by simple inspection of the C_{ijk} data. This will normally eliminate all but one of the n possible warehouse locations that can be used to service goods en route from factory i^* to destination k^*. We can now revise our notation, dropping the middle (warehouse number) subscript in each vari-

---

[8] For if any shipment from i^* to k^* is made through some other warehouse, j', the arrangement cannot be optimal. This is so because that shipment can be rerouted through the least-cost warehouse, j^*, at a saving in cost and with no change in amount delivered.

able since it is no longer necessary to consider the full range of possible warehouses. Substituting this notation in (1), (2), and (4) and dropping (3) obviously leaves us with a standard transportation problem, the optimum values of whose variables can be found by the standard methods.

This solution has a remarkable property that deserves emphasis. It is likely to involve the employment of many more warehouses than one might *a priori* expect to be optimal. To take an extreme example, suppose one package is to be shipped from factory i' to customer k'. If there is a warehouse j' which would otherwise not be used by the company, but which offers minimum costs for regular large-scale shipments from i' to k', then the linear programming solution requires arrangements to be made to have warehouse j' handle this one package shipment! This is an illustration of the fact, discussed in Section 6 of Chapter 6, that a linear approximation to an increasing-returns programming problem will generally involve too many nonzero-valued variables in its solution.

It is clear that nonlinearities in this system may in fact be expected to appear in the objective function (1) (and in the warehouse capacity constraints (3) if they are relevant). An obvious type of nonlinearity will arise out of the transportation rate structure since any shipment so small that it necessarily involves less-than-carload lots will move at higher rates. Some warehousing contracts also involve similar rate structure changes. Both of these nonlinearities help to increase the cost incurred in using a larger number of warehouses to handle a given sales volume because this must cut the average volume per warehouse, and small shipments through any one warehouse will be charged for at higher rates.

Two other nonlinearities work in the same direction. The use of additional warehouses increases negotiation, bookkeeping, and administration costs (fixed charges). Also, there are usually economies of large scale in the amount of inventory that should be kept against the flow of shipments through a warehouse. In fact, standard inventory analysis suggests that, optimally, important inventory components will vary approximately as the square root of the volume of shipments going through the warehouse.[9] This is very clearly an increasing-returns objective function case—the larger the scale of operation of any warehouse, the lower will be its unit costs of operation. It should be noted in closing that, because of the computational difficulties which are inherent in this type of problem (Chapter 6, Section 5), the computational procedure which was developed to deal with this case had to confine itself to a relatively modest goal. It was designed only to find a local rather than a global optimum. That is, it was set up to find a combination of warehouse locations which had the following characteristics:

[9] See the inventory model of Chapter 1 for an illustration of this type of result.

1. It was more efficient (or at least never less efficient) than the current company arrangement, i.e., it was virtually certain to yield some cost savings.

2. No *minor* changes from this computed set of warehouse locations could yield any reduction in costs (the result was sure to be a local optimum.

3. However, there might well have been some (unknown) radical rearrangement (the global optimum) which would have been even more economical. We found no practical way of either locating or ruling out such a possibility.

9. Simplification in Model Construction

A common characteristic of the models which we have been discussing, and, indeed, of just about all models of operations analysis, is the fact that they are oversimplified pictures of the real world. The pricing model ignored variations in marginal cost, the transportation model implicitly assumed away the higher rates which prevail for less-than-carload-lot shipments and other nonlinearities, and similar observations hold for the other models described in this book—the reader would do well to verify this for himself in at least one or two cases.

It is right and proper that this should be so. Any situation in the business world is compounded of a bewildering variety of major and minor elements, and, unless the less important features are erased from the picture, rigorous analysis becomes hopelessly complicated or impossible. The difficulties of statistical fact-finding and mathematical computation mount rapidly with the degree of complication of the model. The decision to omit an element from the model must therefore be a matter of *balancing off the loss in realism against the gain in reduced computation difficulty.* There are no rules or cut-and-dried procedures for this selection process, and all that can be offered the reader here is the unhelpful admonition that he exercise caution and judgment and check the facts over carefully before constructing his model.

In any event, the model builder must be aware that what is left out is often as important as what is put in. Moreover, he must remember that there is no magic in mathematics. The results of the mathematical computations cannot be expected to be any better than the model on which they are based. He should therefore never allow himself to be misled by the aura of mathematical rigor which surrounds the calculations of operations analysis.

REFERENCES

Bowman, Edward H., and Fetter, Robert B., *Analysis for Production Management,* Irwin, Homewood, Ill., 1957.

Churchman, C. West, Ackoff, Russell L., and Arnoff, E. Leonard, *Introduction to Operations Research,* Wiley, New York, 1957.

McCloskey, Joseph F., and Trefethen, Florence N., *Operations Research for Management,* Johns Hopkins, Baltimore, 1954.

Sasieni, Maurice, Yaspan, Arthur, and Friedman, Lawrence, *Operations Research—Methods and Problems,* Wiley, New York, 1959.

CHAPTER TWENTY-TWO

Electronic computers[1]

It is only about a decade since the first modern electronic computer went into operation. But in this brief period these machines have become an integral part of our world. Despite their great cost they have become a standard piece of equipment of the natural and social sciences and of the large business firm. Some American firms operate more than a half-dozen of the largest computers, and they are now manufactured on something resembling assembly-line methods.

The rate of technological development has been equally impressive. Rapid change has occurred in the design of various parts of the equipment as well as in the techniques of their operation. It has been impossible to

---

[1] This chapter deals only with *digital* computers. There is another type, called an *analogue* computer, which, as its name implies, operates in effect by constructing a scaled-down version (model) of the problem and reporting on the results. It is very much like building a small-scale bridge and testing its ability to hold weight before putting up the actual span. Of course, the analogue computer's model does not usually bear such an obvious resemblance to the item to be tested. Since the usual analogue machine is electronic (there are some hydraulic analogue machines but they are used for demonstration rather than calculation), the analogy usually consists only in a formal resemblance between the problem and the physics of electricity. To take a trivial example, we can multiply by electric analogue with the aid of the well-known relationship current × resistance = voltage. That is, to multiply 36 by 53 we can run a current of 36 units (amps) through a resistance of 53 units (ohms) and read their product on a volt-meter.

Analogue computers are particularly well suited to problems involving differential equations. They are less accurate than digital computers (usually giving no more than three or four significant figures) but more readily adaptable to changes in the data and structure of a problem.

write an up-to-date textbook on the subject. Now it even appears that the large, impressive roomfuls of equipment which constitute today's most powerful computers are, thanks to transistors and printed circuits, about to give way to substantially smaller, more compact machines.

This chapter attempts to give a simple and relatively general account of the subject. It discusses the sorts of economic problems for which machines may advantageously be used, the available types of machines, their cost and speed, what is involved in getting the machine to solve a problem and, finally, it describes in very rough terms what goes on inside the machine.

Before we get down to the specific issues of the chapter, one important characteristic of computers must be pointed out. It is easy to become impressed with computers—they can do so many astonishing things. Machines have been trained to catch spelling mistakes (but only for a limited number of words), to draw blueprints, to fit equations, to derive some (simple) mathematical proofs, and even to do some fairly crude translation. Most important, perhaps, is the fact that they cope with complex mathematical problems which, because of the length of the required solution process, were formerly unsolvable.

It becomes easy, then, to think of the machines as electronic "brains."[2] But the basic fact is that *computing machines cannot think for themselves*. They must be told what to do at every step of the way and if an instruction is left out the machine will either botch up the problem and give nonsense results or it will come to a dead stop, in complete helplessness.

This means that, before any problem can be put on a machine, skilled specialists must often work long and hard preparing the requisite instructions which must be absolutely complete and specific. Sometimes these preparations take months and, as a result, this preparation of instructions, which is called *machine programming* (no relation to linear programming) is often a far-from-negligible part of the cost of problem solving. The inability of machines to think for themselves and the resulting high cost of programming will recur at several crucial points in this discussion.

---

[2] This temptation is increased by the various stories one hears of neurotic symptoms manifested by computers. There is, for example, the case in which the operators fed a problem into the machine and then changed their minds and put a second problem in instead. The machine insisted on working only the first problem despite protracted efforts by experts to find out what had gone wrong. Finally the repair team gave up and decided to permit the machine to work off its "frustration" and work on the initial problem. After spending some time on it (long enough, the comment runs, to master its principles), the computer suddenly switched by itself to the second problem and worked out its solution.

1. Problems Suited for Machine Computation

Like many new developments, the use of electronic computers has at times threatened to become a fad. Some companies seem to have installed computers, at least in part, for prestige purposes, and there have been cases where their use has proved disappointing and financially inexpedient. This has, of course, been largely a result of misuse of computers. Before acquiring and using them it is necessary to understand the sort of problem for which they can be employed advantageously.

This information is not just relevant to the decision of whether to get hold of a machine. Once the firm has a computer it is likely to find that there is a lineup of people and problems waiting to use it. Near 24-hour-a-day machine schedules are not uncommon. It is therefore important to give priority to problems on which the machine can be used most effectively. There are, obviously, similar problems involved in the efficient use of computers for pure research agencies even though the profitability of their operation is not a prime consideration.

Because it is so expensive and time-consuming to prepare the machine instructions for any problem, it will rarely pay a firm to have such a program prepared unless it can be used many times. This, then, is our first criterion for the use of computers: machine priority in business must usually be given either to problems for which standard programs exist or where similar problems are likely to recur.

It is for this reason that a very high percentage of machine time in industry has been devoted to preparation of payrolls and other similar types of routine record keeping and calculation. However, even here, it is necessary to check whether the operation is of sufficient scale and complexity to justify the use of expensive computer time.

Increasing use of computers is also being made as a management decision-making tool. For example, problems involving choice of inventory levels, transportation routes, determination of proportions in blending, allocation of advertising expenditure among various media, and statistical investigation of advertising effectiveness have all been dealt with by methods in which electronic computers are required. The machines can find or at least approximate optimal solutions by use of mathematical programming and other related mathematical techniques. In any case, they can often give us far better answers than standard "back of the envelope" decision calculations. Experience indicates that more detailed calculation of this sort is likely to permit reduction in, e.g., transportation or inventory costs of the order of magnitude of 10 to 20 per cent. Hence, for the firm whose inventory and transportation problems are of a variety which is amenable to currently available analytic techniques and whose costs in these areas are relatively large, the use of computers on such decision problems is likely to pay hand over fist.

Aside from such optimality calculations, computers have been used to help in decision-making by running proposals through "dry run" tests. These Monte Carlo methods which were described briefly in the previous chapter, use artificial random "data" to test proposed decisions. For example, we can test how often the firm is likely to be out of stock if its inventory is reduced by a certain amount. In this way years of "experience" can be produced artificially in a matter of minutes.

There is a second criterion which is useful in indicating where machine computation is likely to be profitable as a management decision tool. If, as is often the case, a considerable degree of interdependence is involved— if decision A affects decision B and that changes C which in turn should influence A—it is often unwise to rely solely on good judgment and business experience. These are all too likely to go astray in the resulting maze of complications.

It may be noted, that high programming costs as well as the following considerations have also influenced the procedures used in machine calculation. Since a modern computer can run through a list of nonrepeating orders long enough to fill up its entire "memory" (i.e., all such information that it can handle) in less than three seconds, it is essential to have a method in which, say, step 20 is, "now go back to step 1," and which, by repeating the same calculation over and over again, arrives ultimately at the answer or an acceptable approximation to it. Such repetitive calculation procedures (which are essentially methods of approaching an answer by a sequence of successively better approximations) are called *iterative* methods.[3]

2. Components, Computer Types, and Prices

The computer consists of several basic parts and a number of auxiliary parts, many of which are optional extras. Here we deal only with basic components:

[3] A standard example of an iterative procedure is the following method for finding the square root, R, of any given number, R^2, say 5. To find this square root we make some guess at the value of R and call this first guess R_1. Note that if our first guess is too high so that R_1 is greater than R, then R^2/R_1 will be smaller than R and vice versa. Hence the true root, R, whose value we seek *must* lie between R_1 and R^2/R_1. Therefore, as a second and necessarily better guess we try the average of these two numbers, $R_2 = \frac{1}{2}(R_1 + R^2/R_1)$, and then repeat this process. For example, if our first guess at the square root of $R^2 = 5$ is $R_1 = 2$, we obtain as our second improved guess,
$$R_2 = \frac{1}{2}(2 + 5/2) = 2\frac{1}{4}.$$
Repeating this procedure we get $R_3 = \frac{1}{2}(2\frac{1}{4} + 5/2\frac{1}{4}) = 2.24$ approx., and so on. We can come as close as we wish to the correct value of $R = \sqrt{5}$ by repeating this calculation a sufficient number of times.

1. The *arithmetic and logical unit* is the calculator proper; its working will be discussed in the last section of this chapter.

2. The *memory* is the component in which information (the relevant data and the instructions of the computational procedure) is recorded and kept available for use by the machine as needed. The principles of operation of the memory will also be discussed later.

3. The *console and control panel*. Here most of the control buttons are located. This is also where we find the flashing lights (seen on television reports on election nights). The lights help the operator to locate any source of trouble. For example, if something is wrong with the program and the machine stops, the lights (using a standard code) will flash a number indicating at what step in the program the stop occurred. The operator may then use the lights to find out what numbers the machine was using at that point, what the previous step was, what the next step will be, etc. When the computer is in action these lights flash on and off (to indicate successive steps) too often to be readable. It is only when the machine stops by itself or is stopped by the operator (so that the lights stop flashing) that they yield information.

The essential difference between "big" (expensive) and "small" machines is that the former are faster, have a larger memory, and cost more. By a "large memory" we mean that the machine can store a large number of data and instructions. In many business operations the size of the memory is relatively more important than speed (in contrast with scientific work). For the speed of the machine is always astronomical by ordinary bookkeeping standards;[4] but in making out a payroll for many thousands of employees it is necessary for the machine to have a large enough memory to store all the relevant facts.

Among the smallest electronic calculators are the IBM 610, the L.G.P. 30 (Royal-McBee Corp.), and the Burroughs E-101. These range in price from $40,000 upwards.

There is a variety of intermediate-size calculators, including the IBM 650, the Burroughs 205-220, the Univac File Computer, the RCA 501, the IBM 7070, and the Minneapolis-Honeywell 800. To illustrate their cost and speed, rental on the IBM 650 runs to about $6000 per month per 8-hour shift (with no operator time included). It is about four times fast as the L.G.P. 30.

The giant calculator class includes the IBM 702, 704, 705, and 709,

---

[4] A standard statement is that a computer can be expected to solve in 15 minutes a problem which would occupy four desk-machine-operating clerks for five years. It is perhaps more meaningful to point out that a small machine can solve ten simultaneous linear equations in ten unknowns in somewhere between 25 seconds and 5 minutes. A large machine can do it in less than 5 seconds. By hand this computation should take about 15 hours.

Remington Rand Univac I and II, Philco S-200, etc. These so-called "million dollar" machines are in fact likely to cost considerably more than that figure. It is difficult to set up any firm prices on those machines because they involve so many optional components—such as spare memory units, auxiliary printing devices, etc. For a basic large machine without any extras, rental is of the order of magnitude of $25,000 a month. Rental of such machine time by the hour runs to about $500–$700 per hour. The speed with which such a machine performs an arithmetic operation is measured in microseconds (millionths of a second), in contrast with the millisecond (thousandth of a second) velocity characteristic of the smaller calculators.

It is to be noted, incidentally, that aside from its tax advantages to the corporation, rental has the advantage that it includes maintenance and enables the renter to obtain more up-to-date units as current components become obsolete.

3. *Programming*

Running the machine is a very simple operation which essentially consists of pushing a few buttons. The only difficult thing about running a problem on the machine is the programming. The difficulties stem from two sources. The first, as already mentioned, is that instructions have to be given with no detail left out—in far more explicit step-by-step listing than we ever employ elsewhere. The second difficulty is that the machine has a limited vocabulary—so that instructions must be translated from English into the language of the machine.

A number of things have been done to reduce the latter difficulty. Work is in progress on the construction of an automatic programmer which can translate from a sort of basic technical English into machine language. However, one of the main difficulties so far has been lack of standardization in the English language, especially when colloquialisms and spelling mistakes are considered. A second approach to the problem is to invent simpler "interpretive languages" (which are themselves fairly formidable from the point of view of the amateur) and then storing a translation key in the machine's memory.

If we are to understand the general nature of an instruction to the machine, the concept of a memory *address* must be explained. The capacity of the memory is rated in "words." For example, the IBM punch card 650 has a capacity of 2000 words. Each such word, which may be either a datum to be computed upon or a computational instruction, consists of a sign (plus or minus) followed by ten numbers (integers). Each of the 2000 word locations in the memory has an identifying number, or address, so that we can always locate the spot where we have housed such a "word."

Let us now follow one of the standard interpretive languages for the 650 (the Bell I system) and see how we can use it to tell the machine to do some arithmetic for us. This language tells the machine that, if located at the proper spot in our punch card, the number 1 means "add," 2 means "subtract," 3 means "multiply," and 4 means "divide," etc. Before the computation begins we must store our data in the machine's memory. This is done by feeding punched cards into the machine which give both the memory address at which the next piece of information should be housed and the number to be housed at that location.[5]

Suppose we want to multiply the number stored at address 381 by the number stored at address 427, and to have the result put into memory location 500. To do this the machine must be fed a card containing the following number: 3 381 427 500. Here the first number (3) is the opperation (multiply). The next two sets of three numbers are the addresses of the numbers to be multiplied and the last three numbers constitute the address of the location in the memory where the result is to be stored.

A program, then, consists of a sequence of such sets of ten numbers which describe the computation from start to finish. Basically, there is no way to make sure everything has been included without trying the program out on a relatively simple problem. Many hours may be spent in this way in "debugging" a program. There is, however, a checking device, called the *flow diagram*, which schematically takes the programmer through his proposed operations. By tracing through the paths indicated by the arrows he can see whether there are any obvious omissions. The accompanying "gag" flow diagram (Figure 1) has pretty much become a standard part of programming lore and indicates the nature of this device better than any verbal description.

Another checking device is the trace routine which instructs the machine to describe what it has been doing after each operation. With such a record before him, the user of the machine can search for the source of any troubles he has encountered in the course of a "debugging" calculation designed to try out his program.

4. How Does It Work?

There remains the intriguing question how a set of circuits, tubes, and other electrical devices can remember numbers and perform arithmetic operations. The discussion, which of course will give only a very superficial view of general principles, is divided into three parts: the machine's number system, the memory, and the arithmetic circuits.

---

[5] This is slightly oversimplified. An identifying card number, a number indicating how many words are on the card (there may be any number up to six), and several other such items of information must also appear on the card.

1. *The number system.* An electric current can be in only two different states (on or off) so that it is capable of handling only two distinct symbols. Our number system, however, has ten distinct symbols, 0, 1, 2, 3, 4, 5, 6, 7, 8, and 9, all other numbers being represented by combinations of these symbols. The first problem is, then, to translate from a ten-symbol number system (the *decimal system*) into a two-symbol system (the *binary system*). The idea is a simple extension of the method used in going beyond the "9" in our ordinary decimal system. Here we start another round by putting a number 1 before the zero to make 10, then a 1 before the 1 to make eleven, and so on. In other words, when we run out of symbols we start all over again by putting a 1 before the entire

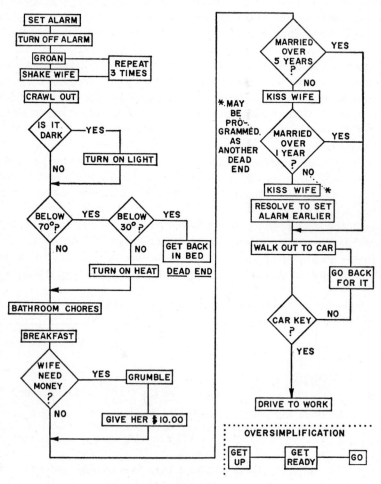

Figure 1

set of numbers, and when we get beyond 99 into the hundreds we just carry this process one stage further. The binary system works in the same way. We have at our disposal only the symbols 0 and 1. When we use these up we put a 1 in front of these and start over again. Thus we get the following numbers: 0, 1, 10, 11, 100, 101, 110, 111, 1,000, etc., corresponding respectively to our ordinary decimal numbers zero to eight,[6] e.g., the number 7 in binary terms becomes the seventh (nonzero) number in this sequence, i.e., 111. This, then, is the number system which is suited for use with an electrical computing system.

2. *The memory.* The operation of the memory is now easy to describe. Devices other than that discussed here have been used and many continue in use. They include such diverse objects as rotating magnetic drums and television tubes. However, the most powerful modern computers use a memory of the sort which is now described. This memory is a honeycomb of tiny doughnut-shaped magnets strung up on wires which run through their centers. By running current through these wires in the opposite direction from the last flow, the direction of the magnetic field of the doughnuts can be reversed. One direction (e.g., that produced by an upward flow of current) is then taken to represent 0 and the other to represent 1. Thus, given enough such magnets, this system can be used to record any number in the binary system.

To "read" the information stored in one of these magnets the machine again sends electric current through the wires, but this time always in the upward direction. If the magnet is recording a 0 (so that the previous current flow was in the same direction), this second flow will induce no further change in the state of the magnet. But if the first current flow was in the downward direction (to record a 1) this second flow will change the direction in the magnet and this, in turn, induces a flow of current through another wire strung through the magnet whose function is to transmit the

----

[6] A simple rule in translating binary numbers is to treat a 1 at the right as a 1, a 1 next to it as a 2, a 1 in the next spot to the left as a 4, and so on, in the doubling sequence 1, 2, 4, 8, 16, 32, etc. Thus, the number 111 becomes $4 + 2 + 1 = 7$. The logic behind this is easily explained. In the ordinary decimal system a number like 2376 can be interpreted as

$$2000 + 300 + 70 + 6 = (2 \times 1000) + (3 \times 100) + (7 \times 10) + (6 \times 1)$$
$$= (2 \times 10^3) + (3 \times 10^2) + (7 \times 10^1) + (6 \times 10^0)$$

(where, by definition, any number, K, raised to the zeroth power equals $K/K = 1$). Thus any decimal system number is a weighted sum of powers of ten. Since in the binary system the number 2 plays the role taken by 10 in the decimal system, the preceding result follows. For example, the binary number

$$1001 = (1 \times 2^3) + (0 \times 2^2) + (0 \times 2^1) + (1 \times 2^0)$$
$$= (1 \times 8) + (0 \times 4) + (0 \times 2) + (1 \times 1) = 9.$$

information. In other words, if when it sends such a testing "shot" of current through a core, no current flow is induced in this readout wire, the machine is told that there was a 0 registered there, whereas if an induced current flow occurs it is informed that a 1 had been recorded at that location.[7]

3. *How electric circuits can do arithmetic.* Since it only involves zeros and ones, calculation in binary system arithmetic is somewhat simpler (though more long-winded) than in the ordinary decimal system. The multiplication table is just a scaled-down version of our own: $0 \times 0 = 0$, $0 \times 1 = 0$, $1 \times 1 = 1$. Addition is only slightly more complicated: $0 + 0 = 0$, $0 + 1 = 1$, and (here is the complication) $1 + 1 = 10$ (which is the binary system notation for the number 2). Other arithmetic operations can be defined in terms of additions and multiplications so that it is only necessary to show how an electric circuit can perform these simple operations.

---

[7] The process for obtaining data, as so far described, would remove all information from the memory. In order to preserve memory beyond one recall, an additional electrical circuit is used to return the magnets to their previous condition after use of the recall mechanism just described.

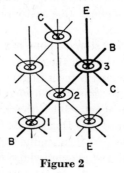

Figure 2

A somewhat more accurate description of a magnetic core memory operation may be illuminating. The schematic drawing in this footnote shows six magnetic cores and the network of wires connecting them. It will be noted that three wires pass through each core—two diagonal wires and one vertical one. Suppose it is desired to read the information stored in one of these cores, say core number 3 (the heavy line drawing). A pulse of current (a flow of current which lasts for only a very brief time period) is simultaneously transmitted through *both* of the diagonal wires B and C which pass through core 3. Now, it is to be noted that each of these wires passes through many cores, e.g., wire B passes through cores 1 and 2 as well as 3. But core 3 is the only one at which both pulses meet, and the circuit is so arranged that only the combination of the two pulses will affect the state of a magnet. In this way the desired memory core is selected. Moreover (as described in the text), depending on the direction of the magnetic field of core 3, the pulses through wires B and C either will or will not induce a pulse which is transmitted through the vertical wire, E, that passes through our core 3. Wire E thus transmits the information contained in core 3 to wherever it is needed.

Let 0 be represented by a flow of current and 1 by an absence of current. Then multiplication can be represented by a circuit with two (fast electronic) switches in parallel, as shown in Figure 3. The two switches represent the numbers being multiplied and the last part of the circuit gives the answer. Thus an open switch represents multiplication by 1 (no current going through the switch) and a closed switch represents multiplication by 0. We then have the possibilities shown in Figure 3.

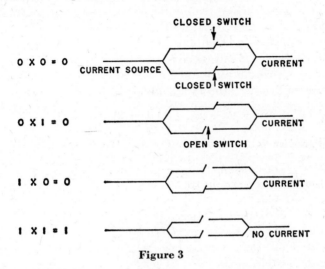

Figure 3

Similarly, we can represent addition (in all except the messy case $1 + 1 = 10$ equals 0 and 1 to carry) by two switches in series (Figure 4).

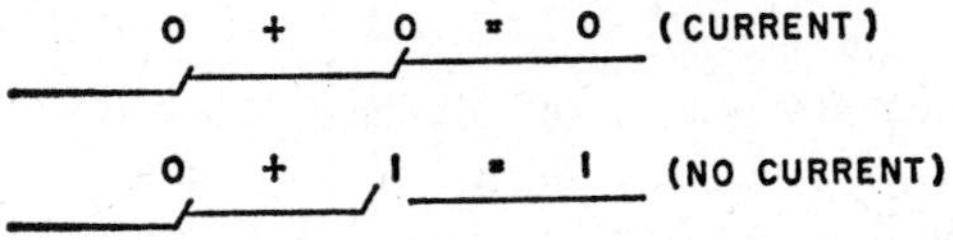

$$0 \quad + \quad 0 \quad = \quad 0 \quad \text{(CURRENT)}$$

$$0 \quad + \quad 1 \quad = \quad 1 \quad \text{(NO CURRENT)}$$

Figure 4

The addition of 1 and 1 requires a somewhat more complicated circuit. However, there is no point in describing such a circuit here since it will contribute little toward the achievement of the basic objective of this chapter, that of offering the reader a very elementary insight into the workings of an electronic digital computer.

Answers to Problems

Chapter II, Section 6

1. (a) $y = \sum\limits_{i=1}^{4} a_i x_i$ (b) $y = \sum\limits_{i=0}^{2} a_i x^i$.

2. (a) $a_0 x^3 + a_1 x^2 + a_2 x + a_3$ (b) $1^2 + 2^2 + 3^2 = 14$.

Chapter IV, Section 2

1. $dy/dx = 77x^6 - 32x$.
2. $dy/dx = -48x^{11} - 8 \sin 4x$.
3. $dy/dx = -42x^{-7}$.
4. $dy/dx = 3e^{3x} \sin x + e^{3x} \cos x$.
5. $dy/dx = (3e^{3x} \sin x - e^{3x} \cos x)/(\sin x)^2$.
6. $dy/dx = (3e^{3x} \log x - e^{3x}/x)/(\log x)^2$.
7. $dy/dx = 60x^3 \cos 5x^4$.
8. $dy/dx = -32x^{-3}e^{2x^{-2}}$.

Chapter IV, Section 5

1. (a) $60x^3$ (b) $-2/x^2$.
2. (a) Maximum at $x = 9$ (b) Minimum at $x = 0$.

Chapter IV, Section 7

1. $Q = 2, A = 3$.
2. $x = -4, z = 3$.

Chapter IV, Section 8

1. (a) $w = 5, x = 7, \lambda = -50$.   (b) $Q = 0.5, A = 2, \lambda = -0.5$.
3. $y_\lambda = \log x^3 w + \lambda_1(\cos x \cos w - 0.3) + \lambda_2(x/w^5 + e^w - 10)$.

Chapter IV, Section 9

5. (a) 25   (b) no   (c) two: $Q_1 = 5, Q_2 = 20$ (d) second derivative of profit: $+0.9$ at $Q = 5$ and -0.9 at $Q = 20$.

Chapter V, Section 10

1. $R = 27$, $x = 0$, $y = 3$, $z = 1$, all slacks zero.
2. $R = 17\frac{2}{3}$, $x = 3\frac{1}{6}$, $y = \frac{5}{3}$, $s_3 = 1\frac{1}{6}$, $s_1 = s_2 = 0$ where s_1 is the slack variable of the first constraint, etc.
3. $R = 26$, $x = 2$, $y = 3$, $s_2 = 1$, $s_1 = s_3 = 0$.
4. $R = 5\frac{1}{3}$, $x = 1\frac{1}{3}$, $s_1 = 3\frac{2}{3}$, $s_2 = y = 0$.

Chapter VII, Section 5

Unrestricted	*Integer*
1. $R = 54$, $s_1 = 8\frac{2}{5}$, $z = 3\frac{3}{5}$, $\quad x = y = s_2 = 0$.	$R = 51$, $y = 3$, $z = 3$, $s_1 = 6$, $\quad x = s_2 = s_3^{g} = 0$.
2. $R = 13\frac{5}{7}$, $s_1 = 3\frac{5}{7}$, $x = 1\frac{1}{7}$, $\quad y = s_2 = 0$.	$R = 13$, $x = 1$, $y = 1$, $s_1 = 2$, $\quad s_2 = s_3^{g} = 0$.
3. $R = 13\frac{1}{2}$, $y = 2\frac{1}{4}$, $s_1 = 2\frac{3}{4}$, $\quad x = s_2 = 0$.	$R = 12$, $y = 2$, $\quad s_1 = 3$, $s_2 = 1$, $\quad x = s_3^{g} = 0$.

Index

A

Abramovitz, Moses, 292n, 295
Ackoff, R. L., 414
Activity analysis, 311–330
  definition of term, 311
  dual prices and decentralized decision-making, 326–327
  existence theorems, 312–316
  existence and uniqueness problems, 311–313
  integer programming and welfare economics, 327–330
  Pareto optimality, 322, 325
  uniqueness theorems, 313, 316–318
  von Neumann model of expanding economy, 318–321
  and welfare economics, 321–326
Adding-up controversy, and distribution theory, 293–295
Additive measures *see* Cardinal measures
Advertising:
  allocation of budget, 398
  objectives of firm, 199–201
  oligopolistic interdependence, 223
Alchian, A. A., 346
Allais, Maurice, 339n, 346
Allen, R. G. D., 63
Allocation of resources, and general equilibrium, 246–248
Analogue computers, 415n *see also* Electronic computers (digital)
Arnoff, E. L., 414
Arrow, Kenneth J., 10, 115, 271–274, 275, 306n, 330
Axiomatization, in decision theory, 380–381 *see also* Decision theory

B

Baumol, W. J., 109n, 125n, 204, 229, 241n, 245, 275, 362n
Bayes criterion and Neumann-Morgenstern utility, 381–384 *see also* Decision theory
Bayes-Laplace criterion, 372–373 *see also* Decision theory
Becker, G. S., 245
Beckmann, Martin, 330
Bennion, E. G., 96
Bergson, Abram, criterion for welfare judgment, 270–271
Bilateral monopolies, 207, 220–222 *see also* Market structures
Binary number system, 422–423 *see also* Electronic computers (digital)
Black, Duncan, 271n
Blau, J. H., 273n
Boehm, G. A. W., 399n
Boulding, Kenneth, 173, 190, 225n, 229, 291, 346
Bowman, E. H., 414

C

Calculus *see* Differential calculus
Cardinal utility (neoclassical), 148–152, 341–342
Cardinal utility theory (Neumann-Morgenstern), 331–346
  axiomatic, basis of, 339–341, 342–344
  "cardinal measurement," 333–335
  construction of N-M (Neumann-Morgenstern) index, 335–337
  expected utility vs expected payoff, 337–339
  measures, classes and strength of, 332–335